THE CHANGING GEOGRAPHY OF BRITAIN

SECOND EDITION

W. E. MARSDEN

School of Education, University of Liverpool

Maps and diagrams by Tim Smith

Oliver & Boyd

ACKNOWLEDGEMENTS

The publishers thank the following for permission to reproduce photographs: Aerofilms: Cover (ii and iii), Plates 1.6, 1.7, 1.13, 1.14, 1.17, 1.18, 1.21, 5.4, 5.5, 5.7, 6.2, 7.5, 7.7, 8.1, 8.5, 8.6, 10.1, 10.2, 11.1, 11.7, 12.1, 12.2, 13.2, 14.4, 14.5, 14.8, 14.10, 14.11, 15.1, 15.3, 15.4, 15.7, 15.8; Airviews, Manchester: Plates 11.4, 14.3, 14.7; Birmingham Post Studios: Plate 13.3; Bolton Evening News: Plate 8.10; British Airports Authority: Plates 7.8, 7.9; British Petroleum: Plate 6.11; British Railways Board: Plates 7.3, 7.4, 7.6; British Steel Corporation: Plate 8.7; Cadbury Schweppes Ltd: Plate 9.1; Camera Press: Plate 9.2 (Colin Davey); Central Electricity Generating Board: Plates 6.8, 6.14; City of Birmingham Public Works Department: Plates 12.3, 12.4, 12.5, 12.6; City of Birmingham Water Department: Plates 4.1, 4.2, 4.3; Commission for the New Towns: Plate 8.8; Contour Designs Ltd: Plate 1.16; Department of the Environment: Plates 11.2, 11.3; Norman Derrick: Plate 14.9; John Dewar Studios: Plates 1.15, 11.5; Howard Doris Ltd: Plate 6.12; Robin Fletcher: Plates 15.9, 15.10, 15.11; Freeman Fox and Partners: Plates 7.1, 7.2; B. R. Hall: Plates 3.1, 3.2, 3.4; Her Majesty's Stationery Office, Crown copyright reserved: Plate 2.1; Hull Daily Mail: Plate 14.6; ICI: Plate 8.9; Eric Kay: Plates 1.3, 1.23; W. E. Marsden: Plates 1.1, 1.5, 1.11, 1.12, 1.20, 3.3, 3.5, 5.1, 5.2, 5.3, 13.5, 13.6; National Coal Board: Plates 6.1, 6.5, 6.6, 6.7, 6.9; Pilkington Bros: Plate 8.2; Popperfoto: Plates 1.2, 1.4, 1.9, 5.6, 6.3, 6.10; Port of London Authority: Plates 14.1, 14.2 (Handford Photography); Scotsman Publications Ltd: Plates 11.6, 15.12; Scottish Tourist Board: Plates 15.5, 15.6: Shell Photographic Service: Cover (i); South Lancashire Newspapers Ltd: Plates 8.3, 8.4; Southport Public Library: Plate 15.2; Telford Development Corporation: Plates 13.1, 13.4; TUC: Plate 6.4; United Kingdom Energy Authority: Plate 6.15; Vauxhall Motors Ltd: Plates 8.11, 8.12; Washington Development Corporation: Cover (iv); Derek Widdicombe: Plates 1.8, 1.10, 1.19; Dennis Wompra: Plate 6.13.

The publishers also thank all those who gave permission to reproduce extracts from their publications (acknowledgement is given beneath each extract in the text).

The Ordnance Survey map extracts (Figs 5.5, 6.2, 8.15, 10.5, 11.5) are printed with permission of the Controller of Her Majesty's Stationery Office, Crown Copyright reserved.

Figure 12.6 is reproduced by courtesy of the Board of the British Library.

The author wishes to acknowledge the following sources which were used as a basis for some of the figures or tables. The Meteorological Office: Fig. 2.3, from the Daily Weather Report, reproduced with the permission of the Controller of Her Majesty's Stationery Office; The Reader's Digest Association Ltd, *Complete Atlas of the British Isles*: Fig. 2.5; Ministry of Agriculture, Fisheries and Food, *Modern Farming and the Soil*, Crown Copyright: Fig. 3.4; City of Birmingham Water Department: Fig. 4.1; *Water Industry Review*: Figs 4.2, 4.3; *Geographical Journal*: Fig. 5.1; K. Briggs: Fig. 5.12; Land Utilisation Survey: Fig. 5.15; National Coal Board: Tables 6.2–6.5 and Fig. 6.7; Department of Energy, *CSO Social Trends*, p. 171: Fig. 6.5; Bale & Gowing, *Geography and Football* (Geographical Association): Figs 6.6, 10.7; British Gas Corporation: Fig. 6.10; Central Electricity Generating Board: Table 6.7; North of Scotland Hydro-electric Board: Fig. 6.15; United Kingdom Energy Authority: Fig. 6.17; British Railways Board: Figs 7.4, 7.6, 7.8; Freightliners Ltd: Fig. 7.5; David and Charles, information from *Directory of Stagecoach Services for 1835* and D. St John Thomas's *Regional History of the Railways of Great Britain: The West Country*: Table 7.1; British Airports Authority: Tables 7.2, 7.3; C. M. Wood, N. Lee, J. A. Luker & P. T. W. Saunders, *The Geography of Pollution: A Study of Greater Manchester* (Manchester University Press): Fig. 7.10; Pilkington Bros: Fig. 8.1; Department of Employment and Productivity: Tables 8.1, 8.4; Commission for the New Towns, Corby: Fig. 8.10; Vauxhall Motors Ltd: Table 8.3; Collins-Longman Atlas 4: Fig. 9.1; Census 1981: Fig. 9.2; R. Dalton & S. Thomas, *Lincolnshire Landscapes* Bishop Grosseteste College: Fig. 10.3; P. Toyne & P. Newby, *Techniques in Human Geography* (Macmillan): Fig. 10.8; City of Birmingham Public Works Department: Table 12.2 and Figs 12.2, 12.3, 12.4, 12.7; Birmingham Reference Library (Local Studies Department): Fig. 12.6; Department of the Environment: Figs 12.8–12.10; Office of Population Censuses and Surveys: Fig. 12.11 and Table 15.1; Telford Development Corporation: Figs 13.2, 13.3, Tables 13.1, 13.2; Port of London Authority: Figs 14.1, 14.3; Table 14.1; J. Bird, *The Major Seaports of the United Kingdom* (Hutchinson): Fig. 14.2; The Sea Fish Industry Authority: Figs 14.5, 14.7, 14.10, Table 14.7; *Digest of Port Statistics*: Table 14.8; F. Sheen of St Bede's RC Secondary School, Ormskirk: Fig. 15.3.

Oliver & Boyd
Robert Stevenson House, 1–3 Baxter's Place, Leith Walk, Edinburgh EH1 3BB
A division of Longman Group Ltd

ISBN 0 05 003672 6
First published 1978, Second edition 1984

Printed in Hong Kong
by C & C Joint Printing Co (HK) Ltd

CONTENTS

Acknowledgements   2

1   **The Physical Basis**   4
Geology and Scenery in Britain   4
Economic Geology   11
Other Influences on the Physical Landscape   11

2   **Weather and Climate**   28
Weather Maps   28
Variations in British Weather   29

3   **Soils**   39

4   **Water Supply**   44

5   **Agriculture**   49
Land Use in Britain   49
Farming in the Lake District   50
Farming in Lincolnshire   56
Other Farming Types in Britain   62
The Post-War Agricultural Revolution in   ritain
Britain   67

6   **Energy Resources**   70
Coal   70
North Sea Oil and Natural Gas   80
Electricity   88

7   **Transport**   92
Roads   92
Rail   95
Air   100

8   **Manufacturing Industry**   105
Coal-based Industries   105
The 'Footloose' Industries of the Twentieth
    Century   121

9   **Population**   126
The Growth of Urban population   126
The Changing Distribution of Population   127

10   **Market Towns and Spheres of Influence**   132

11   **The Growth of a City: Edinburgh**   139

12   **Conurbations**   150
Birmingham and the West Midlands   150
The Conurbations of Britain   161

13   **A New City: Telford**   163

14   **Ports**   172
London: a Commercial Port   172
The Ports of Britain   177
Southampton and Fawley   178
Fishing Ports   180
Passenger Ports   187

15   **Tourism**   190
Seaside Resorts   190
Tourism and Conservation   196

Index   207

1 THE PHYSICAL BASIS

GEOLOGY AND SCENERY IN BRITAIN

If you go by train across the USSR, Canada, or Australia, you may travel for hundreds and even thousands of kilometres without noticing major changes in the scenery. In Britain it is almost impossible to journey for hundreds of kilometres without noticing striking changes.

One of the main characteristics of Britain's physical landscape is its variety. A simplified geological map (Figure 1.1) looks complex enough, but if you look at the geological map in your atlas you will notice that the situation is even more complicated than our map suggests. This variety of geology is one basic reason for

Figure 1.1   Simplified geological map of the British Isles

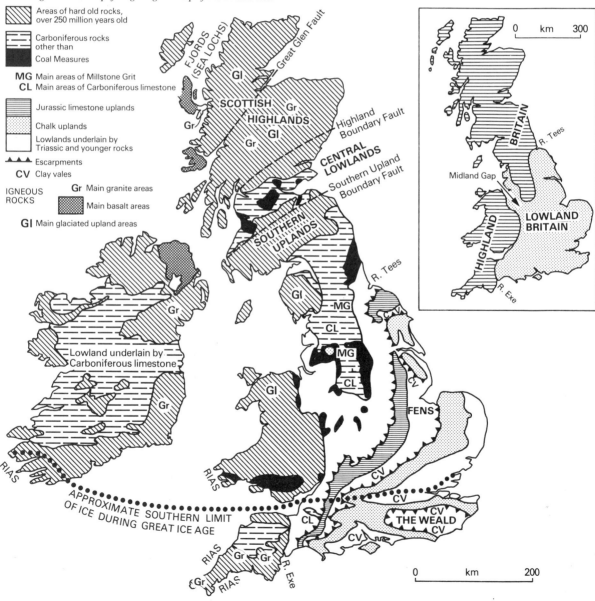

the variety of British scenery. We are going to investigate in more detail why this variety exists, by selecting particular areas of study in which the landscape takes forms which have been influenced strongly by the underlying geology. The basic geology of different areas of Britain is given in Table 1.1.

Table 1.1

Geology and Scenery	Areas of Britain
Igneous rocks	
(i) Granite	Dartmoor, Bodmin Moor, Land's End; Cairngorms
(ii) Basalt	Skye, Mull; Antrim Plateau
Carboniferous limestone	Peak district, Ingleborough/Malham districts; Mendips
Millstone Grit	Central Pennines, Rossendale Uplands, Bowland Fells
Scarplands	
(i) Jurassic limestone	Cotswolds, Lincoln Edge, North York Moors
(ii) Chalk	North and South Downs, Salisbury Plain, East Anglian Heights, Lincoln and Yorkshire Wolds

Exercises

Refer to Figure 1.1, your atlas, and any other relevant information source.

1. On an outline map of the British Isles:
(*a*) Shade in and name areas of Lowland Britain over about 30 metres in height; and areas of Highland Britain over 150 and 900 metres, respectively, using different types of shading.
(*b*) Mark the Tees–Exe line, which separates Highland from Lowland Britain.
(*c*) Make a separate key, and on this mark the symbols used on the map for representing (i) basalt areas, (ii) granite areas, (iii) Millstone Grit areas (iv) Carboniferous limestone areas, (v) glaciated uplands, (vi) escarpments, (vii) clay vales.
(*d*) Name the areas covered in (*c*).
2. (*a*) Name a part of Highland Britain not directly affected by glaciation.
(*b*) Name a clay vale which was, and one which was not, covered by ice in the great Ice Age.
(*c*) Name an important lowland area west of the Tees–Exe line.
(*d*) Name two major types of rocks linked with escarpments.
(*e*) What are the main differences in the geology of the areas on (i) either side of the Tees–Exe line; (ii) between and on either side of the Highland and Southern Upland Boundary Faults?
(*f*) Check the terms Carboniferous, Jurassic, Triassic, etc. on a geological time scale.

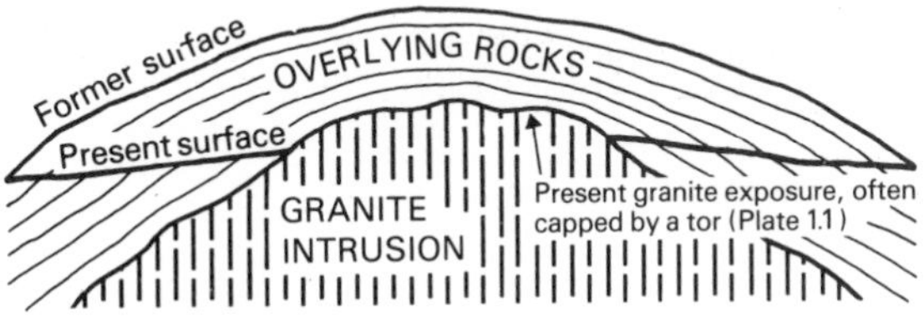

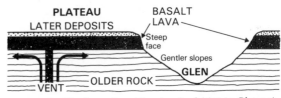

Figure 1.2 The formation of granite upland

Figure 1.3 The formation of basalt upland (Antrim Plateau)

Igneous Scenery

A variety of types of scenery have developed on the various igneous rocks. Here we are going to concentrate on features of granite and basalt areas. *Granite* was originally molten material, *intruded* into overlying rocks. It solidified below the surface (Figure 1.2), later to be exposed by removal of the overlying rocks. *Basalt* began as molten lava, associated with non-explosive volcanic activity. It was *extruded* in flows over many square kilometres of the surface, and has in some cases been covered by later deposits (Figure 1.3), as in the Antrim Plateau of Northern Ireland.

Granite Scenery

After exposure, granite is generally weathered into smooth outlines although, being a tough rock, it forms upland areas, as on Dartmoor. The relatively level summits, often in areas of high rainfall, are associated with poor drainage, forming upland bogs, with surface water collecting in the many hollows in the surface.

Granite Tors

The tops of granite uplands are often characterised by castle-like mounds of rock, called *tors*. Those of Dartmoor and Bodmin Moor are particularly famous, but tors can also be found in the Cairngorms, as Plate 1.1 indicates. Notice the well-marked pattern of joints in the rocks, and the loose boulders.

It is thought that the main influence on tor formation is weathering below the surface. Where the joints were closest together, most rapid weathering took place. When the granite was exposed by removal of the overlying material, the smaller, looser fragments were removed more quickly, or left as isolated boulders, while the less closely jointed material remained together, often with rounded edges and a 'heaped up' appearance, as the tor (Figure 1.4) indicates.

5

Plate 1.1   A granite tor in the Cairngorms

Plate 1.2   'Fingal's Cave', Staffa: basalt columns

Former situation

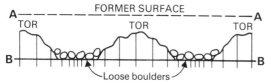

Figure 1.4   The formation of tors

Basalt Scenery

The classic area of basalt scenery in Britain is the Antrim Plateau in Northern Ireland, a flat-topped upland, bounded by a steep face where the basalt suddenly emerges (*outcrops*) (Figure 1.3). The deposits below the basalt tend to be associated with gentler slopes, running down to the valleys (*glens*) which cut through the plateau.

The Giant's Causeway
The most celebrated piece of scenery in this area is the Giant's Causeway, on the north coast of Antrim. When basalt cools it contracts, and the resulting stresses form joints, in this case hexagonal (six-sided). When exposed, almost perfectly divided hexagonal columns are revealed, over quite a large coastal expanse in the case of the Giant's Causeway.

Similar basalt columns are found on the Isle of Staffa (Plate 1.2) off the west coast of Scotland, the caves of which inspired the composer Mendelssohn to write his Hebridean Overture, 'Fingal's Cave'.

Carboniferous Limestone Scenery

Characteristic Features of Carboniferous Limestone

Carboniferous limestone has a well-developed joint system which allows water to pass freely through it. It is thus a *permeable* rock. It is also subject to chemical weathering by rain water, which is in effect a weak form of carbonic acid:

$$H_2O + CO_2 \rightarrow H_2CO_3$$
$$\text{(water)} \quad \text{(carbon dioxide)} \quad \text{(carbonic acid)}$$

The calcium carbonate of limestone is converted into calcium bicarbonate, which is soluble and can therefore be removed by water. Thus Carboniferous limestone is not only permeable: it is also *soluble*. These qualities lead to a number of characteristic features in Carboniferous limestone scenery.

Limestone Pavements
Where the limestone is exposed, and also below the surface, its well-developed joint pattern allows water to enter, and solution (chemical) weathering can take place. The joints are widened and their edges are 'fluted' or rounded off, as can be seen on Plate 1.3, a photograph taken near Malham Cove, Yorkshire. The widened joints are known as *grikes*, and the blocks of limestone that form the 'tables' between as *clints*. Soil may develop in the grikes, allowing grass and even trees to grow. The

Plate 1.3   Limestone pavement showing fluting, clints and grikes above Malham Cove, Yorkshire

Figure 1.5   A block diagram showing characteristic features of Carboniferous limestone areas

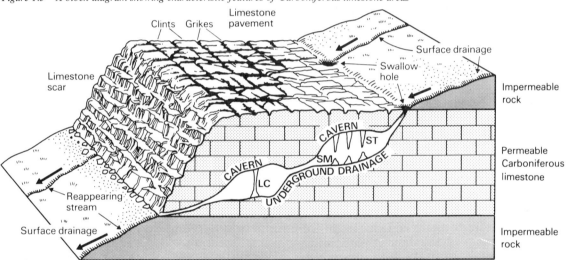

LC Limestone column   ST Stalactites   SM Stalagmites

whole mass of clints and grikes forms a *limestone pavement*. Where pavements outcrop on the sides of hills they form *limestone scars* (Figure 1.5).

Disappearing and Reappearing Streams
The features of Carboniferous limestone result in an interrupted drainage pattern.

(*a*) *Swallow-holes*   The Carboniferous limestone in some areas, as at Malham Cove, is capped by Millstone Grit. This is an impermeable rock, which allows water to flow over it. On reaching the limestone, however, the streams may gradually disappear into it through the stream beds, or disappear much more dramatically through swallow-holes (Figure 1.5), of which one of the most famous is Gaping Gill in the Ingleborough district.

(*b*) *Limestone caverns*   Underground, a whole system of passages through the rock develops along joints and bedding planes, as the limestone is dissolved (Figure 1.5). During the Ice Age and its aftermath, there was probably much more water about than today, making solution of the limestone more powerful. As a result,

7

Plate 1.4   Spring at head of Austwick Beck

spectacular limestone caverns can be found in the Ingleborough district, the Peak district, and the Mendips.

Where water has dripped from joints in the roof, it has evaporated to redeposit limestone in the form of thin elegant *stalactites*. Water dripping on to the floor has led to broader stumpier *stalagmites*. In some cases the two have joined, forming limestone columns or pillars (Figure 1.5).

(c) *Dry valleys and gorges*   At the surface, valleys which were formed before the rivers disappeared are left as dry valleys. Such valleys might have developed at the time of the great Ice Age, when the ground was frozen and so would allow surface water to flow across the limestone. In some areas impressive *limestone gorges*, with near vertical walls, have formed. An example is Gordale, near Malham, in the Pennines. Such gorges are difficult to explain, though one theory is that they were formed by the roofs of limestone caverns collapsing.

(d) *Reappearance of streams: springs*   Where the underground stream reaches impermeable rock, perhaps along the line of a fault, it reappears, and surface drainage is resumed. Plate 1.4 shows a stream reappearing as a spring at the head of Austwick Beck in the Ingleborough district.

Millstone Grit Scenery

Another important rock making up the Pennines is Millstone Grit, a coarse, relatively impermeable, sandstone. This, together with the heavy rainfall experienced in these uplands, leads to a great deal of surface drainage. The flat-topped moorlands of the Millstone Grit are characterised by very poor drainage, with extensive peat bogs, on which the soil is acid and waterlogged. The valleys of such areas are often used for water storage, and many reservoirs are found (see Chapter 4).

Where the Millstone Grit outcrops at the surface, as in the Kinderscout district of Derbyshire, its resistant nature may cause sharply outlined ridges, or *edges*. Plate 1.5 is a photograph of 'The Roaches', a gritstone edge

Plate 1.5   The Roaches, a gritstone edge

8

Plate 1.6   Mam Tor, Derbyshire

north of Leek, rising to about 450 metres in height. Sometimes the outcropping gritstone is weathered into strange shapes, to form *Millstone Grit tors*, such as Brimham Rocks in South Yorkshire.

In some areas, the heavy, impermeable gritstone overlies weaker rocks such as shales. In certain circumstances, this may result in *landslides*, as in the case of Mam Tor in Derbyshire. The process of landslipping leaves a *landslip scar*, from which the rocks have moved, below which are the *hummocks* of material which has slipped down, as shown in the background and foreground, respectively, in Plate 1.6.

Exercises

3. Outline the similarities and differences between:
(*a*)   granite and basalt scenery;
(*b*)   Carboniferous limestone and Millstone Grit scenery;
(*c*)   granite and Millstone Grit scenery.
4. Draw simple labelled block diagrams to show (*a*) the surface features of a Carboniferous limestone upland, (*b*) a landslip.
5. Find Ordnance Survey maps of areas of the Pennines (or other parts of Britain), where Carboniferous limestone and Millstone Grit outcrop. Draw labelled contour sketch maps to bring out the essential characteristics of each.

Scarpland Scenery

Figure 1.1 showed the geology and scenery of much of Lowland Britain as consisting of a series of Jurassic limestone and chalk uplands, separated by clay vales.

These uplands take the form of *cuestas*, made up of a steep slope, or *escarpment*, and a more gentle *dip slope* behind. Plate 1.7 shows the escarpment of the South Downs, with the dip slope on the left, and the beginnings of the clay vale on the extreme right of the picture. The dip slope reflects the dip of the rocks, as can be seen on Figure 1.6 showing the limestone cuesta of Lincoln Edge, and the chalk cuesta of the Lincoln Wolds.

Jurassic limestone and chalk rocks are between 100 and 200 million years old, much younger than the Carboniferous rocks of the Pennines. While less resistant than these older Pennine formations, they are tough rocks compared with the adjoining clays, and therefore stand out as uplands in the setting of Lowland Britain.

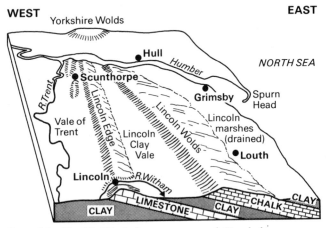

Figure 1.6   Simplified block diagram across north Lincolnshire

9

Plate 1.7 The escarpment of the South Downs

Although Jurassic limestone and chalk scenery are not exactly the same, the similarities outweigh the differences and we shall concentrate here on the characteristics of chalk scenery.

Chalk Scenery

Like Carboniferous limestone, chalk is a permeable rock. Unlike Carboniferous limestone, chalk is also *porous*. This means that the rock contains innumerable tiny pore spaces, each of which can hold water. A rock stratum holding water like this is known as an *aquifer*. In porous rocks, there is slow seepage of water, with the pore spaces filling up to a certain level, known as the *water table* (Figure 1.7). The level of the water table varies with the seasons and weather conditions. In wet weather it will be higher than under drought conditions;

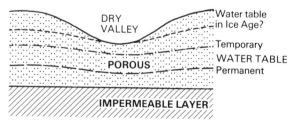

Figure 1.7 Water table and dry valleys

in winter higher than in summer (when there is more evaporation). In drought periods wells sunk into the normally 'permanent' water table may dry up.

As we have seen, chalk cuestas generally consist of an escarpment and dip slope, the line of the escarpment sometimes being marked by a line of chalk quarries. It is also often broken through by major rivers to form *gaps*, which in some cases become the site of gap towns, as in the case of Lincoln (Figure 1.6).

Because surface water seeps readily into the porous rock below, chalk scenery is typified by dry rolling downlands, as shown in the left of Plate 1.7. At one time largely used for sheep pasture, much of the downland is now ploughed for arable farming. The downs are diversified by *dry valleys* which, like those of the Carboniferous limestone, are thought to have been formed during and after the Ice Age, when there was more water about, and the ground was perhaps frozen and rendered non-porous (Figure 1.7). Since that time, the water table has fallen, rivers no longer flow, and the valleys are left dry. In winter, however, some of these valleys may contain small streams or *winterbournes*.

Where the chalk meets an impervious layer below, such as clay, the water comes to the surface in the form of a *spring*. Thus along the line of the escarpment, and perhaps also the dip slope, a *spring line* will occur,

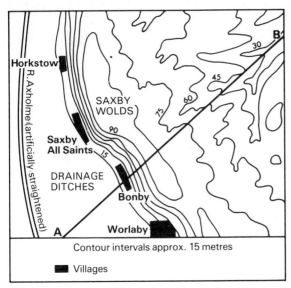

Horkstow

R. Axholme (artificially straightened)

SAXBY WOLDS

Saxby All Saints

DRAINAGE DITCHES

Bonby

Worlaby

30
45
60
73
90
15

A
B

Contour intervals approx. 15 metres

■ Villages

Figure 1.8   Contoured map of part of the Lincoln Wolds

popular for the siting of villages (for water supply), which also lie on *dry point sites* above the damp clay lowland (Figure 1.8). Some small settlements can be picked out on the spring line of the South Downs escarpment in Plate 1.7.

Exercises

6. Refer to Figure 1.1, an atlas map, and other sources of information. Draw a simplified map of the North and South Downs, outlining the chalk, the clay vales, and the central sandstone ridge of the Weald. Label the escarpments; dip slopes; major rivers; gaps and gap towns; and areas of chalk cliffs.
7. Refer to Figure 1.8.
(*a*) Trace this map into your books, and label it as appropriate with dry downland scenery, escarpment, dip slope, dry valley, clay vale.
(*b*) Draw a section along the line A–B, and label it similarly.
(*c*) Outline the advantages of the sites of the villages shown on the map.
8. Outline the main similarities and differences between Carboniferous limestone and chalk scenery.

ECONOMIC GEOLOGY

The geological formations so far described are of profound importance to the economic prosperity of Britain, and will be referred to again in later sections. There is space here only to summarise the main contributions.
(1) *Granite areas* such as Dartmoor are the source of *kaolin* (china clay), formed by the chemical weathering of mineral components of the granite. The areas round

these granite uplands of south-west England are sources of tin, copper and many other minerals.
(2) The *Carboniferous limestone* areas contain innumerable limestone quarries, providing lime for the cement and chemical industries, and limestone flux for the steel industry. These areas were formerly important producers of lead.
(3) *Millstone Grit* was formerly used for grindstones for the steel industry, and for building stone (note the walls on Plate 1.5). The Millstone Grit uplands are a major source of water for the industrial towns of the Pennine fringe.
(4) The *Jurassic limestones* are today Britain's main domestic source of ironstone which resulted in the growth of steel towns such as Scunthorpe.
(5) *Chalk* is another source of lime, much used in the cement industry (see page 175).
(6) The *clay vales* contain important areas of brick clays, as for example in the Peterborough and Bedford areas of the south-east.

As we shall see in later chapters, the scenery of most of these areas attracts tourists, but the quarrying and mining activities provide a considerable threat to the amenity value of such areas (see Chapter 15).

OTHER INFLUENCES ON THE PHYSICAL LANDSCAPE

The underlying geology is thus a vital influence on the forms the physical landscape takes. But this landscape also closely reflects the forces working upon it. We have already noted how chemical weathering helps to produce characteristic forms in Carboniferous limestone areas. We are now going to look into three other influences which have been of great importance in sculpturing the scenery of Britain: *river action*, *ice action*, and *sea action*.

One thing all three processes have in common is that they need to have *tools*, usually lumps of rock, to do their work. They are important not only in *eroding* the land, but also in *transporting* and *depositing* the material they have eroded. The deposits in themselves form particular landscape features.

River Action

It is convenient to divide a river's course from its source to the sea into its *upper course*, *middle course*, and *lower course*; and to look at each of these sections in terms of the *river channel*, the *valley slopes*, the *valley floor* (which together form the cross or *transverse profile*), and the *long profile*, i.e. following the line of the course of the river itself.

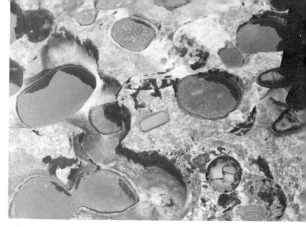

Plate 1.9   Pot-holes in the bed of the River Ure

The Upper Course

The River Channel

In the upper course, the channel floor is often of bare rock, with loose boulders of all shapes and sizes lying on its uneven floor, as we can see in the photograph of the upper Tees valley (Plate 1.8). The river is shallow and appears to be running swiftly, which is why the upper course is sometimes referred to as the *torrent stage*. When the river is in flood, enormous boulders can be moved downstream. These just lie on the river bed in normal times, though they are gradually worn down to a smaller size. This loose material is known as the river's *load*.

Plate 1.8   The upper Tees valley, above High Force

The turbulence of the river swirls round loose pieces of rock to form *pot-holes* (Plate 1.9). Note how some are separate and some are joined. The photograph shows how uneven the river bed is at this stage. Continued erosion causes the pot-holes to join, and this gradually lowers the river bed. Thus *vertical erosion* takes place and can lead to the formation of a *slot gorge* (Figure 1.9).

The Valley Slopes

At the same time as this vertical erosion, wastage of the valley slopes is taking place. Weathering of the upper valley slopes leads to the gradual movement of rock and soil downslope under gravity. In the case of landslides (page 9), movement downslope is rapid. This downslope movement of material leads to the wearing back of the valley slopes, creating a *V-shaped* cross profile. Where the river is not flowing straight, the slopes, when looked at from along the line of the valley, will appear to interlock, and are known as *interlocking spurs* (Figure 1.10).

The Valley Floor

In the upper course, the river's channel is more or less the same width as the valley floor, though a narrow flood plain (see below) may be beginning to develop.

The Long Profile

Figures 1.9 and 1.10 show the transverse V-shaped profile of the valley. We must also consider the profile at right angles to this, running down the line of the river, i.e. the long (or longitudinal) profile. In the upper course

Figure 1.9   Block diagram of the processes at work in the upper course of a river

Figure 1.10   Block diagram of the upper course of a river valley

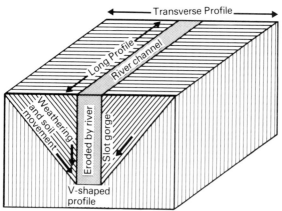

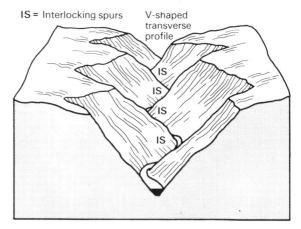

Plate 1.10   High Force on the River Tees

this is often steep and uneven. *Waterfalls* and *rapids* are common features of the long profile at this stage. They are formed where hard bands of rock cross the river. In the case of the High Force on the upper Tees (Plate 1.10), this hard band is made up of a tough volcanic intrusion, known as the Whin Sill.

The waterfall descends to a *plunge pool*, and the action of the spray assists in the wearing back of what are often weaker rocks below the hard band, thereby undermining this band, and causing material eventually to fall in (Figure 1.11). In this way the waterfall retreats upstream, leaving a gorge in front, as the diagram shows. Plate 1.11 shows the view looking downstream from the High Force on the Tees, and illustrates the formation of the gorge. Plate 1.8 is the view upstream from the waterfall, the direction in which the waterfall is retreating.

Figure 1.11   Block diagram of a waterfall

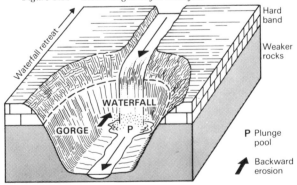

Plate 1.11   The formation of a gorge. The view looking downstream from the High Force on the River Tees

The Middle Course

The River Channel

In this section of the river, the channel is deeper, wider, and the floor more even than in the upper course. The load it carries is more varied than in the upper course. Boulders may still lie in the river channel, but much has been broken down into finer sand or silt, and is carried in suspension. Some of this may lie on the river bed (Plate 1.12).

The Valley Slopes

These have been worn back and lowered from the position shown in Figure 1.9, though they still tend to retain a V-shape.

The Valley Floor

The main feature of the middle course is the development of a *narrow flood plain*. By this stage, the initial curves in the stream have developed to become

Plate 1.12   A river bluff and slip-off slope

13

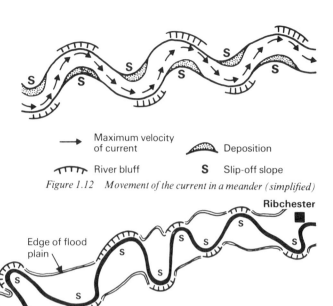

Maximum velocity of current   Deposition

River bluff   **S** Slip-off slope

Figure 1.12   Movement of the current in a meander (simplified)

Ribchester

Edge of flood plain

Flood plain

River flow

River bluffs   **S** Slip-off slope

0   km   1

Figure 1.13   The meanders of the Ribble

meanders. In running round a meander, the main force of the current swings to the outside of the bend (Figure 1.12). Greater erosion takes place here to form a *river bluff* (Plate 1.12). Undercutting of the bluff causes material to slump into the river, adding to its load.

On the inner side of the meander the current is slower and material is deposited to form a *slip-off slope* (Plate 1.12 and Figure 1.12). This meandering action thus causes lateral erosion, leading to the development of a narrow flood plain. Figure 1.13 is a sketch showing the *meander belt* of the River Ribble, with its narrow flood plain, more or less the same width as the meander belt. In times of flood, the whole of this flood plain may be covered by water. When the water evaporates, a layer of silt is deposited, helping to build up the *alluvial* deposits which form the floor of a flood plain.

The Long Profile

The long profile of the middle course of a river is less steep than the upper course. It may seem strange, therefore, that the river is flowing more or less as fast as in the upper stage, though it may not appear to be doing so. This is because the greater volume of water in the river at this stage compensates for the loss of gradient. In this section, irregularities such as waterfalls and rapids have been ironed out, and the long profile is relatively smooth.

The Lower Course

The River Channel

In this section of the river, the channel is much deeper and wider than further upstream. In large rivers, the channel can be many kilometres wide, though this is not the case in Britain. The load the river is carrying is now entirely *in suspension*, or fully dissolved. It is made up therefore of very fine material, with no stones or boulders, which have been broken down upstream. At its mouth, the river may deposit this material as a delta, though deltas do not occur in Britain, except at lakes (see Plate 1.14). Sandbanks or mudbanks are deposited, however. Sandbanks occur at the mouth of the River Mersey, and mudbanks in the Ribble estuary.

The Valley Slopes

These may be several kilometres away from the river channel, and not in fact visible from it. Where the slopes do occur, they are much gentler, except where a mass of resistant rock rises from the flood plain, as is the case of the flood plain of the Forth at Stirling, where volcanic outcrops occur (Figure 1.15).

The Valley Floor

This has become the most significant part of the valley, with a number of characteristic features.

(*a*) *Natural levées*   A *wide flood plain* has developed at the expense of valley slopes. In times of flood, vast areas may be inundated, with large quantities of alluvium

Figure 1.14   Natural levées. For clarity the levées have been drawn with vertical exaggeration

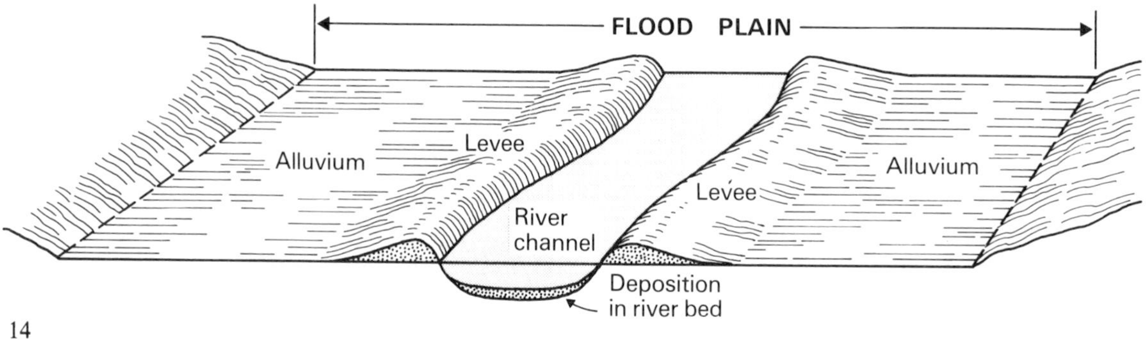

FLOOD   PLAIN

Alluvium   Levee   Alluvium

Levee

River channel

Deposition in river bed

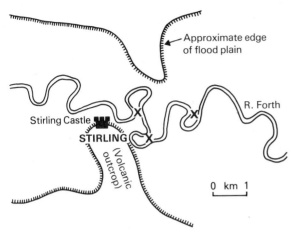

Figure 1.15   The meanders of the Forth at Stirling

deposited. When the river in flood overtops its banks, coarser material is deposited first, and finer material further away from the channel. Thus natural embankments or *levées* are built up parallel to the river channel (Figure 1.14). Sometimes these are artificially 'topped up' as a defence against the flood hazard. Deposition also occurs on the river bed, and the level of the river may well rise above the level of the flood plain, increasing the possibility of flooding.

(b)   Ox-bow lakes   The meandering of the river becomes more intense in the lower stage, with the flood plain much wider than in the meander belt. A fine set of swinging meanders can be found at Stirling, in the lower course of the River Forth (Figure 1.15) and on the River Calder at Castleford (OS map extract, page 72).

The meanders change shape and position, with erosion on the outside of a bend, perhaps in flood, leading to a meander being short-circuited. In this way ox-bow lakes are formed, as has happened at Castleford. In the course of time, such lakes may be filled in with vegetation, and only be recognisable as former lakes from the air. Looking at Figure 1.15, it is easy to see that in time the river may leap over the meander at points 'X', to cut off ox-box lakes.

In this situation, flooding is likely and as a defence against this hazard rivers are sometimes artificially straightened, as in the case of the River Axholme in Lincolnshire (Figure 1.8). This increases the gradient of the river, which helps the flow of water downstream. Artificial straightening is often combined with the construction of artificial levées.

The Long Profile

The gradient downstream is very gentle at this stage, though the great volume of water means that the river is still flowing at about the same speed as further upstream. Checking of the gradient on reaching the sea results in the deposition of material, as already noted (page 14).

Exercises

9. (*a*)   Draw a larger copy of Figure 1.16 in your exercise book. Mark on it the three separate sections of the river's course, and list underneath the main characteristics of each.
(*b*)   Distinguish the main processes dominating each of the three sections of the course. In which is deposition most significant, and why?

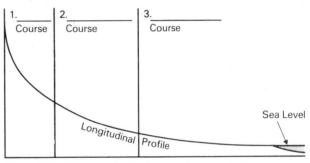

Figure 1.16   Diagram of a river's course (see exercise 9)

10. With the help of Figures 1.12, 1.13 and 1.15, draw as three or four small labelled diagrams the stages in the formation and destruction of an ox-bow lake.
11. With the help of annotated diagrams describe and explain the processes at work on Plates 1.8, 1.10 and 1.11.
12. Refer to the OS map extract of Castleford (page 72). Describe and explain the drainage features as far east as easting 48.

Ice Action

During the great Ice Age of the Quaternary period, which affected this country between about 100 000 and 600 000 years ago, the ice sheets waxed and waned as climatic conditions changed. When the climate was colder, the ice extended south. When conditions became warmer, the ice fronts *melted* and the land was gradually freed from ice. It must be emphasised that the ice did not *retreat*, in the sense of moving backwards. The furthest south the ice sheets reached in Britain was approximately the line of the Thames and Severn estuary (Figure 1.1). But southern England, beyond the ice fronts, suffered frozen conditions during the glacial periods (see page 10).

In Highland Britain, mountain glaciation took place, while in Lowland Britain more extensive ice sheets spread southwards, down the Irish Sea and the North Sea, the latter linking with the ice sheets of continental

15

Plate 1.13   Mer de Glace, Swiss Alps

Europe. Both were responsible for erosion, transportation, and deposition of material, although it would be fair to say that erosion was more pronounced in the highlands, and deposition in the lowlands.

Mountain Glaciation

Though small amounts of mountain glaciation took place in other areas, the regions of Britain where it was dominant were the Scottish Highlands, the Lake District and Snowdonia.

Erosional Features
The mountain glaciers of Britain have long since disappeared, and under present climatic conditions the mountains are too low for snow to lie all the year round, and thus for ice to collect. For a glimpse of what conditions were like in our mountains during the Ice Age, we have to go, for example, to the Alps. Here great beds of snow still collect over the years, become compacted into ice, and move down pre-existing valleys as *glaciers*. Plate 1.13 shows the upper part of the Mer

de Glace glacier in Switzerland. Note the clean surface of the ice at this level and the line of crevasses in the middle ground, where the ice has fallen over a break in the long profile of the valley. Notice also tributary glaciers coming in from the left and right. The mountains are either snow-covered, or exposed as bare rock. This bare rock is liable to *frost-shattering*. At night, water freezes in the joints and expands, allowing more water in on the next occasion. In this way joints are widened, and the rock prised apart. The loosened rocks become *scree*, and move down the slope to the glacier below, to be transported away.

In the right background, sharp peaks emerge above the snow and ice. These are known as *nunataks*, and are particularly liable to frost shattering. Note also the scree slopes just above the junction of the glaciers in the foreground.

(*a*) *Striations*   Armed with material provided by frost-shattered rocks, the rocks below and at the side of the glacier are polished and also scratched by the ice and its tools to form *striations*. After glaciation, these provide evidence of the direction in which the ice travelled.

16

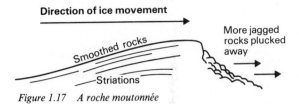

Figure 1.17   A roche moutonnée

(*b*) *Roches moutonnées* (Figure 1.17)   These are out-crops of rock which were smoothed and scratched on the side from which the ice approached. The leeward side is steeper with more jagged outlines, where the ice plucked away lumps of rock as it moved on. Like striations, roches moutonnées provide evidence of the direction in which the ice moved.

(*c*) *Corries* (cirques, or cwms)   In the high mountains, *corrie glaciers* developed from snowfields in hollows in the mountainsides (Plate 1.13). As the snow compacted into ice it moved downhill, pulling from the backwall. At the back of the glacier, a *bergschrund crevasse* developed. Figure 1.18 is a section showing the process of corrie formation at work, enlarging the original hollow in the mountainside to a characteristic armchair shape, as in those of the Cairngorms (Figure 15.5, page 199).

(i) At the back of the corrie, water runs down the bergschrund crevasse, and freezes in joints in the backwall, causing frost-shattering; (ii) as the corrie glacier moves downhill, it plucks away lumps of rock, causing the backwall to retreat; (iii) this material is used by the glacier for erosive purposes, and where the ice is thickest there is most erosion, giving the characteristic rock basin, which on melting often contains a *corrie lake*; (iv) lower down the ice is thinner and erosion less

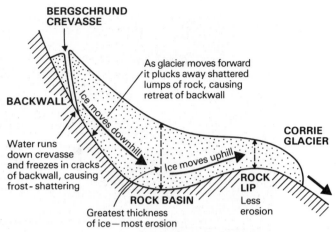

Figure 1.18   Section to show the formation of a corrie

effective, and a *rock lip* is left, sometimes topped by morainic material (see below).

(*d*) *Arêtes and horn peaks*   Where corries on either side of a watershed back on to each other, the retreat of their backwalls during glaciation may leave a knife-edged ridge, known as an *arête* (Figure 1.19), of which Striding Edge on Helvellyn in the Lake District is a famous British example. Where several corries back on to each other, a mere remnant of the former mountain mass may be all that is left after corrie action has taken place. The Matterhorn in the Swiss Alps is a magnificent example of a mountain remnant left in this way, known as a *horn peak*. Note the arête and horn peak in the top left of Plate 1.13.

(*e*) *Valley glaciers*   The corrie glaciers of the high mountains move down to join the main valley glaciers. The erosive force of valley glaciers trims off former interlocking spurs, and transforms them into *truncated*

Figure 1.19   Formation of an arête

(1) During glaciation

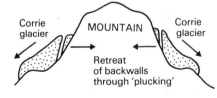

(2) After glaciation

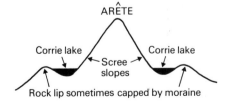

Figure 1.20   Valley features in glaciated highlands

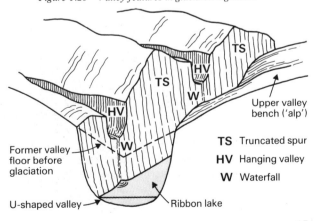

17

Plate 1.14   Buttermere and Crummock Water

spurs (Figure 1.20), examples of which can be seen in the background of Plate 1.13. The valley is over-deepened, cut down below its former level. The V-shape of the former valley is changed in its lower part to a *U-shape* (Figure 1.20). The remains of the former V-shape are represented in some areas by high valley benches or 'alps'.

There are many good examples of U-shaped valleys in the glaciated mountains of Britain, such as Great Langdale in the Lake District (Plate 5.1, page 52). The over-deepened valley floors are sometimes occupied by long narrow lakes, or *ribbon lakes*, of which Coniston in the Lake District is an example.

Hanging valleys (Figure 1.20) represent the former valleys occupied by tributary glaciers. These were smaller, and less powerful as erosive agents. When the ice melted, they were left hanging above the main valley. Where they are now occupied by a river, the tributary joins the main river via a waterfall.

(*f*) *Fjords*   At the coast, glaciated valleys have been drowned to form *fjords*, which have all the normal features of a glaciated valley. At the mouth of the fjord, a *rock lip* may have been left where ice action was weaker. This plus the deposition of morainic material may leave a series of islands known as a *skerry guard*. At the inland end of the fjord, or where tributary valleys reach it, the current of the river is checked and material is deposited to form a *delta*. Such deltas may also be found in ribbon lakes: Buttermere and Crummock Water in the Lake District have been divided by a delta (Plate 1.14).

The most spectacular fjords in Europe are to be found in Norway. Less spectacular examples, but still scenically very attractive, are the sea lochs of the coast of north-west Scotland. Plate 1.15 shows such a sea loch, Loch Leven.

Plate 1.16, showing part of Snowdonia, illustrates a whole array of features of a formerly glaciated region. These include the *horn peak* of Snowdon itself; the arête of Crib Goch; former *nunataks* in the Tryfan area; a whole series of *corries*, including, for example, Cwm Glas (cwm being the Welsh name for corrie); *corrie lakes*, such as Glaslyn; *U-shaped valleys*, such as Llanberis: *ribbon lakes* such as Llyn Peris; and *truncated spurs*, as in Llanberis. Notice too how the sharper glaciated features tend to be on the north-facing sides of the mountains.

Depositional Features

Morainic material   Material plucked from the floor of the valley by the sole of the glacier, and scree and other material coming from the valley sides, are transported by the glacier. Some of the material accumulates at the sides of the glacier to form *lateral moraine*. Where two glaciers unite, their lateral moraines join together to form *medial moraine* (Plate 1.13). The rock debris at the floor of the glacier is deposited as *ground moraine*. A large amount of material accumulates at the snout of the glacier and is deposited as *terminal moraine*. The various types are shown on Figure 1.21. Moraine generally takes the form of an unsorted mass of clay and boulders, as can be seen in Plate 3.1 (page 32).

Plate 1.15   Loch Leven

Lowland Glaciation

Lowland ice transported and deposited vast amounts of morainic and outwash material, laid down by streams, from the ice, leaving vast tracts of *boulder clay* (see Plate 3.1) (or *till*) and *sands and gravels*. Finer material in some cases dried out and was blown by the wind to be deposited as *loess*. River systems, flowing against the direction of the ice, were diverted.

During the great Ice Age, continental ice sheets swept south from Scandinavia, scraping away the surface soil, leaving today the rocky, hummocky, lake-studded landscape of the Baltic Shield. Boulder clay and sands and gravels were deposited in great amounts on the North European Plain. The north-flowing rivers of this plain were diverted into an approximate east–west direction along the front of the ice, creating valleys known as *urstromtaler*. The hummocky nature of the topography has again resulted in many lakes.

Similar ice sheets covered the lowlands of Britain as far south as the Thames and Severn, again depositing large amounts of boulder clay and sands and gravels. In some cases the boulder clay was smoothed by the ice into elongated hills, about 15 metres high, 200–400 metres broad, and 600–800 metres long, known as *drumlins*. Good examples can be found in the Lancaster area and Ribble valley in north-west England, and in County Down in Northern Ireland. Drumlins in County Down are shown in Plate 1.17. They can be picked out

Figure 1.21   *Simplified plan of the depositional effects of valley glaciers*

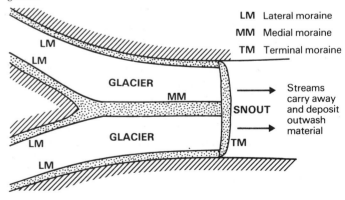

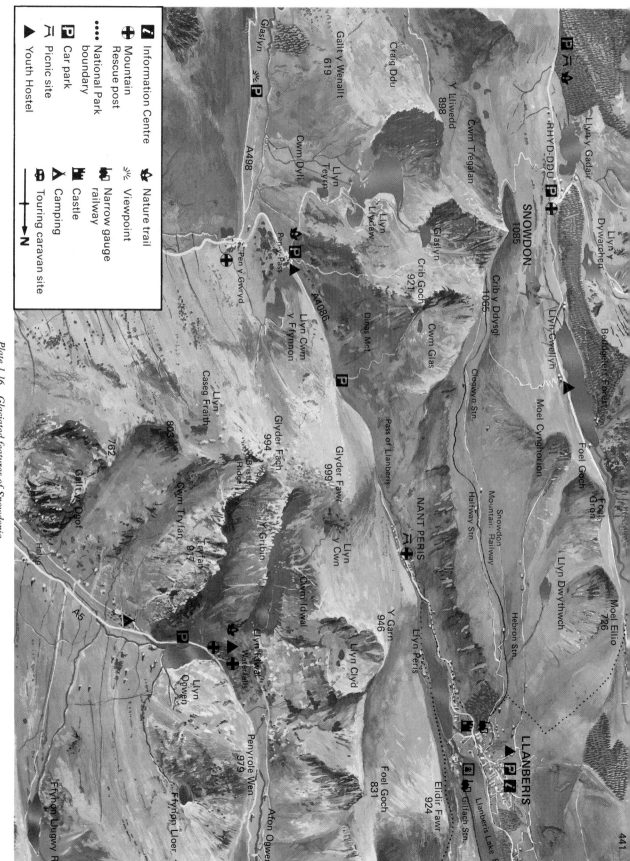

Plate 1.16 Glaciated features of Snowdonia

Plate 1.17   Strangford Lough, County Down: drumlins

as the islands in Strangford Lough, and as the well-drained arable land, with the hollows (like most hollows in drumlin country) being badly drained. The long axis of the drumlin indicates the direction of ice movement.

Eskers are another depositional feature but, unlike drumlins, are made up of sands and gravels. They are long sinuous ridges, running for kilometres across country, approximately in the direction in which the ice formerly moved. They represent the infilling of tunnels in the ice, through which water flowed. When the ice melted, the sands and gravels carried by the water in these tunnels was deposited as an esker.

There are relatively few erosional features associated with lowland ice, but where outcrops of resistant rock stood in the way of the ice they prevented weaker material behind from being carried away, leaving a *crag and tail structure*. Such a structure provides the site for the old part of Edinburgh (Plate 11.1, page 139). Like roches moutonnées, crag and tail structures show the direction of ice movement, but in this case the jagged outlines face the direction from which the ice came, and the smooth gentle slope is found on the leeward side.

Exercises

13. Refer to Plate 1.16.
(*a*) Give other examples of glaciated features additional to those mentioned on page 18.
(*b*) Lay a sheet of tracing paper over the Plate, and draw an annotated sketch of the glaciated features of Snowdonia.
(*c*) Try to indicate the relationships between this Plate and Plate 1.13.

14. With the help of contoured sketches or block diagrams, demonstrate the differences between glaciated and non-glaciated valleys.
15. What are the main differences between (*a*) mountain and lowland glaciation; (*b*) corrie and valley glaciers?
16. Outline the different ways in which striations, roches moutonnées, drumlins, eskers, and crag and tail structures provide evidence of the direction of ice movement.
17. With the help of annotated diagrams, show how you would be able to distinguish between (*a*) a roche moutonnée and a drumlin; (*b*) a drumlin and an esker.

Sea Action

The variety of geological formations shown on Figure 1.1 help to produce a variety of coastal landforms round the British Isles. Like river and ice action, the sea is responsible for the erosion, transportation and deposition of material, mostly through the work of waves.

Erosional Features

Caves and Blow-holes
When waves beat against the base of cliffs, air is driven into joints and bedding planes in the cliff face and compressed. As the wave retreats, the compressed air escapes with considerable force, and thus stresses are produced, and rock material is gradually loosened and dislodged. The joints and bedding planes are in consequence widened and *caves* are formed (Plate 1.2). In some cases the compressed air may escape through the roof of the cave to form a *blow-hole* (Plate 1.18), as shown on the photograph, taken at Cadgwith on the Cornish coast. The roof of the cave may collapse to form a long fissure in the cliff face.

Plate 1.18   A blow-hole, Cornish coast at Cadgwith

Cliff Formation

The waves also use pebbles from the beach to batter at the base of the cliff. This is particularly likely where (i) the slope of the beach is steep, allowing waves to reach the base of the cliffs unimpeded, (ii) there is a long unbroken stretch of sea, over which the winds can whip up large waves. The distance over which this can happen is known as the *length of fetch*. Thus the length of fetch of south-westerly winds is much greater on the coasts of south-west England, say, than on those of south-west

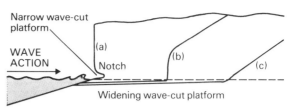

Figure 1.22   Cliff development

Lancashire. The coasts of enclosed seas do not therefore experience such large breakers as those facing the great oceans.

As the waves batter at the base of the cliffs, a notch is formed and gradually enlarged (Figure 1.22). In time the overhanging cliff collapses. This can happen almost overnight where the cliffs are of non-resistant rock, as in Holderness in Yorkshire and the Cromer area of Norfolk.

As the cliff retreats, its 'foundation' is exposed as a *wave-cut platform*. On Plate 1.19 the chalk cliffs, in this case on the Sussex coast, were at one time well to the left of their present position. As they have retreated, the clearly marked wave-cut platform has been left. Where cliff retreat is relatively fast, as in this case, the action of the sea will remain dominant and the cliffs almost vertical.

The widening wave-cut platform increasingly dampens the force of the waves through friction, and when this happens normal forces of weathering and soil and

Plate 1.19   The Seven Sisters, chalk cliffs on the Sussex coast

Plate 1.20 A natural arch at Botany Bay, Kent

rock movement occur higher up the cliff, resulting in the upper part of the cliff assuming a more gentle slope (Figure 1.22). Eventually, the vertical part of the cliff disappears, and the very wide wave-cut platform becomes backed by a gentler slope (stage (c) on Figure 1.22).

Natural Arches and Stacks

Where caves develop on either side of a headland, they may cut back under the action of forces previously described, and meet each other to form a natural arch. This has happened in the well-jointed rocks of the Kent coast at Botany Bay (Plate 1.20). These arches will eventually collapse to form stacks. That is, the block of cliff on the right of the photograph will become a stack when the natural arch collapses. The Needles off the Isle of Wight are excellent examples of chalk stacks.

Figure 1.23 Movement of beach material

← Swash

←--- Backwash

Prevailing wind and wave approach

Movement of beach material

Beach

Shore

Plate 1.21 Groynes and longshore drift at Brighton

Depositional Features

The Action of Longshore Drift

Waves do not necessarily approach the coast at right angles. The direction of the prevailing wind may lead to the waves moving in at an angle to the beach. When this happens, the waves move up the beach as *swash*. But, after the waves break, the water runs down the beach as *backwash*, at right angles to the coast (Figure 1.23). In this way, material is moved along the beach in the direction of the dominant wind.

If too much material is carried away by *longshore drift*, the protecting action of the beach is removed, and waves can again reach the shore behind, causing marine erosion. In some areas, *groynes* have been built, to prevent beach material being carried away, as shown on Plate 1.21, at Brighton. Note the beach material piled up behind the groynes. In which direction is the longshore drift?

23

The Development of Spits

Where the material transported by longshore drift reaches an opening in the coast, such as a river estuary, a long narrow bank of material may be built out, known as a *spit*. The end of the spit may be curved backwards by wave action from another direction, to form a recurved spit, as shown on Plate 1.22 and Figure 1.24 of Hurst Castle spit on the Hampshire coast. In the slack waters protected by the spit, *salt marsh* develops. Other famous spits in Britain include Spurn Head, built out into the Humber estuary. Chesil Beach, which connects the Isle of Portland to the mainland, was formed in a similar way. Sometimes the spit builds right across an opening in the coast, to form a *bay-head bar*, leaving a lake behind, as shown in the field sketch of Slapton Sands in Devon (Figure 1.25).

Exercises

18. Draw a series of labelled diagrams in section and in plan to show the development of natural arches and stacks, making use of photographs and other information in the text.

19. Find a large map of the coast of Humberside and trace the outline of the Humber estuary and the coast to the north of it. Mark on Spurn Head, and label the direction of longshore drift (not length of fetch), the spit, salt marsh and erosion of cliffs.

20. Draw an outline map of the Irish Sea, and a series of arrows crossing the sea in the direction of the main points of the compass, focussed on the coast of south-west Lancashire. From which direction is the greatest length of fetch? Why is this so?

21. Figure 1.26 is based on a field sketch made in the nineteenth century by the great Scottish geologist, Archibald Geikie, of the coast of part of Caithness in the far north of Scotland. Identify the coastal features at A, B, C and D, explaining carefully how each was formed.

Figure 1.24   Development of Hurst Castle spit

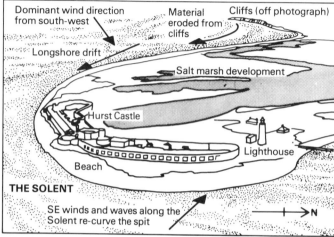

Plate 1.22   Hurst Castle spit

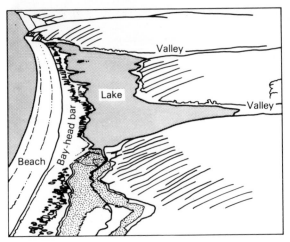

Figure 1.25 Field Sketch of Slapton Sands, Devon

Figure 1.26 Stacks of Duncansby, Caithness

Changes in Sea Level

As has already been noted, the most significant event in our recent geological history has been the Ice Age. This was associated with fluctuations in climate. As the ice sheets grew in colder periods, water was taken up from the seas, resulting in falls in sea level round the world. In warmer periods the ice sheets melted and sea levels rose. Another factor was the removal of weight of ice from a land area when the ice sheets melted, resulting in a rise of the land surface. This is termed an *isostatic* change. Thus, since the Ice Age, a complex series of events has occurred; removal of the weight of ice causing rises in the land surface (in effect like a fall in sea level); and melting of ice causing rises in sea level, drowning coastal estuaries.

Rises of the Land

Inland Features
A rise in the land surface has dramatic effects, enabling river systems to start cutting down into the newly uplifted area. The rivers are *rejuvenated* with, as it were, a new and lower sea level to aim at.

(a) *River terraces* Rivers in their flood plains can therefore start cutting down again, and river terraces are formed. Look at Figure 1.27 and imagine the river at level 1. A rise of the land surface or a fall in sea level allows the river to cut into its former flood plain as far as level 2, and a second flood plain is developed, the older one being left in the form of *paired river terraces*. A further uplift of the surface allows more incision, forming a third flood plain, with two sets of river terraces above. These terraces are valuable sites for farming, settlement and communications, as they are generally of fertile alluvial material, flat, and on dry points above the level of flooding.

(b) *Incised meanders* Sometimes the river incises itself into its former meanders, cutting down into the rocks

Figure 1.27 *The development of river terraces (the drawing is exaggerated vertically)*

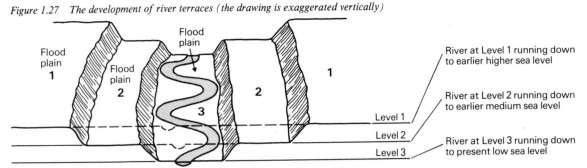

25

Plate 1.23   A raised beach at Gruinard Bay, Scotland

below the former flood plain, as shown on Figure 1.28. The former inside bank of the meander is left as a *meander core*. This can become an important settlement site, as it is defended by water on three sides, forming a natural moat. A famous British example is on the River Wear at Durham (Figure 11.3c, page 141).

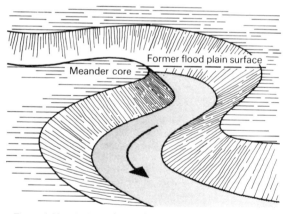

Figure 1.28   An incised meander

Coastal Features

Raised beaches   In the same way as river terraces are formed inland, an uplift of the land surface (or fall in sea level) can produce raised beaches at the coast. Just as river terraces are remnants of former flood plains, so raised beaches are remnants of older beaches (Figure 1.29). At the back of the raised beach there may be an old cliff line, perhaps with abandoned caves. Plate 1.23 shows a raised beach at Gruinard Bay in north-west Scotland, with an old cliff line behind. As with river terraces, raised beaches provide good sites for settle-

ments and communications. Some of the crofting settlements of north-west Scotland are on raised beaches (Figure 5.12, page 64).

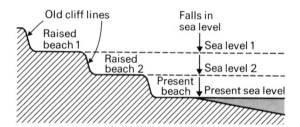

Figure 1.29   The development of raised beaches (the drawing is exaggerated vertically)

Rises in Sea Level

Rises in sea level result in drowning of valleys, whether glaciated or normal river valleys, at the coast.

Fjords
As we have seen already in the section on glaciation, fjords are drowned glaciated valleys (see page 18).

Rias
In parts of Britain not directly affected by glaciation, namely south-west England, south-west Wales and south-west Ireland, the lower parts of river valleys have been drowned to form rias, as shown on Plate 1.24.

Unlike fjords, rias

(i) have relatively gently sloping sides, although the lower slopes can be quite steep, as Plate 1.24 shows;

(ii) have soil-covered rather than bare rock slopes, often wooded on the steeper lower part, with farmland above (Plate 1.24);

26

Plate 1.24   A drowned valley or ria, Looe, Cornwall

(iii) have floors which slope gradually down towards the coast, as in a normal river valley, whereas a fjord might be shallower near its mouth;

(iv) have tributaries entering at the level of the main ria channel, not hanging above, as can be the case with fjords. Like fjords, however, when tributaries reach the drowned channel, their flow is checked and deltas or delta-like deposits are left.

Large rias make magnificent natural harbours. One of the best examples in Britain is Milford Haven, now our greatest oil port. Fowey is a deep-water port involved in the export of kaolin from the granite uplands of the south-west. Places like Looe (Plate 1.24) are minor fishing ports and holiday centres. The larger rias can make cross-river communication difficult. In the case of the Fowey estuary, the lowest bridge point is almost 10 kilometres upstream at Lostwithiel. On smaller estuaries there may be a bridge nearer the coast, as at Looe (Plate 1.24).

Exercises

22. How would you be able to tell that a river terrace was not the present flood plain of a river?

23. (*a*) Refer to the photographs of the Looe estuary (Plate 1.24) and of Loch Leven (Plate 1.15). Outline the features which enable you to distinguish one as a ria and the other as a fjord.

(*b*) Make a table with three columns, like this:

Characteristics	Fjord	Ria
1. 2. 3. ⋮		

In the left-hand column fill in the general characteristics, such as cross profile; long profile; tributaries, etc., then complete the other two columns as appropriate.

(*c*) Try to draw a labelled block sketch of Plate 1.24.

24. In what ways has the Ice Age affected the landscape on Plate 1.23?

2 WEATHER AND CLIMATE

WEATHER MAPS

Every day on television or in newspapers we can see simplified weather maps prepared by the Meteorological Office, accompanied by a forecast for the following day. Meteorologists study the patterns of weather over the earth's surface and provide maps, or *synoptic charts*, which give an overall view of weather conditions at a particular time, and allow predictions to be made about the weather to come.

The charts shown on television, though clear and straightforward, do not show much detail. They are prepared from more complicated maps. The symbols used on these more detailed maps are shown on Figure

2.1, which is linked with a diagram showing how the symbols are actually plotted on the weather map (Figure 2.2). Where a classification is required, as in the case of cloud cover and wind strength, criteria have to be laid down to enable an assessment to be made. The degree of cloud cover can be visually assessed by dividing the proportion of the sky covered by cloud into eighths. Thus four-eighths means a sky half-covered by cloud. Wind strength can be accurately measured by instruments. The effects of different wind strengths are measured by the Beaufort scale (Table 2.1), giving in this case the effects of wind on land.

Figure 2.1   The symbols used on weather maps

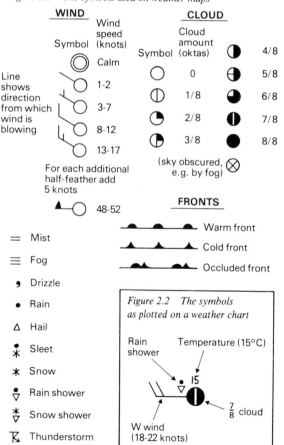

Figure 2.2   The symbols as plotted on a weather chart

Figure 2.3   A synoptic chart

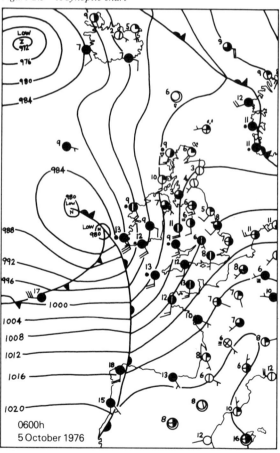

Beaufort number	Description	Effects on land	Speed knots	km/hour
0	Calm	*Smoke rises vertically*	0–1	0–1
1	Light air	*Direction shown by smoke but not by wind vane*	2–3	2–5
2	Light breeze	*Wind felt on face; leaves rustle; ordinary vane moved by wind*	4–6	6–11
3	Gentle breeze	*Leaves and small twigs in constant motion; wind extends a light flag*	7–10	12–19
4	Moderate breeze	*Raises dust and loose paper; small branches moved*	11–16	20–28
5	Fresh breeze	*Small trees in leaf begin to sway; crested wavelets form on inland waters*	17–21	29–39
6	Strong breeze	*Large branches in motion; whistling heard in telegraph wires; umbrellas used with difficulty*	22–27	40–50
7	Moderate gale	*Whole trees in motion; inconvenience felt when walking against wind*	28–33	51–61
8	Fresh gale	*Breaks twigs off trees; generally impedes progress*	34–40	62–74
9	Strong gale	*Slight structural damage occurs (chimney pots and slates removed; fences blown down)*	41–47	75–87
10	Whole gale	*Seldom experienced inland; trees uprooted; considerable structural damage*	48–55	88–102
11	Storm	*Very rarely experienced inland; accompanied by widespread damage*	56–63	103–117
12	Hurricane		Above 63	Above 117

Table 2.1 The Beaufort wind scale

Figure 2.3 is an actual synoptic chart, showing conditions over Britain and Europe at 0600 hours on Tuesday, 5 October 1976. Notice that apart from the symbols indicated on Figure 2.1, it contains *isobars*, lines linking up places of equal pressure, given in millibars, 4 millibars apart. Isobars are like contour lines. Just as contours which are close together indicate a steep slope or gradient, so isobars which are close together indicate a steep pressure gradient, and therefore strong winds. Thus strong winds are being experienced to the south-west of Ireland on Figure 2.3. Where the isobars are further apart, winds are light, or calm conditions may prevail. The winds blow in general from areas of high pressure to areas of low pressure, although the direction of movement is more complex than this, as we shall see later.

Exercises

1. Give a written account of the weather conditions represented in the following symbols. Give the wind direction as well as wind speed, and relate this to the Beaufort scale.

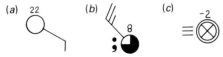

(a) 22   (b) 8   (c) -2

2. Refer to Figure 2.3. Name an area in the British Isles which is experiencing each of the following:
(a) complete cloud cover with rain; winds of about 35 knots from a south-south-easterly direction;
(b) a 4/8 cloud cover with mist; winds of about 10 knots from a southerly direction;
(c) a 1/8 cloud cover; light air from a northerly direction.

VARIATIONS IN BRITISH WEATHER

The most striking feature of British weather, like British scenery, is its *variability*. People living in equatorial regions can confidently expect hot wet weather all the year round, with most rain falling in thundery conditions in the afternoons. People living in the steppes of the USSR and the prairies of Canada can expect that their summers will fairly consistently be hot, and their winters cold.

All that the people in Britain can be confident about is that in any year the weather will be variable. The Easter period, for example, might enjoy warm calm conditions, allowing sunbathing: on the other hand, it might experience a cold snap of Arctic air, with snow falling in the mountains. While summer will be warmer than winter, it may still be quite cool and rainy. Alternatively, though probably less frequently, there may be a long hot dry spell, as in the summer of 1976.

Over a long period of time the weather can be averaged out to give the *climate* of an area. This allows us to generalise and say that, in Britain, winters are usually mild (certainly by the standards of our latitude), averaging between about 3 °C and 5 °C over the country; and summers warm, averaging between about 14 °C and 18 °C. Rainfall can be expected at any time of the year, though with more in the winter season. In summer, the months of July and August are generally wetter than those of May and June.

Quadrant		J	F	M	A	M	J	J	A	S	O	N	D		
(1) SE England	°C	4.1	4.2	5.6	8.1	10.8	14.1	16.3	16.5	14.8	11.3	7.7	5.3	Range	12.2
	mm	57	42	37	36	38	44	57	56	53	65	68	52	Total	605
(2) SW England	°C	6.2	5.8	7.3	9.2	11.7	14.5	15.9	16.2	14.7	11.9	8.9	7.2	Range	10.0
	mm	105	77	73	55	65	58	71	80	82	94	115	115	Total	990
(3) NE Scotland	°C	2.4	2.8	4.5	6.6	9.0	12.0	14.0	13.6	11.7	8.8	5.6	3.7	Range	11.6
	mm	77	54	52	50	62	53	92	73	65	90	91	78	Total	837
(4) NW Scotland	°C	4.3	4.4	5.7	7.0	9.3	11.6	13.3	13.3	11.8	9.3	6.9	5.5	Range	9.0
	mm	107	75	63	65	52	68	87	88	97	118	111	110	Total	1041

Table 2.2 Temperature and rainfall figures for four areas

Exercise

3. Table 2.2 shows the climatic averages of temperature and rainfall for four different stations, each representing the general conditions experienced in the four quadrants of the British Isles. Monthly average temperatures are given, together with the range of temperature over the year as a whole. Monthly average rainfalls are given in millimetres, together with the total for the year.
(a) Draw a climatic graph for each of the four stations. Use bar graphs for the rainfall figures and line graphs for the temperature. The horizontal axis should show by letters the twelve months of the year; the left-hand vertical axis should show temperatures in degrees centigrade, and the right-hand axis rainfall in millimetres. The placing of these should be adjusted to allow the line graph to stand clear above the bar graph. (See Figure 2.16.)
(b) On the basis of your graphs, describe the basic differences between the four parts of the country in terms of:
(i) temperature levels and range of temperature;
(ii) amounts and incidence over the year of rainfall.

Why does British weather vary so much?

To answer this question, we must consider Britain in its overall situation in the northern hemisphere, for the forces which determine British weather rarely begin over Britain itself. The answer is a fairly complicated one, since at least seven factors have to be considered: (1) latitude; (2) ocean currents; (3) air masses and their origins; (4) depression activity; (5) relief; (6) anticyclonic activity; and (7) convection.

Latitude

A glance at the atlas will demonstrate that Britain, for its size, covers a wide range of latitude from about 50° to 60° north. This affects the temperature distribution. The angle of incidence of the sun is less in the higher latitudes, in which Britain lies, than in the tropics. In general, temperatures vary inversely with latitude, i.e. the higher the latitude the lower the temperature. In theory, places in northern Britain will therefore be cooler than places in southern Britain.

This tends to be true in the summer. In Table 2.2 for example, the two stations in southern Britain have higher summer temperatures than the two stations in Scotland. But this is not necessarily the case in winter, when the angle of the sun in the sky in British latitudes is low. Note that station 4, in north-west Scotland, has higher average winter temperatures than station 1, in south-east England. Note too that the stations on the west side of the country have higher winter averages than those on the eastern side of the country. Clearly a different factor is operating there.

Ocean Currents

On the other side of the Atlantic, Labrador, in the same latitudes as Britain, experiences very severe winter conditions, in contrast to British mildness. The main reason for this difference is the presence of two different ocean currents. Figure 2.4 shows that the coast of Labrador is affected by the cold Labrador Current. In contrast, Britain gains the benefit of the warm North Atlantic Drift. This starts in the warm waters of the Caribbean as the Gulf Stream, then becomes the North Atlantic Drift. Notice how it pushes north the January 0 °C isotherm, to give the coasts of Britain and Norway ice-free conditions, contrasting with the frozen harbours of Labrador.

Winds passing over the North Atlantic Drift therefore bring mild weather, particularly to the west side of Britain. When the land mass warms up in summer, the effects of this warm current are not felt. In fact winds coming off the sea at the season are generally cooler.

Thus factors (1) and (2) go some way towards explaining why (a) southern Britain is warmer than northern Britain in summer; (b) western Britain is milder than eastern Britain in winter; (c) places in northern Britain might have less cold winters than those in the south, despite their latitude.

But there are many other factors still to consider.

30

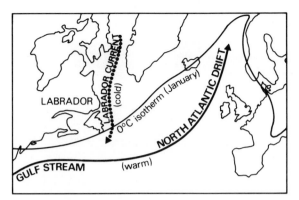

Figure 2.4 The North Atlantic Drift

Air Masses: The Battle of the Atlantic

Figure 2.5 gives a picture of the battle of different air masses over the North Atlantic, which has profound consequences for British weather. High-pressure areas are found near the Pole and in the tropical waters round the Azores, as shown. Great masses of air (of which the winds experienced in Britain are part) move from these areas towards the low-pressure belt in between, which lies over the North Atlantic. It is along this belt that the depressions which influence British weather so much are formed (see later).

Britain is thus affected by the following types of air mass, each bringing with it its own weather components:

Arctic (A) air from due north: very cold and moist.

Maritime polar (MP) air: cold and moist.

Continental polar (CP) air: cold and dry (but see Figure 2.6).

Maritime tropical (MT) air: warm and moist.

Continental tropical (CT) air: hot and dry.

Variations in the pressure systems of the northern hemisphere mean that these different air masses can affect us at different times.

Summer

Britain tends to experience wet summers when the predominant wind direction is from the west, bringing MP or MT air. If mostly MP, summers will be cooler than the average. Occasionally there are hot dry spells, as a result of a southerly flow of CT air, which originates over the Sahara. Summer conditions are also very much influenced by anticyclonic activity (see later).

Winter

The nature of the air masses received in Britain is perhaps even more critical in the winter. If the predominant air masses are MP, Britain tends to receive strong winds, squally showers (perhaps of snow), and relatively low temperatures. If they are MT, coming from the south-west (Figure 2.5), milder conditions result. If they are A or CP, cold winds sweep down from the Arctic and North Sea, or westwards from the USSR and Scandinavia, and bring cold conditions and snow, particularly to northern and eastern areas, having collected moisture over these sea areas. If the CP air originates further south, it has a long land and short sea crossing and is therefore still cold, but much drier than the air which has a long sea crossing (Figure 2.6).

Figure 2.6 illustrates why the Cairngorms are more suitable as a winter sports area than, say, the Lake District or Snowdonia. The Cairngorms, in the north-east of Britain, receive a much greater proportion of A and CP air, bringing snow as a result of the long sea crossing. (See also the relief effect, pages 34–5.) The

Figure 2.5 The 'Battle of the Atlantic': air masses and depression tracks

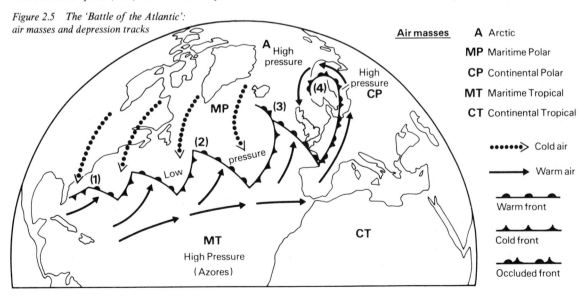

Soil photographs *(relating to pages 41, 42)*

Plate 3.1   Boulder clay and sands   *Plate 3.2   Lowland peat profile*   *Plate 3.4   Shirdley Hill Sand (glass sand)*

Plate 3.3   Lowland peat landscape near Southport (Figure 3.4)

Plate 3.5   Shirdley Hill Sand near Ormskirk (Figure 3.4)

Lake District and Snowdonia are sheltered from these influences. In years when the Cairngorms receive more than the usual proportion of MT air, rain falls rather than snow, and the skiing conditions are less good. (See also Chapter 15.)

Depressions

Figure 2.5 showed the growth of a depression, from its youth in the west of the Atlantic (1), to its maturity (2), the beginnings of old age (3), and its final decline as an occluded front (4). This is an oversimplification in that, for example, not all depressions move in the west–east trajectory shown. Some depressions, on reaching Britain, may be more youthful, or older, than the one shown on Figure 2.5.

Figure 2.7 illustrates in plan and in section, in a simplified way, the processes operating in the growth and decline of a depression.

Stage 1: Here cold MP air is sweeping behind the warmer MT air. The line of division does not remain a straight one: a 'kink' has developed in it which is the start of a depression, with the beginnings of a warm front (WF) in front, and a cold front (CF) behind. At this stage, there is still a considerable amount of warm

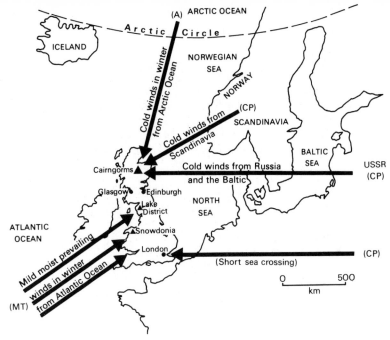

Figure 2.6   The effects of different air masses on Britain

air at the surface, as the section across A–B shows, forming the *warm sector*.

Stage 2: In the mature depression, the cold air is pushing into the warm sector, and catching up on the cold air in front of the warm front. The area of warm air at the surface is much less. Notice too that the warm front has a comparatively gentle surface, and the cold front a steeper one.

Figure 2.7   The growth of a depression

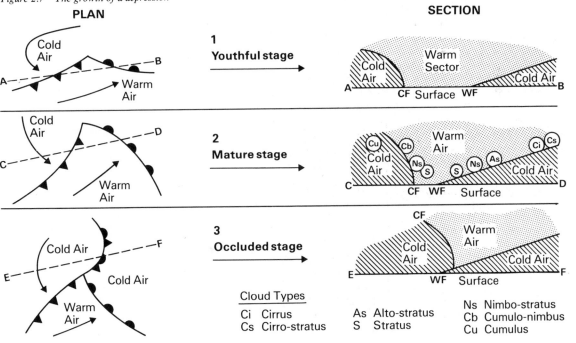

33

Stage 3: Here the cold air behind has caught up with the cold air in front of the warm front, and *occlusion* has taken place. Cold air covers the whole surface area, with the warm air aloft.

Figure 2.7 illustrates that the growth of depressions has to be considered in three-dimensional terms, and emphasises that the representation we see on synoptic charts (Figure 2.3) is only in plan.

Weather Associated with the Passage of a Depression
(*a*) *The warm front* As the warm front approaches, the cloud base becomes lower (Figure 2.7, section). Starting with high wispy cirrus (Ci) or cirro-stratus (Cs) cloud, we then get heavier alto-stratus (As) and nimbo-stratus (Ns). As the cloud base becomes lower, rain begins to fall. The pressure drops but temperatures gradually rise as the warm sector approaches.

(*b*) *The warm sector* In the warm sector, conditions are mild (MT air), and humid (or muggy), with low-level stratus (S) cloud and light rain or drizzle. Visibility is poor. Pressure is low, particularly at the centre of the depression (Figure 2.8).

(*c*) *The cold front* The weather change tends here to be more sudden. Tall rain-bearing clouds such as nimbo-stratus (Ns) and cumulo-nimbus (Cb) move in, giving heavier outbreaks of rain (Figure 2.8). The temperature falls steeply, but pressure begins to rise (Figure 2.9).

(*d*) *Behind the cold front* Following the cold front comes MP air, giving cool or cold squally showery weather, with broken cumulus (Cu) and cumulo-nimbus (Cb) clouds.

Alignment of Depression Tracks
The alignment along which the depression tracks cross the North Atlantic has important consequences for British weather, especially in the winter. If the depression tracks lie across Britain as a whole (Figure 2.8) or to the south of the country, it lies in a Maritime Polar airstream and conditions are cool. On the other hand, if the depression tracks lie to the north of Britain, there will be mild conditions under the influence of MT air.

Relief

Figure 2.8 suggests that, in the passage of a depression, rainfall is liable to be particularly heavy on the highlands. The fact that the air masses affecting Britain for much of the year come from the west would naturally suggest that the west side of the country will be wetter than the east. But this is not in itself sufficient explanation of the striking differences between the mountains of

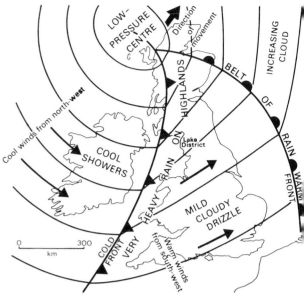

Figure 2.8   A depression crossing Britain

the west, where annual rainfall totals can be above 2000 mm, and the lowlands of the east, where they can be as little as 600 mm.

The additional factor is relief, and the so-called *orographic* effect helps to account for these variations. The moist winds from the west are forced to rise by the mountains of Highland Britain (Figure 2.10). As the air

Figure 2.9   The passage of a cold front

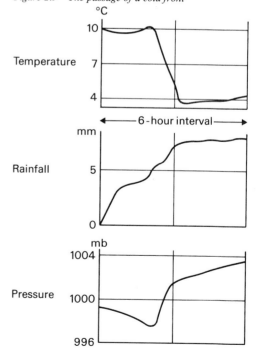

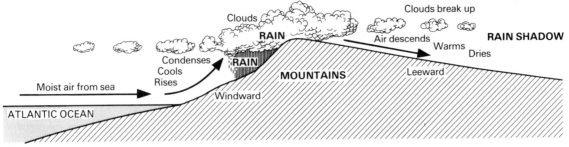

Figure 2.10   Relief (orographic) rain

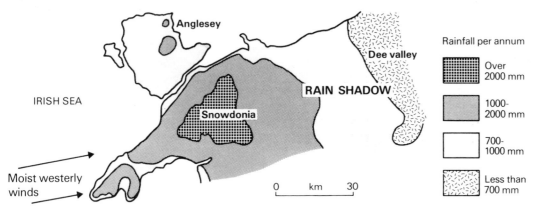

Figure 2.11   North Wales: the effect of relief on rainfall

rises it cools and the water vapour in it condenses to form clouds, which in turn give rainfall. Thus the windward slopes of the mountains have heavy rainfall. On the leeward side, the descending air warms and dries, giving a *rain shadow* effect.

Look now at Figure 2.11 to see this effect in action in North Wales. The heaviest rainfall is in the high mountains of Snowdonia, with over 2000 mm per annum. Further east, totals decrease until in the Dee valley there is less than 700 mm per annum, even though it is still on the western side of Britain. The North Wales resorts also are protected, one of the factors that makes Llandudno and other places popular with holiday-makers.

Relief also has an effect on *temperature*. Mountains are cooler than low-lying areas to the extent on average of 1 °C for every 165 metres of altitude.

Anticyclones

As we have seen, winds move from areas of high pressure to areas of low pressure. Sometimes high-pressure areas, or *anticyclones*, settle over the British Isles. In these circumstances, the isobars are further apart, with light winds circulating clockwise round the anticyclone (as against the anti-clockwise movement in

a depression), and calm conditions at the centre (Figure 2.12). Under anticyclonic conditions the air is descending, not rising as in a depression. As it descends the air warms, and skies are clear. But there are considerable differences in the weather conditions experienced from winter and summer anticyclones.

Figure 2.12   Winter high over Britain

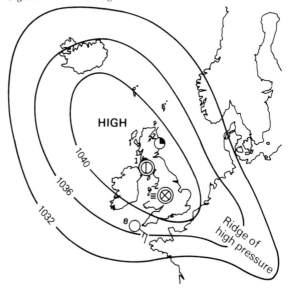

Winter Anticyclones

(*a*) *Fog* Anticyclones are associated with clear skies. On winter nights, there is much radiation of the earth's heat into the atmosphere, leaving cold conditions at ground level. Where there is water vapour in the air this condenses to form *dew at* ground level, and *mist or fog near* ground level.

The fog is particularly persistent in lowlands and valleys, because the denser cold air flows slowly down-slope and ponds in valley floors (Figure 2.13a). This can also take place in the spring when fruit is blossoming and can have serious effects for, for example, fruit farmers. Hence they tend to plant their orchards on the slopes above the bottom of the valley (see Chapter 5).

This ponding of cold air means that there is cold air below and warm air above, giving a *temperature inversion* (Figure 2.13b). Note that the smoke rising from the factory chimney cannot rise into the warm air, which acts as a 'lid', and so has to move horizontally below the line of the inversion.

Under these conditions, lowland temperatures may not rise above freezing all day, if the fog persists, as indicated in the Midlands on Figure 2.12. In contrast, the mountains of Snowdonia might at the same time be enjoying bright sunshine. The weaker rays of the winter sun are not so effective at dispersing fog, especially in urban areas (see below). But as the anticyclone collapses, and winds begin to strengthen, the fog is cleared.

(*b*) *Smog* In urban areas, a lethal combination of water vapour mixed with smoke particles from homes and factories can produce a 'dirty fog' or smog. This tends to be more persistent than fog because the action of the sun's rays is even less effective under these conditions, and poor visibility can persist for days on end. Fortunately, anti-pollution measures are improving the situation in industrial towns.

Summer Anticyclones

Summer anticyclones are accompanied by light winds or calms and long spells of sunshine. Conditions are very warm or hot, with afternoon temperatures rising above 25 °C. Rising heat (thermals) from the ground forms tall cauliflower-shaped fair weather cumulus clouds.

Thunderstorms Over a period of time the heat builds up and thundery conditions develop, often as the prelude to the collapse of the anticyclone, perhaps after two weeks or so, and there is a return to more unsettled conditions.

Figure 2.14 shows a thunder cloud, a large cumulonimbus with its characteristic anvil top. Such clouds can rise to 8000 or 9000 metres in height, with ice crystals at the top. Inside the cloud are turbulent updraughts of air. The water particles in the cloud become negatively and positively charged. Electrical discharges (*lightning*) pass between these differently charged particles. The air in the path of the discharge becomes intensely heated and sound waves (*thunder*) are set up. The flash can take place within the cloud, giving *sheet lightning*, or from the positively charged lower parts of the cloud to the negatively charged ground, giving *forked lightning*.

Figure 2.13 Conditions under winter anticyclone

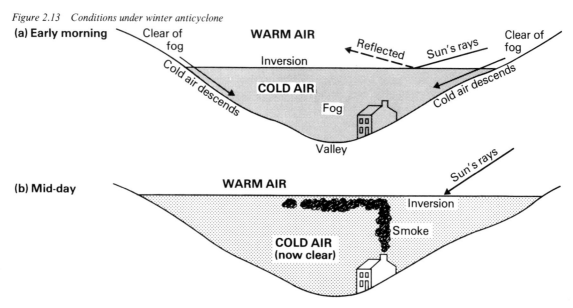

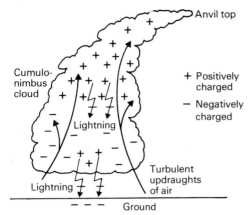

Figure 2.14   *A summer thunderstorm cloud*

Convection

The production of cumulus and cumulo-nimbus clouds is part of the process of *convection*. Rising air in the mid-day and afternoon sun produces such clouds, which can build up into rain clouds to give *convectional rainfall*, the type experienced daily in equatorial areas. The sheltered eastern side of Britain, and particularly the south-east, tend to get these long warm anticyclonic spells more frequently than other parts of the country, and a higher proportion of their summer rainfall is of a convectional type.

The more frequent presence of such conditions in the south-east also produces warmer average temperatures in summer, as indicated for station 1 in Table 2.2.

Summary

The variations between the stations in the four quadrants of Britain in Table 2.2, which introduced us to the complexities of British weather, thus reflect the influence of a considerable number of variables. The impact of these is summarised on Figure 2.15.

Figure 2.15   *Britain: general climatic factors*

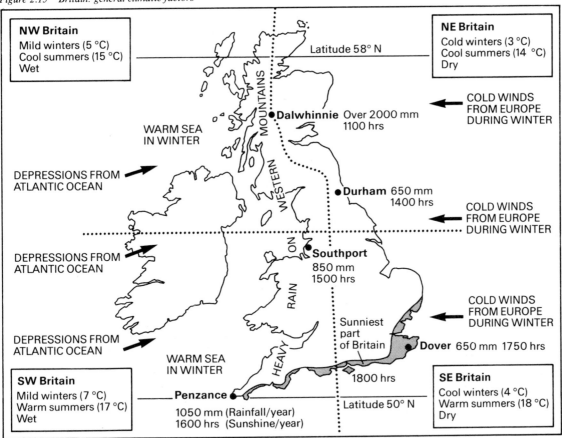

Exercises

4. Outline the main differences between depressions and anticyclones in terms of (a) pressure and wind directions; (b) temperature conditions; (c) rainfall conditions; (d) visibility.

5. Refer to the climatic graphs, Figure 2.16.

(a) Describe the temperature and rainfall conditions of Stations A and B.

(b) In which parts of Britain are the two stations to be found? Give reasons for your answers.

6. Refer to Figure 2.11.

(a) Compare this with a relief map of North Wales, and describe in detail the correlations between the two maps.

(b) Find three other parts of Britain in which similar conditions occur.

7. Refer to Figure 2.3. Imagine that the depression shown lies over the southern part of the North Sea, at about 1800 hours on the same day. Further occlusion has taken place. The cold front now lies approximately along a line from the Wash to south-western England. Describe the weather conditions liable to be present:

(a) on the coast of East Anglia;

(b) in the Isle of Wight;

(c) in Wales.

Mention all the conditions illustrated on synoptic charts. As an alternative, you might draw a chart similar to Figure 2.2 for a station placed in each of these three areas.

8. Refer to Figure 2.15. On the basis of information given and your understanding of the text, write an explanatory account of the major variations, by region, of British weather.

9. (a) Describe how the satellite photograph (Plate 2.1) shows cloud, showers, and clear skies in relation to the shape of the depression.

(b) Refer to Figures 2.5 and 2.7. What stage has the depression in Plate 2.1 reached?

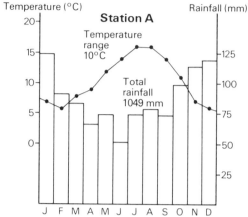

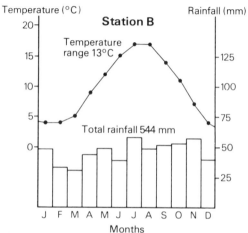

Figure 2.16 Climatic graphs (temperature and rainfall)

Plate 2.1 Satellite weather photograph of passage of depression, 8 February 1982 (with isobars superimposed)

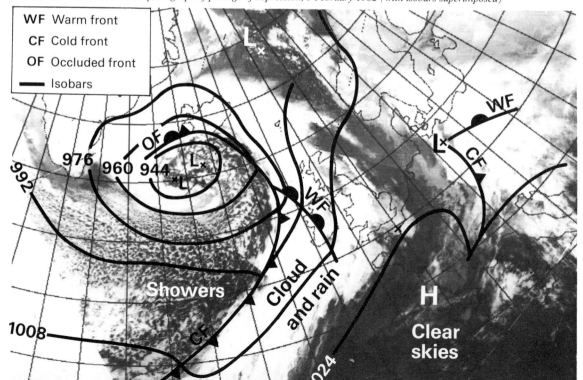

3 SOILS

Before we study farming in Chapter 5, it is vital to understand something of the formation and properties of soils. *Soil is the natural medium in which plants grow.* We often read that 'good' or 'fertile' soils help farming. But what constitutes a 'good' or a 'fertile' soil?

Soil Properties

Soil Material

Soil is made up of *mineral matter* (derived from weathered rock), *organic matter* (derived from plants and animals), *water* and *air*, and *plant roots* and *soil animals*. Air and water take up about half the soil body in an average agricultural soil. Plants find nutrients in the mineral and organic matter and in the water in the soil.

Soil Texture

One of the most important qualities of soil is its texture, the degree of coarseness or fineness of material in the soil. In some soils there are large boulders and other lumps of material, which are very coarse indeed. But here we are thinking of the general texture of the soil itself.

Coarse-textured Soils

These are soils with a high proportion of sand particles, ranging from about 0.2 mm to 2 mm in diameter. When rubbing a moistened sample of such a soil between the fingers, the coarse fragments can easily be felt. There are many pore spaces, so the soil is *porous* and can hold water easily and allow it to run through.

Fine-textured Soils

These contain a high proportion of fine particles, largely of clay, with a diameter of less than 0.002 mm. When moistened, a sample can be moulded into shapes between the fingers, and stains the hands. The individual particles cannot be felt. Clays are *impermeable* and tend to be easily waterlogged.

Another fine-textured soil is a silt, containing particles of from 0.02 to 0.002 mm in diameter. The alluvial soils of flood plains and river estuaries are examples.

Medium-textured Soils

These contain a mixture of particles, including coarse sands, fine sands (0.2 mm to 0.02 mm in diameter), silts and clays. Mixed soils such as this are known as *loams*.

Most British soils are mixed. Clay soils, although predominantly of clay, contain some silt and sand (Figure 3.1a). Loam soils grade into each other. A clay loam (about 35% clay) and a loamy sand (about 75% sand) are also identified (Figure 3.1b and c). Most good arable soils come within the general category of loams.

Peat is also an important soil in Britain, not identified in the above classification (see page 32).

Figure 3.1   Soil textures

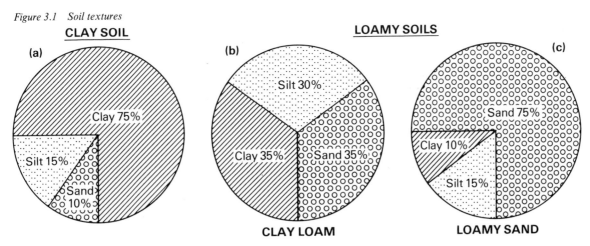

Soil Profiles

Apart from their varying distribution, soils change with depth. The *soil profile*, as it is called, covers the area between the surface and the parent rock below. It is usually divided into three *horizons* (Figure 3.2), which are more or less horizontal layers, made visible when a trench is dug into the soil.

The A Horizon

The A horizon is made up of a mixture of mineral and organic components. Here organic material from decaying vegetation accumulates and becomes mixed with the mineral matter of the underlying soil. Where rainfall is heavy, this material, and especially the mineral matter, is washed downwards or *leached*, to leave an ashy grey layer at the bottom of the A horizon (Figure 3.2).

The B Horizon

The upper part of the B horizon is composed of the mineral matter leached from above, which may form a hard, reddish-brown pan, where iron is present. Little or no organic matter is found in this layer. Lower down, the finer mineral material is mixed with coarser material, weathered from the parent rock below (Figure 3.2).

The C Horizon

This is the unweathered parent material below.

Acidity and Alkalinity

Another important characteristic of soil is its degree of acidity (or alkalinity). An acid soil contains no lime, while an alkaline one contains a great deal of lime (calcium carbonate). The degree of alkalinity is measured by the *pH value*. Soils range from pH2 to pH12. Above pH9 the soil would be very alkaline, above pH7 it would be alkaline, and below pH4.5 very acid.

The acidity of the soil is an important factor in soil fertility. In very acid soil, there exist fewer nutrients for plant growth. The best soil for plant growth is one that is slightly acid, about pH6, where the elements are soluble and available for plants to use. Most British soils tend to be more acid than this, and thus require liming to increase their fertility.

Factors Affecting the Nature of the Soil

Parent Material

Soil development can be limited by the nature of the parent material, which may be solid or drift geological

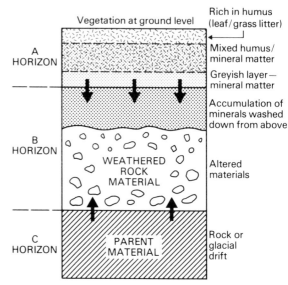

Figure 3.2   Soil profile

formations (Figure 3.2). Thus weathering of hard old rocks, such as gabbro, granite, Millstone Grit and Carboniferous limestone into soil is slow, which may lead to *thin* soils, unless other factors intervene (see below).

The parent material also affects the acidity of the soil. For example, soils on sandstone and granite tend naturally to be acid; those on limestone and chalk, alkaline.

Relief and Drainage

Rocks are weathered naturally into soil. On slopes there is a tendency for this soil to creep downwards. Figure 3.3 shows how as a result the soil thickness on the slope becomes less, while soil accumulates at the foot of the slope. Clearly this process is slower where there is a vegetation cover. Where bare soil is exposed, rapid *soil erosion* can take place, through the *gullying* of small streams.

Figure 3.3   The effects of relief on soil

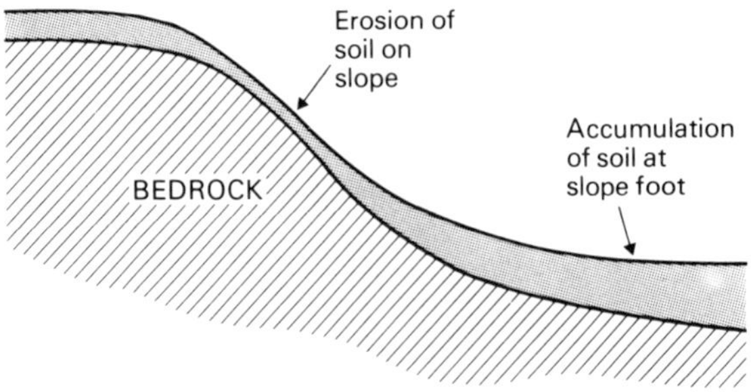

Erosion of soil on slope

Accumulation of soil at slope foot

BEDROCK

Drainage on slopes will tend to be freer, and the soils thus drier, containing more air spaces. At the bottom of slopes, or on flat-topped summits, soils will tend to become *waterlogged*, especially in the presence of heavy rainfall and impervious material below.

River Action

Rivers both help to erode soils, and transport the material to deposit it elsewhere, for example during flooding. The material is deposited as a silty soil, *alluvium*, on flood plains, and also on the mud-flats of estuaries.

Glacial Action

Ice sheets and glaciers have had a decisive influence in redistributing soils. In mountain areas the soil cover has often been stripped away, and redeposited on the lowlands. Vast amounts of glacial drift make up the parent materials of many of our lowland soils. Two basic types can be found.

(*a*) *Boulder clay* This is unsorted morainic material, made up basically of clay, but containing also boulders and pebbles of varying sizes. Such soils are acid and have a fine but sticky texture. They are *impermeable* and liable to waterlogging, especially in wetter parts of the country. Plate 3.1 (page 32) shows a sticky boulder clay in the Lake District. The darker A horizon at the top contains much more organic matter.

(*b*) *Sands and gravels* These were laid down by streams running out of the ice. Here the pebbles tend to be smaller, rounded and more even, and laid down in layers. The soil is again acid and coarse-textured, but *porous*.

Climate

Rainfall
Heavy rainfall naturally increases the possibility of waterlogging, particularly in clayey and silty areas, and in conditions of impeded drainage, as in hollows and flat areas. Clay soils tend to be *heavier* in wetter areas than in drier areas of Britain.

Drought
A period of drought can lead to the drying out of well-drained sandy and peaty soils, which become liable to *wind erosion*, a serious problem in the Fens, for example.

It is made worse by the removal of hedgerows, which has happened increasingly in recent years in many arable areas of Britain.

Frost
Although frost is bad for certain crops, it is helpful in winter for breaking up soils, particularly in clay areas, giving more air spaces in the soil. Farmers find such soils easier to plough in the spring which follows a cold frosty winter.

Vegetation

This is very important in providing the soil with its *organic material*, in the form of leaf or grass litter, for example. This material is a vital aspect of the fertility of any soil.

Podsols
An exception occurs under *coniferous forest* conditions, where relatively infertile *podsols* develop, particularly in sandy conditions. Coniferous trees can flourish in sand and gravel soils. They do not produce leaf mould, however, only sharp needle-like leaves which accumulate on the surface. These are not broken down into organic nutrients for the soil. Such soils are largely mineral, and the washing down of mineral material gives the podsol a very pronounced ash-grey layer (see Figure 3.2). Soils under coniferous forest are therefore infertile. It should be emphasised that podsols can develop under conditions other than coniferous forest.

Peat Soils
(*a*) *Moorland peats* These have developed on flat-topped moorland summits, where rainfall is heavy, drainage is poor, and where a plentiful supply of moorland vegetation breaks down quickly into peat. These conditions apply on the Millstone Grit summits of the Pennines, for example. The upland peats are acid, spongy (containing a lot of moisture), and form peat bogs. They are unsuitable for farming activity, except for rough pasture for sheep and cattle. But they form ideal storage for water supply, allowing a gradual seepage of water downwards to the streams and reservoirs (Chapter 4).

(*b*) *Lowland peats* The lowland peats of the Fens, south-west Lancashire and the Somerset levels are also made up of decayed vegetable matter, also occur on level ground, and are spongy in character, but there the resemblance with upland peats ends. They consist of the remains of past deciduous forest vegetation.

After the Ice Age, Britain went through a wet cool period of climate, when the trees died, and the vegetation rotted down and accumulated over the years as thick layers of peat. The old trunks or roots of trees (stocks) can sometimes be seen sticking out of the peat.

This peat is of a much less acid type than that of the uplands. When artificially drained, as it is in the areas previously mentioned, it gives a black fertile soil, deep, rich in organic material, porous, and easy to work (Plate 3.2, page 32). Unfortunately, peat dries out when exposed to the air, and the finer surface material is liable to wind erosion. Shrinkage of the peat causes fields to fall below the level of roads (Plate 3.3, page 32), and requires the re-laying of drains every so often. Eventually the soil is lost altogether, and the underlying material exposed.

Human Intervention

Perhaps the major influence on soils is humankind. Our influence may be a negative one, for example:
(a) by ploughing downslope we can cause gullying;
(b) by removing hedges we can help wind erosion;
(c) by putting heavy machinery on clay soils in wet weather we can harm the soil texture;
(d) by growing the same crop year after year we can drain it of the same nutrients, and introduce soil pests.

It is of course in the farmer's interest in the long run to treat the soil well, even though it may be more expensive to do this in the short run. Farmers can thus:
(a) add organic matter through ploughing in stubble, manuring, etc.;
(b) add mineral nutrients through putting in chemical fertilisers;
(c) rotate crops, using, for example, a leguminous crop, which puts nitrates back into the soil every few years;
(d) irrigate the soil in dry conditions.

The natural clays, loams and sands are thus changed over the years by human intervention. There is in south-west Lancashire, for example, a soil known as Shirdley Hill Sand (Plate 3.4, page 32), found round the market town of Ormskirk (Figure 3.4). This was originally sand dune material, formed when the coastline was much further inland. The sand is in itself lacking in organic material, but over the course of time grass and trees grew on it, and as humus (organic matter) built up, so cropping began. Over the centuries a rich black A horizon has developed, giving the soil the name the Ormskirk 'black sand', very good for vegetable growing (Plate 3.5, page 32). Soil profiles show a dark A horizon, with the light sand below (Plate 3.4). This Shirdley Hill Sand is a very pure form, suitable for glass making. Plate 3.4 shows it being extracted near St Helens for the glass industry (see Chapter 8).

What is a Fertile Soil?

We are now in a position to say that a fertile soil is one that:

(a) is *deep* enough to allow the root development of crops;

(b) has a *loamy* texture, with a good balance of air spaces and water content;

(c) is *well drained*, and not liable to waterlogging, which deprives the soil of its air, and does not allow soil animals such as worms to thrive;

(d) contains adequate *organic* and *mineral* nutrients;

(e) is just *slightly acid*, which allows the mineral nutrients to be made available as plant food.

As we have seen, however, human intervention can make soils that would be relatively infertile in their natural state productive through artificial means.

Soils and Farming

Anticipating Chapter 5, we may summarise that:

(a) loam and lowland peat soils (where artificially drained) are good for arable farming and vegetable growing;

(b) clay and alluvial soils are usually best left under grass and used for pastoral farming: but clay and certainly clay loam soils in less wet areas can be used for arable farming;

(c) thin rocky upland soils are limited in use to hill sheep farming, although on less steep slopes cattle can be grazed;

(d) upland peats can only be used for rough pasture for sheep and cattle.

These are of course very broad generalisations, subject to a good deal of local variation.

Exercises

1. Outline the differences between (*a*) sand and clay soils; (*b*) podsols and lowland peats.

2. Refer to Plate 3.1 (page 32). Draw an annotated soil profile to indicate the difference between the underlying boulder clay (till) and the overlying sands and gravels.

3. Compare and contrast the farming landscapes shown on Plates 3.3 and 3.5 (page 32).

4. Refer to Figure 3.4. Seven different types of soil are shown in the key.

(*a*) Draw up a table, with the seven types of soil in the left-hand column. Make a separate row for each of the following: texture; acidity (high/low); drainage; organic matter; area found. Fill in details as appropriate.

(*b*) Try to predict the relative fertility of each of the seven types, and the kind of farming associated with each. This can later be checked against information in Chapter 5 (pages 49–69).

5. Give reasons why:

(*a*) cereal growing is not important in Snowdonia;

(*b*) the peat soils of the Fens are not used for sheep rearing.

6. For your home region, try to find a classification of soils like that shown in Figure 3.4. Assess the impact of these soils on local farming.

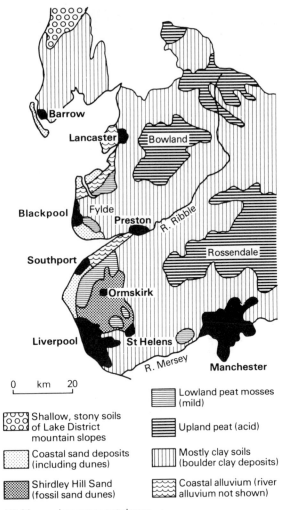

0   km   20

▨ Shallow, stony soils of Lake District mountain slopes

▨ Coastal sand deposits (including dunes)

▨ Shirdley Hill Sand (fossil sand dunes)

▤ Lowland peat mosses (mild)

▤ Upland peat (acid)

▥ Mostly clay soils (boulder clay deposits)

▧ Coastal alluvium (river alluvium not shown)

NB Many urban areas not shown

Figure 3.4   The soils of Lancashire

4 WATER SUPPLY

Birmingham's Water Supply

Plate 4.1 is a photograph of the attractive unspoilt valley of the River Claerwen in the mountains of central Wales. The picture was taken many years ago. The tracks, the bridges, the farmland, some of the woodlands and the large private residence no longer exist, because the land on which they stood now lies under the waters of the Claerwen reservoir, which supplies part of the water requirements of the city of Birmingham.

Birmingham's need for increasing its supplies of water is obviously linked with the expansion of its population. At the beginning of the eighteenth century Birmingham had 15 000 people. At the beginning of the nineteenth century numbers had increased to 70 000. A hundred years later, the population had risen more than tenfold to $\frac{3}{4}$ million, while by 1981 it was nearly 1 million.

By the late nineteenth century, therefore, local supplies of water by themselves were insufficient, and Birmingham had to look further afield. In 1876, the city of Birmingham acquired the Birmingham Waterworks Company, an early example of a private enterprise being taken over by a public authority. Attention was turned to the River Severn and the Welsh mountains as possible sources of supply, and the latter were eventually chosen. An Act of Parliament (1892) was needed to

allow the city to build reservoirs in the valleys of the Elan and the Claerwen, tributaries of the River Wye (Figure 4.1). No dam was built in the Claerwen valley, however, until more than fifty years later.

Plate 4.2 shows part of the reservoir system and the gathering grounds of the *Elan valley scheme*. Water is taken from here by the Elan aqueduct to Birmingham (Figure 4.1). There were many local protests at the drowning of the Elan valley. The reservoirs involved the demolition of eighteen cottages, one church, one chapel, one school and two residences. Farmers lost their land, and anglers their fishing rights, although the farmers were compensated and fishing was permitted in the reservoirs. At the same time, the reservoirs are impressive landscape features in themselves, attracting tourists and creating a few jobs for local inhabitants.

By the mid-1960s the demand for water in Birmingham exceeded the supply from the Elan valley and it was decided to supplement this, and provide for future growth, from the River Severn. The *Clywedog scheme* was finally authorised in 1963 and came into operation in 1968. The reservoir is a regulating reservoir, designed to control the flow of water along the Severn. Hence in times of drought and low water, water from the reservoir is let out into the Severn. This means that Authorities such as Birmingham can rely on the

Plate 4.1   The River Claerwen valley, central Wales

Plate 4.2   The Elan valley reservoir

flow and are able to extract continuous supplies of water from the river.

Plate 4.3 shows the *Trimpley works* on the Severn, where Birmingham extracts its water from the river (Figure 4.1). The intake is from the river on the left (below the wooded slope), while the treatment works (to purify the water) and the pumping station are on the right. From here the water is pumped to the Frankley works on the outskirts of Birmingham itself (Figure 4.1).

Further supplies for the region are being developed by tapping the *ground-water* resources of the Triassic sandstones of Shropshire.

Exercises

1. Name different groups of people who were affected by the drowning of the Claerwen valley (Plate 4.1).
2. Imagine that the reservoir in Plate 4.2 is no longer there. Recreate the conditions before the drowning of the valley. In what part of the river's course was this valley? Give the evidence on which you have based your choice.

The Advantages of the Welsh Mountains for Water Supply

(1) *Average rainfall totals are high*, about 1800 mm per annum in the mountains of central Wales, giving a plentiful supply of water.
(2) The Wye and the Severn have many tributaries in their upper reaches, such as the Elan and the Claerwen in the case of the Wye (Figure 4.1), giving *extensive water gathering grounds* and large volumes of water.
(3) The many *narrow valleys* of the mountains make the impounding of reservoirs by dams (Plate 4.2) easier than it would be in wide valleys; in addition the hard old base rocks of the mountains provide *firm sites* for dams.
(4) Although the local people of the valleys which were drowned were very seriously affected, farming in the region was never very prosperous. Though regrettably some people had to be moved from their homes, there were not large numbers of them. The water undertaking does also provide a certain amount of work for local people, particularly in relation to the surrounding

45

Plate 4.3   Trimpley works on the River Severn

coniferous plantations (Figure 4.1). Sawmilling is associated with the Elan valley scheme. Hill sheep farming does, however, continue to be the main occupation of the area.

(5) As Figure 4.1 shows, the water supplies are *accessible*, the Elan valley being located within about 112 kilometres of Birmingham. The further the supplies are from the urban areas which need them, the greater the expense of transporting the water. As we have seen, even taking the water 112 kilometres was costly to Birmingham.

Exercises

3. State the different types of land use shown on Plate 4.2.

4. Compare the advantages and disadvantages of (*a*) local; (*b*) 'imported' supplies of water, to a large town.

The Water Supplies of Britain

Figure 4.2 shows how water supply is used. Most goes to households in unmetered form, which means that each householder pays a *water rate*, however much or little is used, according to the rateable value of the house. Note also that a small proportion of the water supply is not drinkable, and is for industrial use. In addition, a large percentage of the supply is lost by leakage and other means. The Water Boards, as part of an economy drive, are striving to reduce the amount lost in these unaccounted ways.

Over the years, there have been increasing demands for water, as we have seen, for *domestic use*, rapidly growing in an age when people are becoming more affluent and more hygienic, demanding water for baths, showers, washing machines, hose pipes, and other

Figure 4.1   Birmingham: water supply from Wales and the Severn

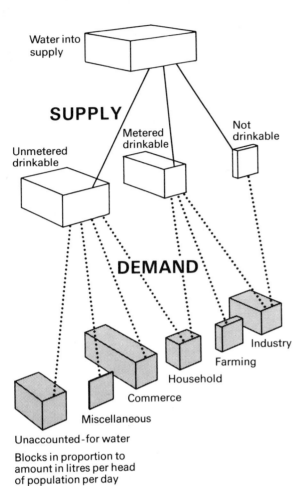

Figure 4.2   Components of public water supplies

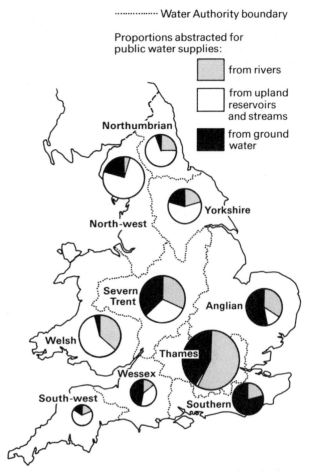

Figure 4.3   Water Authorities and water supplies of England and Wales

purposes; *industrial use*, where the demands of factories and power stations are increasing even more rapidly; and *agricultural use*, as farmers in the crop farming areas are realising the advantages of applying irrigation water to their fields in dry periods, especially in the drier south-eastern parts of Britain. Overall, Britain is fortunate in having such a reliably moist climate and therefore generally adequate supplies of water. A greater problem is to manage water supply as cost effectively as possible. A major difficulty is that the water is not in the right place. Rain falls most heavily on the mountains, but the large urban areas which consume the water are mostly on the lowlands. Thus in very dry years, such as 1976 in Britain, some areas may have ample supplies while others are desperately short of water.

To try to solve these problems, individual smaller-scale Water Authorities have been combined to form large regional Water Authorities (Figure 4.3), and

schemes are in hand to make possible large-scale transference of water in times of need from surplus to shortage areas.

Figure 4.3 shows the proportions of water supply derived from rivers, upland reservoirs, and from ground water, in the various Water Boards of England and Wales. Notice that those of Highland Britain (Figure 1.1) draw most of their water from upland reservoirs and streams, while in Lowland Britain a greater proportion comes from rivers and ground water. For example, porous Jurassic limestones and chalk store water in *aquifers*. Villages have traditionally grown up along *spring lines* along the foot of scarps (Plate 1.7). Note that the London region, under the Thames Water Board, relies almost entirely on river water, taken largely from the Thames; and on ground water from wells sunk deep into the chalk which underlies the Thames Basin.

Conflict

In few other human activities does conflict between interested groups of people occur more regularly than in those related to water supply. There is conflict (i) between different Local Authorities competing for water supplies in the same area; (ii) between the local inhabitants of valleys, about to be submerged by reservoirs, and the urban water undertaking; (iii) in the case of Wales, between the English Water Boards and Welsh nationalists who do not think that water should be taken out of Wales, and who object even more in some cases to paying higher water rates than in parts of England; (iv) between conservationists, and the Water Boards or industrialists, as in the case of the Cow Green reservoir in Teesdale, which supplies water to the industries of Teesside, but which threatened to submerge areas containing some of the rarest plants in Britain; and (v) between competing uses of rivers and reservoirs. Some reservoirs are stocked with trout and are used generally for water sports, for example. Some Local Authorities allow their reservoirs to be used in this way; others do not, for fear of pollution.

The main argument is that between the economist and the conservationist. In terms of conservation, water from the sea might be used. But the cost would be very great, and the economic argument is against turning to the sea at present.

Another alternative would be to install water meters, so that we would have to pay for water like gas or electricity. This would certainly help to conserve water, but the cost of installing millions of meters is enormous.

The most sensible way in the British case, however, is to encourage individual families and industrial concerns to use water carefully, through, for example, dual flush lavatory systems, and showers rather than baths.

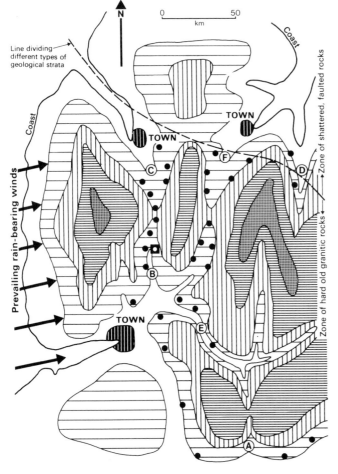

Figure 4.4 Choosing the reservoir site

Exercises

5. Refer to Figure 4.3.
(a) Name *four* Water Authorities obtaining over half their water from upland streams and reservoirs; *two* with over half from ground water; and *one* with over half from river water.
(b) Suggest reasons for the differences between Water Authorities in terms of supply and demand, by looking also at Figures 1.1, 2.16 and 9.1.
6. *Either* write an essay *or* arrange a class debate on the question 'Conserving Britain's Water Supplies'. Whichever you do, base your arguments as much as possible on facts you can find. Where opinions or emotions are concerned, make sure that you can distinguish these from the facts. Look up accounts in newspapers about water supply issues and try to analyse:
(a) how the different sides in the issue put their case in different ways;
(b) why it is so difficult to make acceptable decisions on the water supply question.
7. Refer to Figure 4.4. On the basis of information given on the map, and with the help of the information on factors affecting water supply on pages 44–7, work out the best site for a dam and reservoir for the urban areas of the map, in any one of valleys A to F. State carefully the advantages and disadvantages of each of the five valleys as a reservoir site.

5 AGRICULTURE

LAND USE IN BRITAIN

Figure 5.1 is a triangular graph showing the proportions of different types of land use in Britain. Britain can be divided into the densely settled areas, forming the *townscape* and *rurban fringe* in which rural and urban areas merge, and less heavily populated areas, which include the *farmscape*, where the predominant land use is farming; the *wildscape*, consisting of areas of bare mountain, marsh and forest; and the *marginal fringe*, where areas of farming are mixed in with forest, mountain, marsh, and so on.

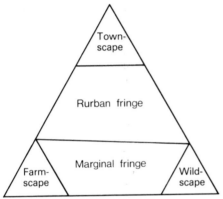

Figure 5.1   Land use in Britain

The graph suggests that a limited proportion of the landscape of Britain is devoted to farming, and the resulting produce has to feed a lot of people, too many in fact, which means that we have to import a lot of foodstuffs. An efficient farming industry is therefore very important, if only to keep down our imports bill.

The main types of farming can be classified as follows:

Subsistence farming, i.e. produce being grown for the farmer's own use. This is hardly found at all in Britain, the nearest example being in the *crofting* communities of north-west Scotland (Figure 5.2). Even here, the farmer usually engages in supplementary activities (page 64).

Commercial farming, i.e. produce for sale. Almost all farming in Britain is of this type. It can for convenience be divided into the following.

(1) *Hill farming* which is traditionally mainly for sheep, but increasingly for cattle, making use of rough pastures for rearing, rather than for fattening of the animals.

(2) *Arable farming*, for crops, with sub-divisions such as

(a) cereals: wheat, barley, oats, etc.,

(b) roots: sugar beet, turnips, potatoes, etc.,

(c) fruit and vegetables: orchards and market gardens.

(3) *Mixed farming* which is widespread in Britain today, with the farmer both growing crops and raising stock, allowing risks to be spread.

(4) *Cattle farming* (like hill sheep farming, can be termed *pastoral*) which may be for meat, *beef cattle*; or for milk and other dairy products, *dairy cattle*.

The distinction we noted in Chapter 1 between Highland and Lowland Britain comes out well on Figure 5.2. There is a close relationship between farming and relief, although other physical factors also operate,

Figure 5.2   General farming types in Britain

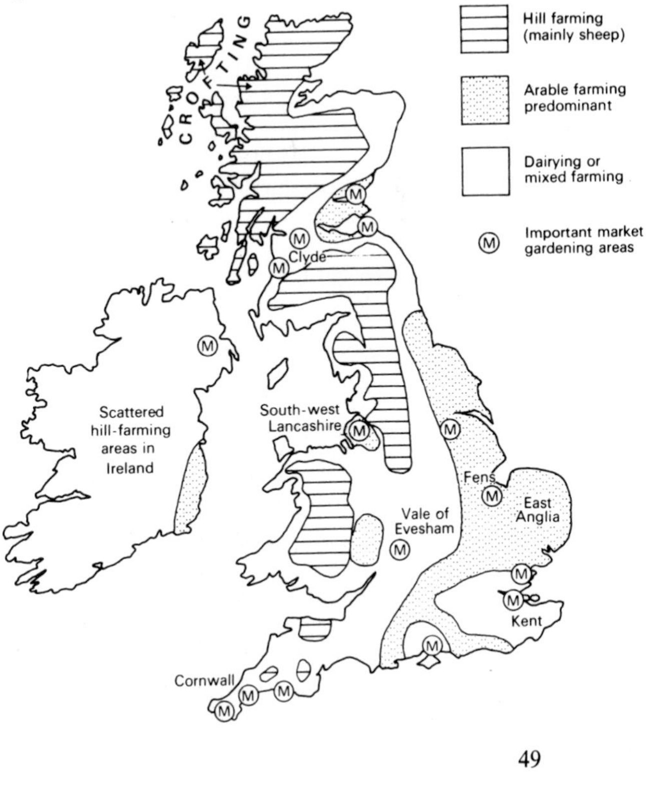

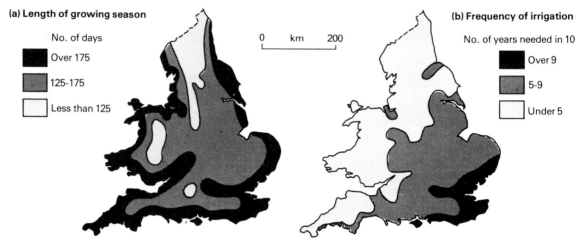

(a) Length of growing season

No. of days

■ Over 175

▨ 125-175

□ Less than 125

0   km   200

(b) Frequency of irrigation

No. of years needed in 10

■ Over 9

▨ 5-9

□ Under 5

Figure 5.3   Farming in England and Wales: (a) length of growing season; (b) frequency of irrigation needed

such as weather factors, including amounts of rainfall, sunshine and frost, discussed in Chapter 2. Two factors that we have not so far touched upon are the *length of the growing season* (when temperatures are above about 6 °C) and the occurrence of *drought*, both very significant to the farmer. Variations in these over England and Wales are shown on Figure 5.3, drought being indicated by the frequency of irrigation needed (Figure 5.3b).

Even more important to the farmer than physical factors are *economic factors*, to which we shall be paying special attention in this chapter. It is not just a question of the general economic forces of supply and demand (for example, if supplies are great, prices for produce fall; if demand is great, prices are higher), but the extent of government intervention, made even more complicated by our entry into the European Community, with its Common Agricultural Policy (CAP).

In this chapter, we are now going to study in depth two contrasted farming areas, the Lake District and Lincolnshire, then more briefly other major types of farming.

Exercises

1. Give an example of an area in Britain coming into each of the categories shown on Figure 5.1.
2. Outline the broad relationships which appear between the main farming types in Britain (Figure 5.2) and the factors shown on
(*a*) Figure 1.1 (geology and relief);
(*b*) Figure 2.16 (general climatic factors);
(*c*) Figure 5.3a and b (growing season and irrigation needs).
Check later whether these broad relationships appear in the more detailed studies.

FARMING IN THE LAKE DISTRICT

As we have seen, the Lake District is one of the major glaciated mountain areas of upland Britain. In such areas, the farms are concentrated in the valleys, as the Ordnance Survey map extract of part of the Lake District shows (Figure 5.5).

We are going to look in more detail at farming in Great Langdale, and particularly at Middle Fell Farm (285061 on the OS extract). The area covered by the farm is shown on Figure 5.4. Notice that the farm includes three types of land:
(*a*) *in-bye land* (or *inland*), in the flat valley floor of Great Langdale;
(*b*) *intake*, on the slopes immediately above the valley floor; and
(*c*) the open fells and crags which, unlike the in-bye land and the intake, are not divided up by fields.

Let us look at these different types of land from two viewpoints. Plate 5.1 is taken from the path coming down the Band (270057 on the OS map extract), towards Stool End Farm (marked A on Plate 5.1). We can see clearly that the 'inland' area is characterised by a number of small fields, enclosed by stone walls. The 'intake' land, also enclosed by stone walls, is shown on the valley sides. Here the fields are somewhat larger and more evenly shaped. Above the intake land are the steep crags, of which only Side Pike (C) can be seen on this picture. Middle Fell Farm is sited at point B.

Plate 5.2 is a closer view of Middle Fell Farm, taken from one of the bridges over Great Langdale Beck (286061). The intake can be seen behind the farm, above which are the steep rock faces and the *scree* (the loose stones broken from the rock face and lying below it) of Raven Crag.

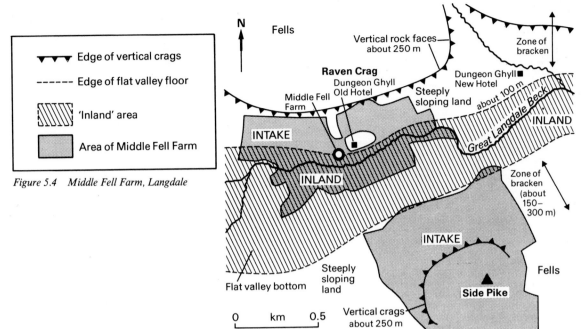

Figure 5.4   Middle Fell Farm, Langdale

Legend:
- ▼▼▼ Edge of vertical crags
- ------ Edge of flat valley floor
- 'Inland' area
- Area of Middle Fell Farm

Fells

Vertical rock faces about 250 m

Zone of bracken

Raven Crag
Dungeon Ghyll Old Hotel
Dungeon Ghyll New Hotel
Middle Fell Farm
Steeply sloping land
about 100 m
Great Langdale Beck
INLAND

INTAKE
INLAND

INTAKE

Zone of bracken (about 150–300 m)

N

Flat valley bottom

Steeply sloping land

0   km   0.5

Vertical crags about 250 m

Side Pike

Fells

Figure 5.5   OS map extract of Langdale

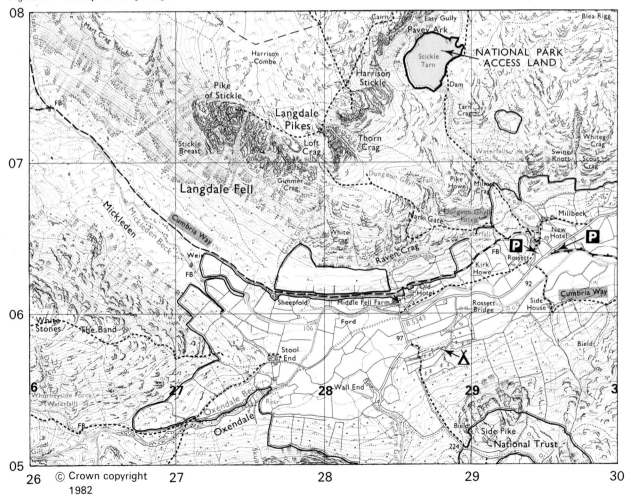

© Crown copyright 1982

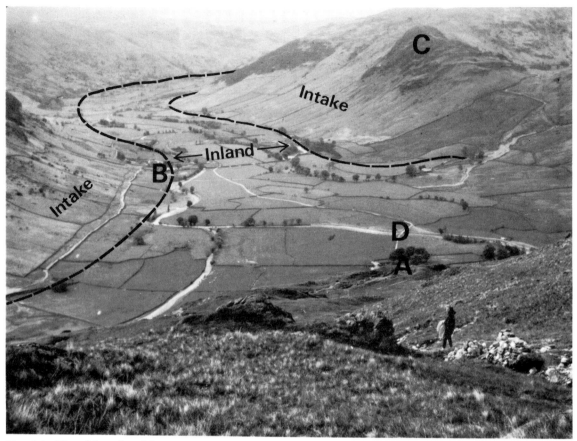

Plate 5.1   View of Great Langdale

Plate 5.2   Middle Fell Farm and the crags behind

Middle Fell Farm

The tenant of Middle Fell Farm rents the property from the National Trust, who own large areas of land in the Lake District. The farmhouse is an old stone-built dwelling dating back to the seventeenth century. The living quarters are now whitewashed over, but the walls of local stone can be seen to the left of Plate 5.2.

The Physical Environment

The building stones have been quarried from the old volcanic rocks which make up the surrounding mountains. The local green slates are a traditional roofing material, and are increasingly being used for ornamental purposes, for example, slate fire-places.

The tough ancient rocks of this area have resulted in the harsh craggy outlines of the Langdale Pikes and other peaks. The relief is clearly a handicap to the farmer. The sides of the valleys are too steep for modern machinery to be used, while the valley floor is flat, causing bad drainage and sometimes flooding. Because of this the farms and villages are usually located above the valley floor on *dry-point sites*.

Weather

The weather conditions experienced in the valley are also a handicap to farming. Rainfall is frequent, and the average annual total varies from about 3300 mm at the head of Mickleden to about 1900 mm at Ambleside, decreasing downvalley. Ambleside is in a partial *rain shadow* (see page 35), but still receives much more rainfall than the average for Britain. Heavy autumn rainfall can make harvesting uncertain, while the frequent low cloud cover results in low sunshine totals through the year. In winter, cold air from the fells sinks into the valley and causes fogs there, at the same time as bright sunshine is being experienced on the fells above. At this season the rays of the sun are cut off by Side Pike from the Middle Fell area of the valley (see Figure 5.6).

Soil

Soil, as we noted in Chapter 3, is the medium in which plants grow, supplying nutrients to the crops, either in the form of minerals or organic matter. Hence soil quality affects farm prosperity. In Langdale, the 'inland' area is largely made up of sticky clays, left by the glacier which once occupied and gouged out the U-shape of the Langdale valley. These clays are very heavy, acid, and liable to waterlogging, especially in view of the flatness of this land and the heavy rainfall of the area. On the intake, soils tend to be thin and rocky, as can be seen on Plate 5.2, where the scree from Raven Crag has invaded the enclosed fields. On the screes and crags above the intake there is little or no soil. On the more level fells, soils tend to be peaty and liable to waterlogging, as are those of the valley sides in the

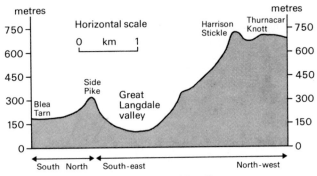

Figure 5.6   *Section across Great Langdale valley*

vicinity of springs. Hence the soils of the Middle Fell Farm area are not a great asset to the farmer.

Natural Vegetation

Where the valley floor is not farmed, or where adequate drainage facilities have not been provided on the farmed land, rushes and mosses can be found, a sure indication of poorly drained land. In contrast, the rich growth of bracken on the slopes tells of good drainage. The zone of bracken in the Langdale valley is marked on Figure 5.4. The bracken is a problem to the farmer as it cannot be cropped by sheep, and tends to invade the pastures of the intake land.

Langdale farmers, however, are not over-worried about the physical factors mentioned above. They limit the choice of types of farming, but in fact the farmers of the valley give little thought to growing crops, adapting their farming activities to the prevailing conditions.

Plate 5.3   *The strengthening of stream banks by artificial walls, Great Langdale*

The main problem presented by the physical environment is seen to be danger of flooding from Great Langdale Beck. There were four bad floods during the 1960s. In recent years, renewed efforts have been made to control the streams, which can rise alarmingly and overflow their banks after the torrential downpours which are not uncommon in this area. One method of control, shown on Plate 5.3, is to straighten and strengthen the stream banks by artificial river walls. The photograph was taken from point D on Plate 5.1 and shows Oxendale Beck at very low water after a dry spell. Middle Fell Farm can be seen in the background.

Such problems are temporary, however, and in general the farmers are more concerned with economic than with environmental hazards.

Exercises

3. Describe and account for the different appearances of each of (a) Great Langdale valley, and (b) Middle Fell Farm on each of Plates 5.1 and 5.2. State the direction in which the camera was pointing when each photograph was taken.
4. Trace the section shown on Figure 5.6 into your exercise book.
(a) With the help of information given previously, label at the appropriate places on the section (i) inland; (ii) intake; (iii) fells; (iv) crags; (v) zone of bracken; (vi) the site of Middle Fell Farm.
(b) Draw in the sun's winter rays coming in at a low angle over Side Pike, and indicate the area in shadow in the valley.
5. In what ways are the sites of Middle Fell, Stool End and Wall End farms (OS map extract) (a) similar, (b) different?

Economic Problems

The basic economic problem of a farmer, like that of a manufacturer or of a housekeeper, is one of budgeting, that is, of ensuring that more money is received (*income*) than is spent (*expenditure*). The margin between the two is *profit*, if income exceeds expenditure; or *loss*, if the reverse happens. The farmer naturally wishes to *maximise* the profits.

How easily this can be done depends in part on (a) the nature of the physical environment of the farmland; (b) the state of the economic system, which influences how much people are prepared to pay for the farm produce when marketed; (c) how much the government are prepared to subsidise the farmer by giving grants; (d) how skilful the farmer is in making the best use of the physical environment, and in choosing the combinations of crops and livestock which will make most money at a particular time; (e) how hard the farmer works; (f) the farmer's attitude to life. For example, old farmers may be less ambitious than young ones, and be more concerned with living a reasonably comfortable life than with making large profits. They might be reluctant to adopt new and more efficient methods because they are used to traditional ones. They might also value an old-established rural way of life, even though it is not a very profitable one.

The Economy of Langdale Farms

Langdale farms vary in size between 40 and 80 hectares. The inland is under permanent grass some of which is cut for hay and some for silage (collected before the hay in early summer, when the grass is fresh and green). All the hay and silage comes from the inland area. The main livestock raised are sheep. Farm boundaries are arranged so that each farm has portions of inland and intake (see Plate 5.1). Grazing rights on the open fells are shared between the farmers, so that in fact the area used by the hill sheep farmer is much greater than the size in figures of the farm suggests.

(a) *Sheep* The Herdwick is the main Lake District breed, and has the advantages of being small and agile, and therefore adapted to climbing the steep slopes and crags; and very hardy, able to cope with the harsh weather and poor grazing of the fells. On the other hand, Herdwick wool is of relatively poor quality and the lambs are slow to mature.

In November, tupping (mating) takes place, and the lambs are born in the following spring, usually in mid-April. During the winter, especially in times of snow and blizzards, the farmers have to take special care of the flocks, to prevent the sheep from being buried in snow drifts. Hence the sheep are brought downhill nearer to the farm until after lambing, when the ewes and lambs are returned to the fells, about the end of May. They remain there until the following winter, although they are brought down for shearing (mid-June to July) and dipping against insect pests (autumn), as well as for marketing at the autumn sales.

(b) *Cattle* Many farms produce *store cattle*, that is cattle reared on a hill farm and then sold for fattening on higher-quality lowland pastures. Cattle reared in the hills usually do well when transferred to better land. The inland pasture is used mainly to provide feed for the store cattle, which graze outside from mid-May to September. In winter they are entirely stall-fed on hay and silage from the farm, although some roots and artificial feed may be bought. Clearly, the more feed that has to be bought in from outside, the less the profits are likely to be. But if the farm itself does not produce enough feed, the farmer has to do this. In recent years there has been an increased tendency in the area to keep *dairy cattle*, and these are profitable enough to justify expenditure on feed from other sources.

Income

The main income of Langdale farmers comes from the *sale of produce*. This includes money from the *lamb and sheep sales* at Ambleside and Broughton-in-Furness. On average, for every 600 sheep reared in Langdale, about 480 lambs are expected to be born to the ewes. Of these, 130 ewe lambs are kept for replacement, leaving 350 lambs for sale. *Wool* is also sold, though here again, in an age of artificial fibres, demand has been declining, especially for poor-quality wool such as that from Herdwick sheep. *Milk* is sold to the Milk Marketing Board at Milnthorpe, and through milk rounds. In summer, much milk is purchased by the local tourist industry. Visitors from the Langdale camp sites call in at farms to buy milk and eggs. *Store cattle* are sold when eighteen months to two years old, at Ulverston, Kendal, Ambleside, and Broughton-in-Furness. The sales take place in the autumn.

Government subsidies are available for hill sheep and cattle, and grants are provided for the purchase of fertilisers and other purposes. Hill farmers regard these as essential to keep going.

Subsidiary income comes from taking in visitors during the holiday season. The population of the Langdale valley as a whole is greatly increased by tourists during the summer.

Cooperation

In 1976 a Lakeland Farmers Cooperative scheme was formed to increase income from the sale of store cattle and sheep, sent together for fattening or wintering to one large lowland farm, with resulting economies and better prices.

A 'Model' of a Farming System

The way in which Langdale farms work is basically the same as that of any other farm system, although the physical environments of different farms, the produce they are concerned with, and their profitability vary considerably. We can make up a theoretical 'model' or framework to show the working of a farm in general terms. Let us try to do this.

In the earlier part of the chapter we noted how the elements of the physical environment work upon, or *interact*, with each other.

(*a*) Heavy rainfall (*weather*), acting on stiff clays (*soils*), particularly in a flat area (*relief*), leads to waterlogging (bad *drainage*) and the formation of rushes and mosses (*natural vegetation*) (Figure 5.7a). At the same time, the natural vegetation rots down to put organic material back into the soil; relief affects the weather, and so on.

(*b*) Similarly, steep slopes (*relief*) associated with thin *soils* but generally good *drainage*, allow bracken (*natural vegetation*) to flourish (Figure 5.7b).

The arrows on Figure 5.7 therefore represent interaction between the various elements of the physical environment which Figure 5.7c attempts to link together. The main model, Figure 5.8, links the physical environment with the economic system, which in practice is done through the farmer and the farm. The farmer puts things into the environment (*artificial inputs*), such as fertilisers, feed and drainage, which, together with the *natural inputs* of the physical environment (Figure 5.7), increase the amount the farm produces: the *output*.

Figure 5.7 Physical environment model (sub-section of Figure 5.8)

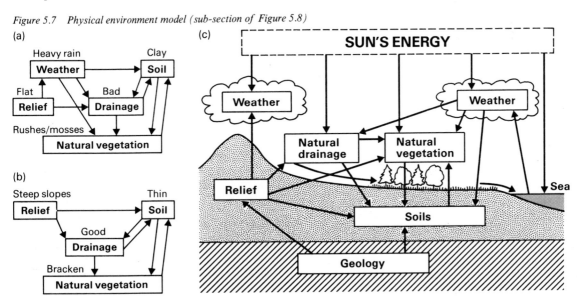

Although the model may seem complicated at first, it is less so if looked at with a particular example of a farm in mind. The model enables us to see that the successful farmer is likely to be the one who makes the best use of the physical environment, who is knowledgeable about the workings of the economic system and the most efficient methods of farming, who is prepared to work hard, and is ambitious to make high profits.

Exercises

6. By reference to the 'models' (Figures 5.7 and 5.8) and to information given in the text, indicate ways in which:
(a) the relief directly and indirectly (through its effect on drainage, etc.) affects the type of farming in the Langdale valley;
(b) government grants help Lakeland farmers to run their farms;
(c) artificial inputs are necessary in increasing farm produce;
(d) the location of the farm in the particular physical environment of the Lake District limits the choice of types of farming.

7. Enlarge the following table, showing the activities of 'The Farmer's Year' in Langdale, in your exercise book, and fill it in as appropriate, using information given in the text. (Note that it is unnecessary to fill in every section if no information is available for it.)

Season	Work with sheep	Work with cattle	Other work
Spring			
Summer			
Autumn			
Winter			

8. (a) On the evidence of the OS map extract, why is Great Langdale an attraction to tourists?
(b) With the help of this and other information in the text, and the extract below, discuss the pros and cons of tourism for the local farmers.

Finding farm labour is one of the main problems of Lakeland valleys, which are steadily losing their 'native' population. In their place, retired people are buying up farm cottages to convert into purely residential dwellings, or well-to-do people are purchasing them to act as holiday homes during the summer. This creates difficulties for local young people wishing to settle down in the area, as it is causing a steep rise in the price of property.

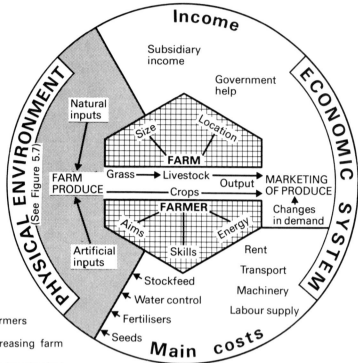

Figure 5.8   Model of a farm system

FARMING IN LINCOLNSHIRE

Now let us see how the theoretical model we have drawn can be used as a framework in another real situation, by studying a Lincolnshire farm, that of Mr G. H. Parker, which is located at North Cotes, on the Lincolnshire coastal marshes south of Grimsby (Plate 5.4).

Lincolnshire: The Physical Environment

Geology and Relief

Looking first at geology and relief, we should note that the rocks of Lincolnshire, mostly limestone, chalk and clay, are much younger and less tough than the old volcanic rocks of the Lake District. Consequently the relief outlines are less sharp and less spectacular than those of Langdale. Look back at the block diagram (Figure 1.6, page 9) which shows a west-to-east section from the Vale of Trent (clay), through the ridge of Lincoln Edge (limestone), then the Lincoln Clay Vale, followed by the Lincoln Wolds (chalk upland), and finally the drained Lincoln marshes (recent deposits of boulder clay and alluvium). It is in this last area that Mr Parker's farm, known as The Grange, stands.

Plate 5.4   Aerial view of part of the Lincolnshire coast

To the west of the farm runs the fairly steep slope of the edge of the Lincoln Wolds, but the rest of the landscape is almost completely flat. The marshlands, which have been reclaimed for farming, are only slightly above sea level, and have to be protected from the sea by dykes, known as 'sea banks' in this area. Plate 5.4 is a photograph of the Lincolnshire coast just to the north-east of North Cotes. After the beach and some coastal dunes, waterlogged ground can be seen, backed by a sea bank, which protects the fields behind. As the picture shows, the boundaries of some of the fields are formed by drainage ditches.

Weather

The weather in this area of Lincolnshire is quite different from that of the Langdale valley. Instead of an annual rainfall total of over 2500 mm, there is less than 650 mm. Occasionally heavy rain may fall in autumn to interrupt harvesting, but the only problem is usually that of too little rainfall in summer, when irrigation water may have to be applied. This is particularly true on the Wolds, where the soils and the underlying chalk are porous and allow water to seep through quickly. On the more impervious soils of the marshes, water stays longer on the surface.

As Lincolnshire faces east, it is open to cold winter winds from Europe. These travel across the North Sea, pick up moisture, and sometimes result in heavy snow-fall, especially on the higher land of the Wolds (see Figure 2.6, page 33). The cold winters of the eastern part of the country are in fact a help to the farmers, because frost breaks up the soil, lets in air, and makes ploughing easier.

The worst disaster experienced by the farmers of this area came in the winter of 1953, when gale-force northerly winds, combined with high tides, led to storm waves overwhelming the sea banks, and flooding the coastal marshlands, including all the land shown on Plate 5.4.

Soils

The *soils* of Mr Parker's farm can be divided into three types.

(*a*) Coastal *silt* (or alluvium) makes up the soils of the coastal marsh and stretches inland for up to 2.5 kilometres. Here the soils are very deep.

(*b*) The '*Middle marsh*' soils to the west are also very deep. These consist of heavy boulder clays laid down during the Ice Age. It should be mentioned, however, that a 'heavy' clay in this relatively dry area is less of a

57

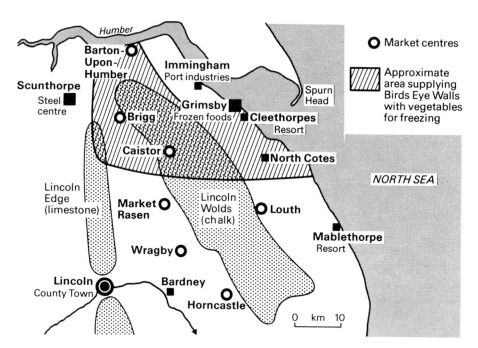

Figure 5.9
North-east Lincolnshire

Key:
- ○ Market centres
- ▨ Approximate area supplying Birds Eye Walls with vegetables for freezing

Map labels: Humber, Barton-Upon-Humber, Immingham Port industries, Scunthorpe Steel centre, Spurn Head, Grimsby Frozen foods, Brigg, Cleethorpes Resort, Caistor, North Cotes, NORTH SEA, Lincoln Edge (limestone), Market Rasen, Lincoln Wolds (chalk), Louth, Wragby, Mablethorpe Resort, Lincoln County Town, Bardney, Horncastle, 0 km 10

problem than one in a wet area, and Mr Parker can plough this land for crops, though its sticky nature limits the types of crop which can be grown on it.

(*c*) Some of Mr Parker's land is near the edge of the Wolds. Here the *clay is mixed with chalk* which gives a fairly light loamy soil. Where the chalk meets the clay, the water seeping through the porous chalk comes to the surface in a series of springs and a *spring line* results. This provided sites for early villages, giving a local water supply, and a dry location above the wet coastal marshes.

Thus while Mr G. H. Parker has to take some account of the physical environment of the area, he has a much wider range of choice of types of farming than the farmers of Langdale, and economic factors are much more influential than physical in deciding what he chooses to produce.

Exercises

9. Contrast the features of relief and drainage shown on Plates 5.1 and 5.4.

10. Refer to Figure 1.6, page 9.

(*a*) With the help of Figure 5.9 work out the horizontal scale of the section.

(*b*) Compare this scale with that of the section across the Langdale valley (Figure 5.6).

(*c*) Compare the relief features on the two sections, but say why it is difficult to do so.

11. Enlarge the table shown below in your exercise book, and make brief notes to bring out the differences in the physical environments of the Langdale valley and the Lincoln marshes.

	Langdale valley	Lincoln marshes
Geology		
Relief		
Drainage		
Weather		
Soils		

12. State briefly why the Lincoln marshes form the more favourable environment for farming activities.

Mr G. H. Parker's Farm: The Grange

Size and Shape

Mr Parker's farm is an 800-hectare unit, very large by British standards. The fields are scattered, largely because the farm unit is built up from the amalgamation of older farms. Land has been bought from over thirty different people. Most of the older farms were 20–40 hectares in size, and some of these still remain in the area. Usually when adjacent land comes on the market, Mr Parker will try to buy it to make his farm an even larger and more compact unit. Many of the fields have also been enlarged. Mr Parker's son now farms one-third of the total farm area.

The Farmer

Mr G. H. Parker of Lincolnshire is a very different type of farmer from those of Langdale. It would be fair to say that farming in the Lake District is still in part a traditional rural way of life, although certain changes have taken place. In Lincolnshire, farmers such as Mr Parker conduct their businesses as considerable industrial enterprises.

Farm Output

We noted earlier that the easier physical environment gives Lincolnshire farmers a wider range of choice of farming activities than their Lake District counterparts. This can be seen in Table 5.1, which shows the variety of produce of Mr Parker's farm.

The rotation of crops is on a six- or seven-year basis, and includes wheat, barley, potatoes, peas, sugar beet, and ley grass. It is important not to grow the same crop year after year in the same field, chiefly because it encourages insect pests and diseases to build up in the soil. In parts of south-west Lancashire, for example, the *monoculture*, or growing of one crop, namely potatoes, year after year, led to the build-up in the soil of an eelworm which attacked the potato roots, and has led to a sharp decrease in the growth of that crop in the area in the last twenty years or so.

All the wheat produced is *winter wheat*, that is wheat drilled between October and December, which lies dormant through the winter and starts to grow the following spring. The *ley grassland* differs from *permanent grassland* in that it is specially sown and left for a particular period of time, in this case two years. It would thus be referred to as a two-year ley. Ley grass can be regarded as a crop. It provides higher-quality grazing than much permanent pasture but is of course more expensive. As a result of the recession, the amount of ley grass has been drastically reduced, as Table 5.1 indicates.

Table 5.1. Produce of The Grange

		Number of hectares	
Crops		1971	1981
Cereals:	(a) wheat	220	413
	(b) barley	165	100
Root crops:	(a) potatoes	75	53
	(b) sugar beet	45	114
Vegetables:	peas	115	115
Temporary grass:	leys	170	30*
	Total	800	825
		Numbers of stock	
Cattle: Beef and store cattle		310	267

*NB   Also 84 hectares of permanent grassland

Inputs on the Farm

Mr Parker has to spend a large amount of money in order to produce this massive and varied output.

Machinery and Buildings

The machinery used on the farm includes four combine harvesters; one beet harvester shared with another farmer; three self-propelled pea-pickers, large vehicles which automatically pick, or vine, the pea crop, and are shared with three other farmers; fifteen tractors; a forklift truck and pallets, for handling bulky produce such as potatoes; and a variety of drills, sprays, harrows, and other small equipment.

In addition to the machinery, there are many modern barns and storehouses dotted over the farm. Some of these are heated with thermostat controls to keep the interior at a constant temperature, in which potatoes, for example, are stored to await the time when good prices can be obtained for them. The highly-mechanised nature of the farming is made possible by the vast output, by the level or gently undulating nature of the ground, and by the large size of the fields.

Labour

Mr Parker's labour force amounts to twenty-five full-time men, and part-time or casual workers who are employed for the potato harvest. The full-timers, who are provided with living accommodation, include two foremen, one handyman, one bricklayer, one carpenter, two mechanics, two lorry drivers, fourteen tractor drivers, and two other men. The skills possessed by these employees are an indication of the highly-mechanised nature of the farming.

Seeds and Fertilisers

The higher the *yields* (the amount produced per hectare) of his crops, the greater Mr Parker's profits will be. He therefore ensures that he buys good-quality seeds, and large amounts of fertilisers, which both help to produce high yields. Although he uses some farmyard manure, the bulk of the fertilisers are chemical, including nitrates and phosphates. A fully-qualified person, shared with neighbouring farmers, is employed to advise and assist with sprays and fertilisers.

Water Control

The main expenditure is on *drainage*. All the fields on the farm are under-drained by plastic pipes, about 75 mm in diameter and just over 300 mm long. About 60 hectares of land have their drains replaced every year, giving an average renewal rate for each part of the farm of once in seventeen or eighteen years. The drains run into ditches, which run along at least two sides of the fields. The drainage ditches in turn run into several outfalls to the sea.

An elaborate drainage system is essential in view of the level nature of the land, and its nearness to sea level. Where artificial drainage does not take place, the land will revert to marshland, as can be seen in the left foreground of Plate 5.4.

Stock Feed
As we have noted, Mr Parker supplies some of the stock feed from the farm. The grass crop is collected
(a) as *silage* (cut when grass is young and green and stored in airtight conditions), some of which is mixed with sugar beet tops;
(b) dried and cut into small pieces as *cake*.

Both of these are major sources of feed. In addition, half of the barley grown on the farm is fed to the animals. The rest of the feed is brought in from outside, and is clearly more costly than that grown on the farm.

Government Help
Without government help, Mr Parker would have to increase considerably the prices of the produce he sells. Apart from the grants for fertilisation and drainage, the government guarantees the price of wheat, barley and sugar beet. This means that however low the price of these products falls when sold, the government will make it up to a minimum amount, on which Mr Parker and farmers like him can depend.

Table 5.2. Agricultural land use in Britain
(selected crops)

	Hectares	
Crops	1971	1980
Wheat	1 097 000	1 441 000
Barley	2 288 000	2 330 000
Potatoes	257 000	206 000
Sugar beet	190 000	213 000
Peas (for processing)	53 000	59 000
Ley grasses	2 307 000	1 965 000

Exercises

13. Refer to Tables 5.1 and 5.2.
(a) Work out the proportions of land under different crops at The Grange in 1971 and 1981.
(b) Describe the changes which have taken place (i) at The Grange, and (ii) in Britain as a whole, as indicated on Table 5.2.
(c) What are the similarities and differences between the two tables?
14. State differences between (a) root and cereal crops; (b) ley and permanent grassland; (c) irrigation and drainage; (d) natural and artificial fertilisers; (e) monoculture and crop rotation; (f) arable, pastoral, and mixed farming.
15. Compare the ways of life of a hill sheep farmer, and a large-scale lowland farmer of an area such as Lincolnshire (or any other similar area).
16. Using the 'models' as frameworks (Figures 5.7 and 5.8), compare the farming systems of Langdale and the Lincolnshire coast. Why has the latter a wider choice?

Marketing
Mr Parker's main income comes from the marketing of produce.

Beef is sold when the cattle are fifteen to eighteen months old at Louth, the nearest market town.

Potatoes, which are bulky and expensive to transport, are sold as close to the farm as possible, and are generally bought by local merchants, from centres such as Grimsby, Louth, and Brigg (Figure 5.9). The majority of the potatoes end up in the Manchester and London markets.

Wheat is dried, stored and then sold the following spring to large flour mills at Sheffield, Hull and Selby (Yorkshire).

A proportion of the *barley* crop is used for feed on the farm. The rest is sold to merchants, also for feed.

Sugar beet is sent to the sugar factory at Brigg, this being one of two such factories in the northern half of Lincolnshire, the other being at Bardney (Plate 5.5), near Lincoln (Figure 5.9). In this factory, raw sugar is produced from the beet and refined into granulated and caster sugar. Syrup and treacle are also produced. Sugar beet is a bulky and expensive product to transport. For every eight units in weight of beet, only one of raw sugar results.

Other materials needed for processing beet are coal and lime, which are also bulky and expensive to transport. Hence it is useful if the sugar beet factory is located within easy reach of the beet-producing area, and of supplies of coal and limestone. Note that the Brigg and Bardney factories are both located in the Lincolnshire beet-producing region near the limestone of Lincoln Edge (Figure 5.9), and are not too far from the Yorkshire coalfield, which lies to the west of Scunthorpe.

One of the by-products of the beet factory is beet pulp which, mixed with molasses, gives a high-energy stock feed. This too is a bulky low-value product, and has to be sold near to the factory. It is therefore an advantage that there is a large local market for stock feed on the nearby Lincolnshire farms. Another by-product is spent lime, sold for fertiliser.

Plate 5.5 Sugar beet factory, Bardney

Plate 5.5 shows that the Bardney factory is linked by railway, river (the straightened River Witham) and road with sources of raw materials and fuel. At one time most of the beet came in by railway, and some by barge along the river. Today all the beet is brought in by road, while the railway is still used for transporting coal and limestone.

Peas: The Frozen Foods Industry

One of the most striking developments in Britain in the last decade has been the rapid growth of the frozen foods industry in Britain.

Mr Parker is one of over 100 farmers in north-east Lincolnshire who have contracted to sell their peas to the Birds Eye Walls frozen foods factory in Grimsby. In the Birds Eye Walls office there is a map showing the distribution of these farms, and the approximate area within which they are found is shaded in on Figure 5.9. The absolute time limit allowed between the picking of the peas and the beginning of the freezing process in the factory is 90 minutes. In fact all the farms have to be within 45–50 minutes road-travelling time of the factory.

Birds Eye Walls experts cooperate closely with the farmers. The firm supplies particular varieties of seeds which mature at different speeds. This stretches out the harvesting season and thus spreads out the work in the factory. Otherwise all the peas would be coming in at the same time. The factory experts also test the soil, and suggest the best fertilisers for each field. At harvest time, pea samples are taken and tested in a 'tenderometer'. This indicates whether the peas are at the stage when they have the most tender texture. When this stage arrives, the signal is given and the mechanical pea-pickers move into the fields, working round the clock, at night by floodlight. The pea-picker combs through the crops, picking off the pods and a proportion of the vine, shelling the peas automatically.

The Grimsby Frozen Foods Industry

There is a tremendous concentration of the frozen foods industry at Grimsby. Apart from Birds Eye Walls, other famous firms have factories there, including Ross (who also process potatoes from Lincolnshire farms), and Findus (also processing beans from the same area). The great advantage of Grimsby is that it is located near the Lincolnshire vegetable-producing area and the fishing ports of Grimsby and Hull (see Chapter 14). Fish for frozen fish products is brought from these two ports. While the pea harvest is on, in July and August, the Birds Eye Walls factory concentrates on pea processing, but the staple work throughout the year is the manufacture of fish fingers, together with some processing of sprouts and carrots (for mixed vegetables) at the end of the year.

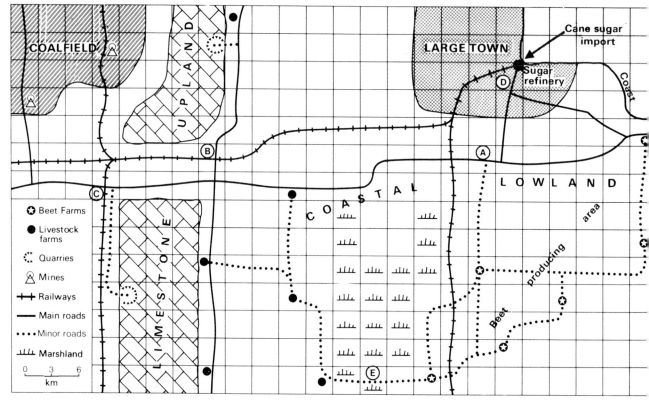

Figure 5.10   *Locating the sugar beet factory*

Exercise

17. A simulation exercise: locating a sugar beet factory. Imagine you are in the position of having to decide on the best location for a new sugar beet factory on the basis of the evidence given in Figure 5.10. You have narrowed the choice down to five sites, A to E. The best one will have the most favourable balance of advantages of access to (a) beet farms; (b) limestone; (c) coal supplies; (d) livestock farms (for sale of beet pulp); (e) a sugar refinery (taking raw sugar from the beet factory). You might also consider the availability of poor-quality agricultural land, which would be cheap to buy. Remember that improved access reduces transport costs.

To work out the accessibility of the five factory sites you should find the total distance which has to be travelled between each site and each of the five factors (a) to (e) above, and all marked in the key of Figure 5.10, by totalling up the squares crossed, on the following points basis:

One point for a square crossed by a railway or main road (see key);

Two points for a square crossed only by a minor road;
Three points for other squares (only rough tracks available).

You must not cut diagonally across squares. You can change from rail to road transport or vice versa only if the two actually cross each other in the same square. The best site is the one with the lowest points total.

Hence for site A you would find the score by adding up the points in travelling from A to (a) a beet farm; A to (b) limestone supply, and so on; and you would repeat this for B, C, D and E.

(a)   Which site emerges as (i) the best and (ii) the worst location for the factory, and by how much?

(b)   Suggest reasons in each case.

(c)   This simulation is of course a tremendous simplification of what would happen in reality. Give some reasons why.

OTHER FARMING TYPES IN BRITAIN

Beef Cattle: North-east Scotland

One of the most relished dishes in Britain is the Angus steak. It comes from the Aberdeen Angus breed of beef cattle, whose home region is the north-east lowlands of Scotland, including the Buchan lowlands and Angus. This is part of an important beef-producing region starting in the north-east of England, and continuing up the east coast as far as the Orkneys.

Some of the farms of the region are in an upland fringe situation, as Figure 5.11 indicates, with a transition from the rough pastures of the moors to permanent grass on the lower slopes, with ploughed fields between these and the damp valley floor. Note these features on Plate 5.6, which shows an Aberdeenshire landscape. The ploughed fields are generally used for turnips, a valuable fodder crop, and for barley or perhaps oats, both also used as fodder. A standard rotation is to have a sequence of cereal crop, root crop, cereal crop, clover, then three years of grass. As elsewhere in Britain, however, the increased use of fertilisers makes the rotation of crops less essential.

The remoteness of this area from the major towns of Scotland, except Aberdeen, makes beef cattle a more advantageous proposition than dairy, though there is some dairying round Aberdeen. Other advantages are that the cattle can make use of rough grazing and the permanent pastures of the upland fringe in summer, and use fodder crops in winter. The relative dry east coast climate helps the growth of fodder crops.

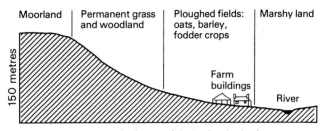

Figure 5.11   Section on the fringes of the Buchan lowlands

Although the Buchan lowlands are important in specialising in beef production, beef rearing is in fact a widespread occupation in Britain. The key feature is probably the rearing of cattle as stores in the uplands, as we noted in the Lake District (page 54), then their transfer to the lowlands for fattening. Beef cattle are particularly important also in the Welsh Marches, the country to the east of the Welsh mountains, as in Hereford and Worcester. Herefords are one of the main breeds of beef cattle. They are also important in southwest Wales, Devon and Somerset, again upland fringe locations.

Plate 5.6   Farming landscape in Aberdeenshire

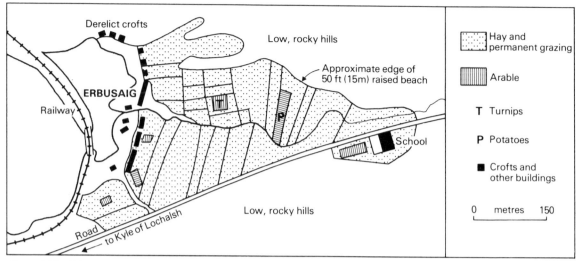

Figure 5.12   Erbusaig, a declining crofting settlement near Kyle of Lochalsh

Crofting in North-west Scotland

A considerable part of the Scottish Highlands is made up of the 'crofting counties', which contain the crofting townships, maintaining, though very much in decline, the nearest approximation to subsistence farming we have left in Britain. Crofts are traditionally holdings of less than 20–30 hectares. The farmland close to the croft, the *in-bye* land (see also page 50) is often divided into separate strips of land, as at Erbusaig in the Lochalsh peninsula (Figure 5.12). This is to give fair shares of poorer and richer land to the farmer. Outside the in-bye land is the common grazing land on the glaciated rocky hills. Each crofter has the right to graze animals on this common grazing land.

Many of the crofting townships are sited on raised beaches at the coast, as is the case with Erbusaig. Others may be on the deltas of the sea lochs, on coastal deposits of blown sand, or on valley terraces above badly drained floors. The heavy rainfall and generally acid soils limit the range of crops which can be grown. Thus the soil at Erbusaig is a mixture of glacial drift and raised beach deposits, which are very liable to water-logging and are lacking in plant nutrients such as nitrogen, lime, potash and phosphates. Coral sand, from round Erbusaig Bay, contains both lime and phosphate, and seaweed contains potash, so both these are spread over the land. Manure from the farm animals and artificial fertilisers are also used.

As can be seen from the map (Figure 5.12) little land is used as arable. Hardy cattle are the main animals at Erbusaig. Sheep and poultry are also important in crofting areas. The map also shows derelict crofts,

symptomatic of the decline of townships such as Erbusaig. Even twenty years ago Erbusaig was losing population, and the only crofters spending all day on their holdings were retired people. The rest use crofting as a part-time occupation, working in Kyle of Lochalsh or more distant Scottish towns. Crofters in other areas work for the Forestry Commission or are engaged in tourism, in some cases letting out crofts for self-catering accommodation.

The Kent Fruit and Hop Belt

Plate 5.7 is a photograph taken in the Kent fruit and hop belt (Figure 5.13) near Canterbury. Notice the orchards in the foreground and, behind the farm in the right centre, a field of hops. In the corner of the field stands the picturesque outline of the oast house, where hops were dried before being sent to breweries, to give beer its characteristic 'bitter' taste. Today the drying takes place in large modern buildings.

Other changes have taken place in the traditional procedures. Hops were once a *labour intensive* type of farming, labour being needed for the elaborate setting up of poles and strings, along which the hops were 'trained', and also for picking. In the old days, large numbers of East Enders from London came for the autumn hop-picking season. Much of the process is now mechanised, and smaller amounts of casual labour are required.

64

Plate 5.7   The Kent fruit and hop belt

The physical conditions required by hops include, in particular, protection from strong winds. They can tolerate a wide range of soils, so long as they are well drained and fertilised, and are less susceptible to frost than fruit.

This part of Kent is well known for its production of apples, pears, cherries, plums and small fruits such as strawberries and gooseberries. The orchards are sited on the lower dip slope of the North Downs (and equivalent sites), beneath the windswept downland summits, and above the frost hollows of the valleys (see Figure 2.13, page 36).

The advantages of this area for fruit growing include, as just described, the presence of sloping conditions above frost hollows but below windswept summits; plenty of woodlands and hedgerows, providing shelter belts from the winds; light loamy soil ('brick-earths') on the lower slopes, which warm up quickly in spring; low annual rainfall (under 750 mm) and long hours of sunshine for ripening the fruit; access by rail and road to the huge market of Greater London; and a long tradition of fruit growing in the area, with effective research and marketing experience.

Apart from Kent, the only other important region for both fruit and hop growing is in the West Country and in Hereford and Worcester.

Figure 5.13   The Kent fruit and hop belt

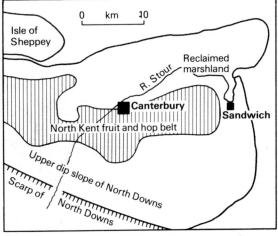

65

Farming in South Lancashire

While particular areas of Britain specialise in particular types, the British farming scene, as with geology, relief, weather and soils, is one of variety. The situation in south Lancashire provides excellent illustration of this variation within a small area. Let us first summarise the soil divisions and the associated geology, relief and climate.

Rossendale Uplands

Table 5.3 shows that this area has points in common with the Lake District. A major difference is an economic factor: access to the industrial towns of south Lancashire, providing a ready market for dairy and poultry produce. A typical Rossendale upland farming scene has moorland summits, which are peat covered (see page 8), with improved pastures on boulder clay soils around and below the farm. But the soils even on these slopes are acid and liable to waterlogging. Large amounts of money are needed for liming and draining to keep the pastures in good condition. Hill farmers cannot afford to do this without considerable government help.

The Boulder Clay Country of the Lowlands

The undulating boulder clay lowlands to the west of the Rossendale uplands (Figure 3.4) are part of a more extensive belt stretching up from the Midland Gap and the Cheshire Plain to the Fylde and the Lancaster area. The soils tend to be acid and sticky, and the rainfall fairly heavy, between 900 and 1000 mm. The land is generally under permanent pasture, broken up into smallish fields with hedges as boundaries. Dairy cattle are very important, supplying milk and cheese for the urban markets of the north-west, but fattening of beef cattle and sheep is also significant. This area and the Fylde are among the most important in the country for poultry rearing.

Shirdley Hill Sand

We noted earlier the first-class quality conditions for arable farming on Shirdley Hill Sand (page 42), which is high in organic matter from centuries of cultivation, deep, loamy and easy to work. The climate is relatively mild and sunny (Figure 5.14), with low rainfall totals for the west coast, lying in the rain shadow of Snowdonia (page 35). Crops grown include cereals, of which barley is now the most important, and a whole range of vegetables, including 'greens', carrots and potatoes. This area was once more important for potato growing, but continuous cropping over the years led to the build-up of pests and serious disease in the potatoes.

Another crop which has declined is peas, now concentrated in areas such as Lincolnshire near the vegetable freezing factories (page 61). On the other hand, vegetables are supplied for canning at the Heinz factory near Wigan. The area is also very suitable in terms of physical conditions for sugar beet growing. But it is not grown in Lancashire because there are no sugar beet factories in this area, and it would be uneconomic to transport it to the factories in eastern England (pages 60–1).

The Peat Mosslands: Market Gardening

The flat mossland areas of south Lancashire are also of first-class quality for arable farming, so long as they are kept artificially drained. This is vital because some of the land is below high-water level. Pumping has to be used to clear away the water, and field boundaries are normally drainage ditches.

The very dark peat soils (Plate 3.2) are easy to work and rich in humus. A similar range of crops can be grown as on Shirdley Hill Sand. On the peats of the Tarleton area between Southport and Preston a characteristic occupation is *market gardening*. This is the production of vegetables and flowers, both in the open

Table 5.3

	Moorland Peat Rossendale	**Boulder Clay**	**Shirdley Hill Sand** (Plate 3.3)	**Lowland Peat** (Plate 3.2)
Geology and Relief	Flat-topped Millstone Grit uplands with incised valleys	Undulating lowlands on glacial drift	Gently undulating lowlands on fossil sand dunes	Flat peat mosslands needing artificial drainage
Climate (Figure 5.14)	High rainfall (over 1250 mm per annum), low sunshine totals, relatively short growing season	Gradation to $\longrightarrow$		Relatively low rainfall (less than 850 mm per annum), increasing sunshine totals (over 1400 hours per annum), and length of growing season

and under glass, on small intensively cultivated holdings. Normally more than one crop per year will be produced. Production under glass is helped by the relatively high sunshine totals of the coastal area (Figure 5.14), and includes lettuces, tomatoes, cucumbers and flowers. Spring cabbages and cauliflowers can be sown under glass and later transplanted in the open. Some farmers combine market gardening with cereal growing. Towns such as Blackpool and Preston, and Greater Merseyside provide a ready market for the produce. Some of the market gardeners sell their produce at roadside stalls.

Market gardening is of course a widespread activity in Britain, and is particularly important in the Fens, areas round Greater London, the Vale of Evesham (for the Midlands), and in Cornwall, where growing is helped by the early springs, which allow vegetables and flowers to be taken to market before those of other parts of the country.

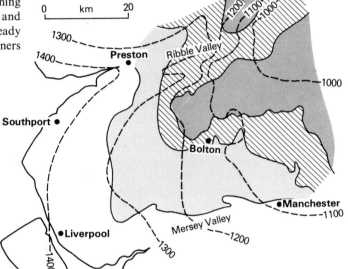

Figure 5.14 South Lancashire: rainfall and sunshine

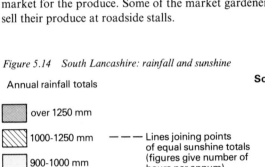

Annual rainfall totals

over 1250 mm

1000-1250 mm

900-1000 mm

less than 900 mm

— — — Lines joining points of equal sunshine totals (figures give number of hours per annum)

THE POST-WAR AGRICULTURAL REVOLUTION IN BRITAIN

In the last twenty-five years the changes which have taken place in British farming have been so rapid and so striking that they have been referred to as an 'agricultural revolution'.

There has been an enormous *increase in the agricultural output*. Britain's farms are producing half as much again as they did in 1945, through more efficient methods of farming. Although we have still to import about half our food, we are now self-supporting in such products as milk and eggs.

There has been a large *extension of crop farming*, (*a*) in clay areas, where more powerful machines are able to plough the heavy soils, once largely under permanent grassland; and (*b*) on the chalk downlands, where cereal crops are gradually replacing the rough pastures, once largely used for sheep grazing.

There has been a great *increase in mechanisation*. The number of tractors used in Britain increased nine-fold between 1950 and 1970. During the same period there was a sharp decrease in numbers of agricultural workers.

There has been a tremendous expansion in the use of *fertilisers and insecticides*. Vast quantities of chemicals

are put into the soil to increase yields and keep down weeds. Plants are sprayed from the air against diseases. Some people think this process has gone too far, and will end not only by killing the insect pests, but also bird life, and may even affect the people who eat the food.

There have been improvements in the use of (*a*) *fast-growing seeds*; (*b*) *the processing of grass* for stock feed; and (*c*) *irrigation practices*, which are found particularly in the drier south-east areas of the country. Hence plants are ripening earlier, grass can be collected green rather than as hay, and water can be provided artificially in drought periods. All this has helped to remove some of the uncertainty from farming.

Factory farming, particularly of poultry, has become widespread. In this system, the birds or animals are confined under artificial conditions. Their only job is to produce as many eggs or as much meat as possible in a short time. Heating, lighting and feeding are all artificial. This is a very efficient system but, in the opinion of many people, a not very pleasant one.

Improved methods of *handling and marketing* farm produce have been developed. One example is that of milk, which in some cases is transported in large tanker lorries, in the same way as petrol. Refrigerator lorries allow the transport of perishable products over longer distances. Another trend in marketing is the increased importance of the *frozen foods* industry, as we have noted in Lincolnshire.

The increased efficiency of farming methods, resulting in improved yields of produce, must be set against a background of severe *competition for land* in an overcrowded island. Serious losses of agricultural land have occurred to provide for (*a*) forestry; (*b*) mineral workings; (*c*) roads; and (*d*) urban development. Many of the traditional sheep pastures of the hills are being taken over by the Forestry Commission to allow the planting of coniferous forests. An increased amount of limestone (for cement and other uses) and clay (for bricks) is being extracted, and the limestone quarries and clay pits are steadily eating into the countryside. Vast new motorways and New Town developments are also using up increasing amounts of farmland.

The new type of farmer in lowland Britain is very much like a factory manager, involved in a *technological revolution*, as farming is becoming more and more mechanised and efficient. Farmland in Lowland Britain is now very expensive, and is bought and sold by investors in the same way as building land in the towns. In comparison, hill farming is becoming less prosperous, and could not continue without government help. But should the traditional way of life of the hill sheep farmer be allowed to die because it is not economically prosperous, or because the upland areas are in demand for forestry? The 'attack on the hills' for water supply, for forest land, and for tourist amenities, is one of the main conservation problems of today, and will be looked at in a later chapter.

This agricultural revolution has made British farming more up-to-date than that of some of our EEC neighbours. The effects of the Common Agricultural Policy (CAP) of the EEC has been to increase prices to consumers. Under both EEC and the British system farming has had to be subsidised. But, broadly speaking, under the EEC system the consumer pays for this through increased prices: under the former British system, food prices were kept low by further government subsidy to the consumer. Efficient British farmers clearly benefit from the grants from the CAP.

Exercises

18. Refer to Figure 5.11 and Plate 5.6.
(*a*) With the help of a tracing overlay, draw an annotated sketch of Plate 5.6, marking on the kinds of features indicated on Figure 5.11.

(*b*) With the help also of Plates 5.1, 5.4 and 5.7, indicated similarities and differences between the farming landscapes of
(i) Great Langdale and the highland fringes of Aberdeenshire;
(ii) Lincolnshire and the Kent fruit and hop belt.
19. Refer to Figure 5.15a, b and c. Figure 5.15a and b are of the same area. Figure 5.15c is of a different area, in which the relief is more or less flat.
(*a*) Suggest, with reasons, in which parts of Lancashire these two areas might be.
(*b*) Outline the relationship between land use and relief on Figure 5.15a and b.
(*c*) Refer back to Figure 5.1. In which category would each area in Figure 5.15 come: farmscape; wildscape; marginal (farm-wildscape) fringe: rurban (farm-town) fringe? On what evidence do you base your answer?
20. This chapter has included studies of, among others, hill farming, mixed farming, and market gardening. Apart from the areas so far considered:
hill farming is also important in the Welsh mountains and the Southern Uplands of Scotland;
mixed farming is very important in East Anglia with, like Lincolnshire, emphasis on crop production;
market gardening is also important in the Fens, the Vale of Evesham, and the south-west peninsula.
From each of these groups choose *one* area.
(*a*) Outline the main types of production found in each of these, assessing the relative importance of physical and economic factors.
(*b*) How do these areas compare with similar types of area you had previously studied? Are physical or economic factors the most important? To what extent?
21. Table 5.4 shows changing patterns of food consumption in Britain between 1970 and 1980.

Table 5.4 Food consumption
(grams per person per week)

	1970	1980
Liquid milk	131.26	117.94
Butter	169.81	114.82
Sugar	480.24	316.67
Beef/veal	221.13	230.48
Pork	80.23	117.08
Poultry	143.45	189.09
Potatoes	1469.66	1160.93
Bread	1080.42	882.25
Frozen vegetables	331.13	472.31
Apples	207.52	222.54

(*a*) Describe the changes indicated between 1970 and 1980.
(*b*) Explain the changes which have taken place, under such headings as (i) changes in cost; (ii) EEC entry; (iii) changing tastes; (iv) changing diets; (v) other factors.
(*c*) Comment briefly on the likely impact of these changes on Britain's (i) dairy farmers; (ii) beef producers; (iii) poultry producers; (iv) grain producers; (v) market gardeners.

(a) Land use

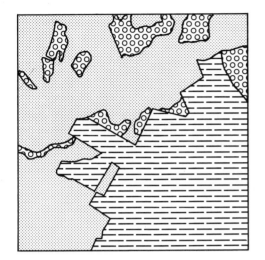

Permanent grassland

Moorland (rough pasture)

Woodland

(b) Relief

Heights in metres

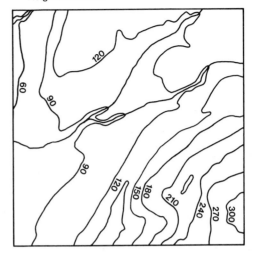

Scale 1: 25 000

NB Roads not shown on maps

(c) Land use

Cereals

Market gardening

Grassland

Factories and wasteland

Housing

Relief: level, under 20 metres

Figure 5.15   Land use and relief

6 ENERGY RESOURCES

COAL

The Selby Coalfield

'Imagine a solid block of high quality, clean coal, the size of the Isle of Wight, from two to four metres in thickness, and that's the Selby coalfield.'
(*Journal of York Chamber of Trade and Commerce Spring 1982*)

Plate 6.1 is a photograph of the surface buildings at the Wistow mine site on the Selby coalfield, which started production in 1982. This is one of six sites on the new coalfield: five shafts, and one (Gascoigne Wood) drift mine. All the mines are linked by underground tunnels and, unlike most traditional mines, the coal comes to the surface at one point, at Gascoigne Wood, by means of conveyor belts, computerised to ensure an even flow of coal. From here the coal is taken to nearby power stations (pages 77–8).

The 4000 miners employed on the Selby coalfield will eventually produce 16 million tonnes of coal per annum, nearly twice the present output of the whole Yorkshire area, and at a productivity rate four times the British average. The coalfield taps a magnificent coal seam, in places 3.4 metres and more thick, named the Barnsley seam. This dips eastwards from about 300 metres deep in the west to 1100 in the east. The coal is so clean that there is no need for spoil heaps.

Castleford

One of the oldest towns in the north Yorkshire coalfield area is Castleford, which has developed over the site of a former Roman fort at the confluence of the Rivers Aire and Calder (423263 on the OS map extract, Figure 6.2). Castleford itself is shown on Plate 6.2. The town is almost surrounded by collieries. Some of the miners live in the terraced houses shown in the foreground of the picture, though many others have moved to modern council housing estates on the outskirts of Castleford. The central area of the town lies in the left middle ground of the photograph between the railway line and the river. The confluence of the Aire and the Calder is just off the photograph. A noticeable feature is the weir (letter W on the photograph) below which the meander of the River Aire is heavily polluted. Across the background runs a straight canal cut. These features also stand out clearly on the OS map extract.

Plate 6.1   Wistow mine site, Selby coalfield

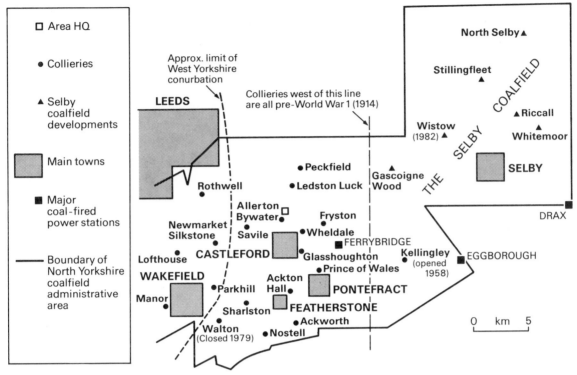

Figure 6.1 *Yorkshire Coalfield: the North Yorkshire area*

The following labels appear on the map:

Legend:
- □ Area HQ
- ● Collieries
- ▲ Selby coalfield developments
- Main towns
- ■ Major coal-fired power stations
- Boundary of North Yorkshire coalfield administrative area

Approx. limit of West Yorkshire conurbation

Collieries west of this line are all pre-World War 1 (1914)

LEEDS

North Selby ▲
Stillingfleet ▲
Wistow (1982) ▲
Riccall ▲
Whitemoor ▲

SELBY COALFIELD
THE SELBY

SELBY

DRAX

Rothwell ●
Peckfield ●
Ledston Luck ●
Gascoigne Wood ▲
Allerton Bywater ●
Newmarket Silkstone ●
Savile ●
Fryston ●
Wheldale ●
CASTLEFORD
Glasshoughton ●
FERRYBRIDGE ■
Kellingley ● (opened 1958)
EGGBOROUGH ■
Lofthouse ●
Prince of Wales ●
WAKEFIELD
Ackton Hall ●
Manor ●
Parkhill ●
PONTEFRACT
FEATHERSTONE
Sharlston ●
Ackworth ●
Walton ● (Closed 1979)
Nostell ●

0 km 5

Plate 6.2 *Aerial view of Castleford*

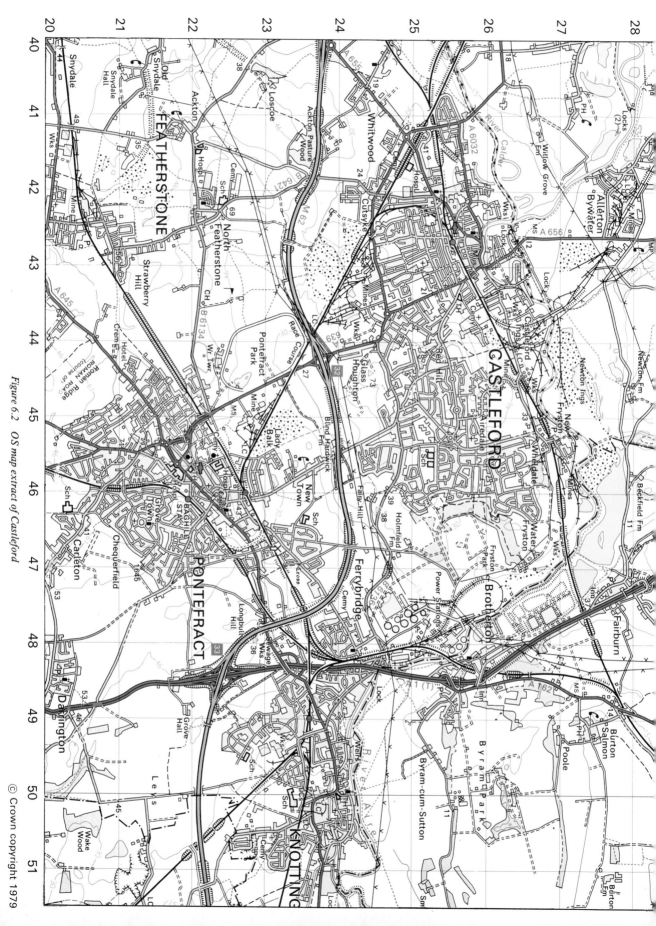

Figure 6.2   OS map extract of Castleford

© Crown copyright 1979

Exercises

1. Refer to the OS map extract of the Castleford area, and also Figure 6.1 and Plate 6.2.

(*a*)   Give the grid references of the square(s) in which the following are found: Ferrybridge power station; Prince of Wales colliery; headquarters of north Yorkshire coalfield area.

(*b*)   What suggests that the Rivers Aire and Calder are important for coal transport?

(*c*)   (i) Outline four stages in the development of communications in the Castleford area; (ii) explain the advantages of this area in terms of communications.

(*d*)   Compare the patterns of settlement in squares 4220 and 4225.

2. (*a*)   Describe variations in the patterns of streets and buildings in various parts of Plate 6.2.

(*b*)   What are the advantages and disadvantages of living in towns such as Castleford?

A Mining Settlement: Featherstone

Featherstone is a small mining settlement of 14 000 inhabitants, lying not far to the south of Castleford (36 000 inhabitants) and south-west of Pontefract (33 000). Until the 1860s, Featherstone was an agricultural village, although small collieries have been recorded in this district since the seventeenth century. Table 6.1 shows how its population growth in the late nineteenth and early twentieth centuries was linked with coalmining. As coalmining developed, so houses had to be built for the workers. Most of these were terraced houses, some of which can be seen on Plate 6.3 (a picture taken in the 1920s) with a huge spoil heap overlooking them.

Plate 6.3   Terraced miners' houses at Featherstone, 1926

Table 6.1   Featherstone

Population		Mining activity
1861	*c.* 700	1868 First colliery opened
1871	2 250	1877 Second colliery opened
1881	6 000	1885 Colliery enlargement
1891	7 500	1892–4 Colliery enlargement
1901	12 000	
1911	14 500	1910–13 Further enlargement
1921	15 000	
1931	15 000	1935 One of collieries closed
1951	14 000	
1961	14 500	
1971	15 000	
1981	14 000	

Before 1891 about 1300 homes had been built; between 1891 and 1911 a further 1300 were put up; and another 1300 between 1911 and 1951. Many of the terraces were built on either side of the main roads, with shorter terraces leading off. A feature of mining settlements such as Featherstone is the large number of men dependent for employment on the local colliery. In the period before the Second World War approximately 70% of the male labour force was employed in mining. This had serious consequences in times of economic depression. Between 1928 and 1933, for example, unemployment in the western part of the Yorkshire coalfield varied between 21% and 57%. In contrast to the situation for men, for most of whom employment is provided by the local mine, there is little employment in Featherstone for women. The working women of the town tend to travel to work by bus to the nearby larger centres of Castleford and Pontefract, and other parts of the West Yorkshire conurbation (Figure 6.1).

The Work of the Miner

Plate 6.4 shows men working at the coal face in the 1930s. The seam here is a thick one and the conditions shown were good for that period. But much of the work was hard manual labour, with picks to hack out the coal, and shovels to load it into the tubs. Notice the pit props on either side of the picture. The miners often had to walk miles to the coal face, and on finishing work had to travel home dirty in their working clothes and bath in a tin tub in the back kitchen of their terraced houses.

In most of today's collieries conditions are much improved. Compare the 'tools' of Plate 6.4 with the massive coal-shearing machine at the modern colliery shown on Plate 6.5. Notice that pit props have been replaced by powered hydraulic jacks which move forward as the coal face advances. After being cut, the coal is loaded automatically on to conveyor belts which take the coal to the foot of the shaft. The miners now travel to the coal face by underground electric or diesel locomotive. When the day's work is finished, the miner has the facility of the pit-head bath, and can travel home clean in everyday clothes. The highly mechanised mines of today, some of which are electronically controlled, produce massive outputs with relatively small amounts of labour, compared with the old mines. Although

Plate 6.4   Coal miners at work, 1935

Plate 6.5   A shearer loader at a modern Yorkshire coalface

74

mining remains a dangerous and unpleasant occupation, safety standards have improved greatly in the last thirty years, as indicated in Table 6.2. Even the 1947 figure is an improvement on nineteenth-century figures. Between 1851 and 1881, for example, on average over 100 miners per annum were killed in the Yorkshire coalfield alone.

Table 6.2 Number of miners killed in British mines

1947	1953	1968	1976	1980
618	401	130	50	39

The North Yorkshire Coalfield

Figure 6.1 gives a rough outline of the extent of the Yorkshire coalfield as a whole. It runs south into the Derbyshire field. Figure 6.3 is a section showing the structure in Yorkshire. The rock strata on the eastern side of the Pennines dip generally eastwards. The Coal Measures *outcrop*, that is, appear at the surface, in the *exposed* part of the coalfield in the west of the region. It must be understood that the term *Coal Measures* refers to a series of rock strata of Carboniferous age, including sandstones and shales as well as *coal seams*. Further east, the Coal Measures are *concealed* beneath younger Permian (including Magnesian limestone which forms an escarpment at the surface (Figure 6.3)) and Triassic rocks. These features are illustrated on Figure 6.4 which is a geological section in the area of the main shaft at Kellingley colliery.

In the early days, most of the coal was mined in the extreme west of the coalfield, where the coal was generally nearer the surface and more easily extracted by shallow pits. Much of the coal of this western area is

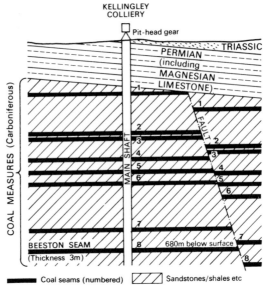

Figure 6.4 *Geological section of Kellingley Colliery*

now used up, and over the years mining has tended to shift eastwards towards the concealed coalfield.

Many of the largest and most modern mines are found in this concealed part of the coalfield, as at Kellingley in the North Yorkshire area (Plate 6.6), set in a rural landscape to the east of the old mining region (Figure 6.1). The boundary between the *exposed* and the *concealed* parts of the North Yorkshire coalfield runs through Pontefract (Figure 6.3). Kellingley was in fact the first mine to be opened on the concealed part of the field in North Yorkshire, although there are many such mines further south. It is the biggest mine in its area, employing nearly 2000 workers, and producing nearly 1½ million tonnes of coal per annum when it works up to

Figure 6.3 *General west–east section across the Yorkshire coalfields*

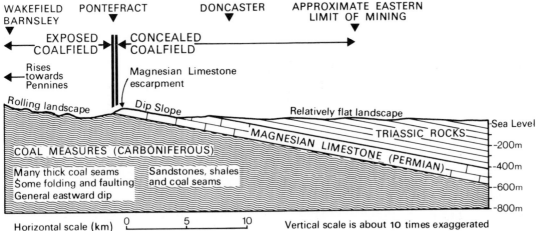

75

its full capacity. Table 6.3 shows the annual production figures and the number of workers employed in the North Yorkshire pits in 1980–1.

Table 6.3

Colliery (see Figure 6.1)	Annual production 1980 (tonnes)	No. of employees
Ackton Hall	620 000	1500
Allerton Bywater	750 000	1230
Fryston	550 000	1055
Glasshoughton	400 000	640
Kellingley	1 700 000	2360
Ledston Luck	340 000	440
Lofthouse	320 000	900
Manor	100 000	260
Newmarket	260 000	650
Nostell	420 000	630
Park Hill	250 000	500
Peckfield	260 000	585
Prince of Wales	570 000	200
Rothwell	325 000	650
Savile	340 000	575
Sharlston	850 000	1250
Wheldale	420 000	890

These figures indicate that there are considerable differences in *productivity*, measured by the output per worker, between pits, which arise in part from the differences in geological difficulties encountered. The Yorkshire coalfield has in general great advantages for mining, compared, for example, with the Lancashire coalfield. The Yorkshire coalfield is very large. The seams are on average thick, as in the case of the Beeston Seam at Kellingley (Figure 6.4), which is about 3 metres

thick, and can be seen being worked mechanically on Plate 6.5. In general the coal seams dip gently eastwards, and are not greatly affected by folding and faulting, though these do occur. The thick, relatively undisturbed, seams make possible the high degree of mechanisation which exists at collieries such as Kellingley. Another advantage of the Yorkshire coalfield is that it has large resources left, especially in the concealed part of the field, where there are vast areas to be developed, as we have seen in relation to the new Selby coalfield.

Exercises

3. (*a*) Distinguish carefully, with the help of labelled sketches (i) coal seams and Coal Measures; (ii) an exposed and a concealed coalfield.
(*b*) Find out the advantages and disadvantages of opencast mining.
(*c*) Draw two separate labelled sketches side by side to bring out the differences between a coalfield with favourable, and one with unfavourable, mining conditions.
4. Compare the underground working conditions on Plates 6.4 and 6.5.
5. Compare the appearance of Wistow mine site (Plate 6.1) with that of Kellingley Colliery (Plate 6.6).
6. (*a*) On an enlarged map of the North Yorkshire coalfield, locate the main collieries with the help of Figure 6.1 and Table 6.3, and draw against each a bar graph, proportional to the number of workers employed at the colliery.
(*b*) Name the largest and the smallest mines in terms of tonnage produced. In which parts of the coalfield are they?
(*c*) Work out the most productive and the least productive mines on the basis of the figures in Table 6.3. Comment on their location.

Plate 6.6   Aerial view of Kellingley Colliery

Users of Coal

Although coal has many by-products, which are employed in the manufacture of a whole variety of chemicals, including dyes, plastics, explosives, fertilisers and antiseptics, its main use is as a fuel source. Users of coal as a fuel in Britain as a whole have changed over the years, as indicated in Table 6.4.

Table 6.4 Main users of coal
(*figures given in millions of tonnes*)

User	1947	1959	1970–1	1975–6	1980–1
Electricity power stations	27.0	46.0	73.5	75.0	89.5
Gas works	22.5	22.5	3.5	—	—
Coke ovens	20.0	25.5	24.5	18.0	11.5
Domestic	36.5	31.5	18.5	11.0	9.0
Industrial	36.0	31.5	18.5	9.0	7.8
Railways	14.5	10.0	0.1	0.1	0.1

Overall, the total production of coal in Great Britain has declined from a maximum of about 215 million tonnes in 1955 to just over 110 million in 1980–1. While the use of coal as a fuel has declined, that of oil and natural gas has increased and is likely to do so further as

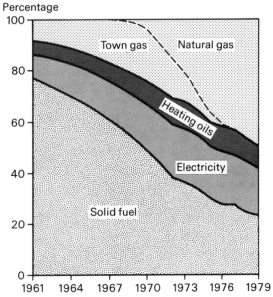

Figure 6.5   United Kingdom: domestic consumption of fuels

Figure 6.5 indicates. As Table 6.4 shows, by far the most important users of coal today are the electricity power stations.

The Transport of Coal to Power Stations from the North Yorkshire Coalfield

Plate 6.7 shows barges on the Aire and Calder Navigation (Figure 6.6) waiting to unload coal mechanically through the barge unloader (the tall structure on the right) at Ferrybridge 'C' power station, opened in 1968. In the background is the 'B' power station (4725 on Figure 6.2). This is one of three major coal-fired power stations located in the area, the others being at Eggborough and Drax (Figure 6.6), the latter being

particularly convenient for the Selby coalfield. The three stations together consume some 19 million tonnes of coal per annum.

No conventional transport system can cope with such demands. The canal, though still used by Ferrybridge and for export of coal via Goole (Figure 6.6), is clearly not adequate for this purpose, and neither is road transport. The transport problem has been overcome by

Plate 6.7   Ferrybridge Power Station

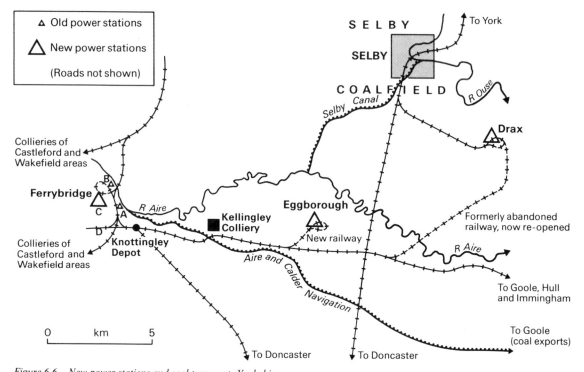

Figure 6.6 New power stations and coal transport, Yorkshire

the development of the so-called *merry-go-round* trains, such as that shown arriving at Drax power station on Plate 6.8. These trains draw hopper wagons of over 30 tonnes capacity. One of these is shown being loaded at a colliery on Plate 6.9. Notice the fine nature of the coal, which is the type required for use in power station furnaces. On arriving at the power station, the 'merry-go-round' train does not stop, but runs very slowly on a loop line, while the hopper wagons are discharged into fixed hoppers under the track.

To work this system in North Yorkshire, an abandoned railway line has been opened to serve Drax, and new loops constructed to serve Eggborough and Ferrybridge 'C'. All the coal supplied to Eggborough and Drax and most of that to Ferrybridge uses this system. It should be noted, however, that in Yorkshire and in the country as a whole, road transport is also used in the movement of coal to power stations.

Plate 6.9 Travelling hopper and retractable chute at a modern colliery

Plate 6.8 'Merry-go-round' train at Drax power station

Exercises

7. (*a*) Draw a graph or graphs to show the changing uses of coal as revealed on Table 6.4.
(*b*) Describe the changes indicated on Figure 6.4.
(*c*) Give reasons for the changes on (i) Table 6.4, (ii) Figure 6.5.
8. Refer to Figure 6.6 and other relevant information in the text.
(*a*) State the advantages and disadvantages of the Aire and Calder Navigation for the transport of coal compared with railways. Why is the lower part of the River Aire itself not used?
(*b*) Can you suggest possible reasons why Eggborough and Drax power stations have been built well to the east of the main area of collieries? This means finding out other factors which affect the siting of coal-fired power stations (see page 89).
9. Describe ways in which technological change has affected the mining and the transport of coal.

The Coalfields of Britain

Coal is perhaps the most important of all Britain's industrial resources, and has been mined on a large scale for nearly 200 years. Its presence in large quantities made possible the Industrial Revolution and rapid growth of manufacturing towns and population through the nineteenth century. All the major British conurbations except Greater London and Merseyside are located on coalfields, and Merseyside is in fact very closely linked with the Lancashire coalfield. The landscape of former coal mining is still present in areas where the collieries are now exhausted.

The coal industry, like railways, is now nationalised, and run by the National Coal Board (NCB). The division of the British coalfields into NCB areas is shown on Figure 6.7.

The fact that the Yorkshire–Derbyshire–Nottinghamshire coalfield is sub-divided into seven NCB areas is a sign of its importance. In contrast, the comparatively small coalfields of Lancashire, Cumbria, North Wales and Staffordshire together form one area. The outputs of British coalfields are shown in Table 6.5.

Table 6.5 Coal output (millions of tonnes)

Coalfield(s)	1963–4	1970–1	1975–6	1980–1
Scottish	16.4	11.2	9.7	7.8
North-east England	32.2	19.0	14.4	14.2
Yorkshire	43.9	34.8	31.4	31.6
Derby–Notts	39.3	32.3	27.9	29.3
Staffs and South Midlands	22.0	17.1	20.3	19.7
Western (see Figure 6.7)	12.7	6.1		
South Wales (and Bristol area)	19.4	11.6	8.3	7.7
Kent	1.6	1.1	0.7	0*
Total	187.5	133.2	112.7	110.3

* included in South Midlands

This decline in production is reflected even more in a decline in the numbers employed by the coalmining industry. In 1952 it had 727 000 employees in 880 mines. By 1980 these figures had declined to 225 000 and 211, respectively. Some coalfields are now in danger of dying out altogether. In the whole north-western area, for example, sixteen out of the thirty-two pits were closed between 1965 and 1971.

The *technological revolution* in mining has made it possible to reduce the number of mines by almost two-thirds, and the number of miners by over half, without a correspondingly steep decline in coal production, which has decreased by less than one-third in the period shown. In 1947 less than four horse power of machinery per worker was used, as against nearly twelve in 1967. To obtain 1000 tonnes of coal required 914 work shifts in 1947, as against 547 in the late 1960s. Figure 6.8 shows the continuing improvement in productivity in mining in recent years, rising from 295 million tonnes per machine shift in 1976–7 to over 330 million tonnes in 1980–1.

Figure 6.7   National Coal Board areas, 1971

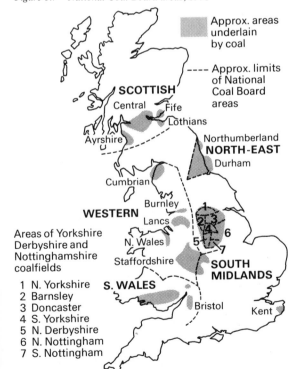

Approx. areas underlain by coal

---- Approx. limits of National Coal Board areas

SCOTTISH
Central   Fife
Lothians
Ayrshire

Northumberland
NORTH-EAST
Durham

Cumbrian

Burnley
WESTERN
Lancs
N. Wales
Staffordshire

SOUTH MIDLANDS

Areas of Yorkshire Derbyshire and Nottinghamshire coalfields

1 N. Yorkshire
2 Barnsley
3 Doncaster
4 S. Yorkshire
5 N. Derbyshire
6 N. Nottingham
7 S. Nottingham

S. WALES
Bristol
Kent

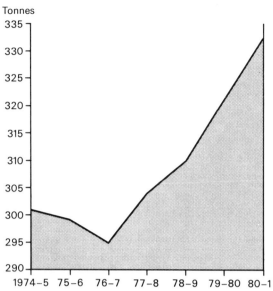

Tonnes

Figure 6.8   Britain's coal output per machine shift since 1974–5

NORTH SEA OIL AND NATURAL GAS

Plate 6.10 is a photograph of a Shell/Esso production platform on the North Cormorant oilfield (Figure 6.12) which began production in 1982. The platform is 260 metres tall and stands in over 150 metres of water. Notice that the living accommodation for the workers is on a separate rig from the production platform.

In June 1975, the first oil from the North Sea to reach Britain was landed at the Isle of Grain refinery in Kent. This represented one of the climaxes in a story which began at Slochteren in the Netherlands in 1961, when one of the world's major natural gas fields was found. As the underlying geological structures here were similar to those under the North Sea, companies were stimulated to undertake the expensive task of exploring the submarine structures. Their efforts were to be rewarded. The North Sea has been shown to cover both major natural gas fields and oilfields. By 1982, Britain was self-sufficient in both oil and natural gas.

Exercises

10. (a) Distinguish between a coalfield and an NCB area, giving examples to show the differences.
(b) Why do NCB areas differ so much in size as measured on the map?
11. Refer to Table 6.5 and draw graphs to show:
(a) the overall decline in coal production between the dates given; and
(b) the differences in production between the different coalfields. What factors account for these differences?

Finding the Natural Gas and Oil

The fact that the gas-bearing and oil-bearing structures lie below the sea, and in most cases well out to sea in deep water, adds greatly to the problems of discovering and exploiting these resources. The original exploration, once promising structures had been found, was undertaken by undersea drilling rigs.

The favourable structures include porous reservoir rocks, which contain the oil and natural gas in the pores

Plate 6.10   Oil production platform on North Cormorant oilfield, North Sea

(a) Simple fold

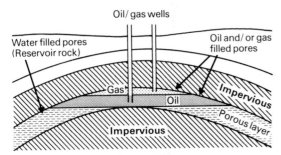

(b) Fault

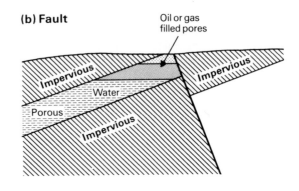

Figure 6.9   Favourable structures for oil and natural gas

in the rock; and 'trap' structures, such as anticlinal folds and faults, in which the reservoir rock is, as it were, trapped against an impervious rock (Figure 6.9a and b). Many favourable structures were to be found in two major areas: (a) the Southern Basin, extending westwards from the Netherlands to eastern England, which has proved to contain large natural gas fields; and (b) a major axis running from north to south between Norway and the Shetlands and northern Scotland, containing the so-called East Shetland and Central Basins. These basins are the source of immense quantities of petroleum, and also contain natural gas (Figure 6.11).

The North Sea has been divided up by international agreement into territorial waters. Figure 6.11 shows how favourably Britain is placed both for reserves of oil and natural gas. Only Norway is as fortunate in the reserves which have been found. It is less fortunate in that a deep sea trench lies between the oil and gas fields and its shores, preventing the use of pipelines to the shores of Norway. Thus oil from the Ekofisk group of fields is by agreement piped to Teesside (Figure 6.11).

Natural Gas

Natural gas was found under the North Sea before oil. The main gas fields discovered so far have been in the British and Norwegian areas, starting in 1965. Gas from the West Sole field is taken by underwater pipeline to Easington in Yorkshire, while that from Leman Bank, Hewett and Indefatigable goes to Bacton in Norfolk. From here the gas is taken by pipelines linking with Britain's major gas pipelines (Figure 6.10).

North Sea gas has had the tremendous advantage of reducing our dependence on imported natural gas, in a period of rapidly increasing demand for fuel. In addition, natural gas is far more efficient than town gas (made from coal), giving twice as much energy as a similar amount of coal gas. From the late 1960s, natural gas was being fed into homes for running domestic

Figure 6.10   UK National Gas Transmission System

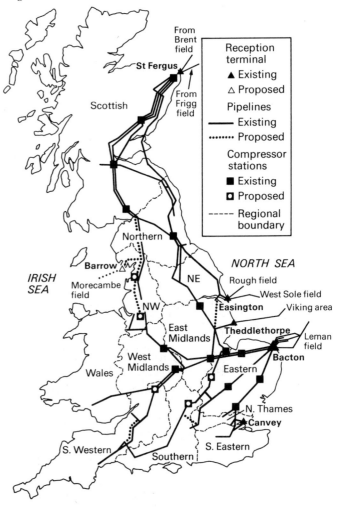

appliances, such as gas fires and cookers. Today almost all of Britain is covered. The reserves of the Southern Basin shown on Table 6.6 have been supplemented by major new discoveries in the Frigg field (shared with Norway), Brent, and in Morecambe Bay (Figure 6.10). The Rough and Morecambe Bay fields are to be used for winter peak supply. Development of Irish Sea fields will bring new employment to declining north-west ports such as Barrow.

Table 6.6 Amount of gas produced (1980) from main British fields

Southern Basin	cubic metres
Leman Bank field	9482
Hewett area	6568
Indefatigable field	6878
Viking area	4689
West Sole field	1445
Rough field	467
East Shetland Basin	
Frigg field	6374
Piper field	521

Oil

Five years after the major gas finds, the Phillips Petroleum Company announced in 1970 a giant oil strike in the south-west corner of the Norwegian sector of the North Sea, which was named *Ekofisk* (Figure 6.11). A little later a gas strike, *Codfield*, was found to the north of Ekofisk and further south in Danish waters, another small oilfield, *Dan*, was discovered. In 1971, four important finds in British waters to the east of Aberdeen were announced. In December 1971 it was reported that one of these, the BP *Forties* field, was potentially one of the world's great oilfields, and would be developed immediately. More was to come. After the Forties field, an even greater source was discovered in the East Shetland Basin. This consists of two giant fields, *Brent* and *Ninian*, a number of medium and small-sized fields, all in the British sector, and the great *Statfjord* field, in Norwegian waters. In 1976 an important discovery, known as the *Beatrice* field, was made. This is not a large field, but it lies close inshore in the Moray Firth (Figure 6.12). Other promising areas lie to the west of the Shetlands, where the *Clare* discovery is awaiting appraisal. Even more important has been the finding of a medium-sized onshore field at *Wytch Farm* in Dorset (Figure 6.11), where production costs are much smaller than is the case with an offshore oilfield.

The Significance of North Sea Oil

In 1971, Britain had to import 108 million tonnes of oil, over three-quarters of which came from the Middle East. By 1982 Britain had become self-sufficient in oil, with great benefit to its external balance of payments. North Sea oil is also of high quality and is located near to the enormous market for oil of the countries of Western Europe.

Within Britain, the impact of the oil finds has also been great:

(a) Employment has been created in such areas as Teesside, Clydeside, the Firth of Forth, the Moray Firth, and north-west Scotland, in the construction of drilling rigs, production platforms, pipelines, and many other accessories.

(b) Further employment has come from the need to construct shore facilities for the unloading of oil and natural gas. Figure 6.12 shows the pipelines to Teesside (for Ekofisk oil); Cruden Bay and St Fergus (for Forties oil and Frigg natural gas); Flotta in the Orkneys (for the Claymore and Piper fields); and, largest of all, Sullom Voe in the Shetlands (for the giant Brent, Ninian and adjacent fields). Sullom Voe (Plate 6.11) has become one of the major oil ports of the world, sending out from its deep-water harbour tankers loaded with oil from the East Shetland fields.

(c) Aberdeen has become the main commercial and marketing centre for the oil industry, with the advantages of being the nearest large commercial centre and port to the newly discovered oil industry, with an existing airport at Dyce. Rapid change has taken place during the 1970s in the Aberdeen area.

(i) The work generated in the area has given it employment percentages much higher than the average for Scotland.

(ii) Land prices, and thus the cost of housing, have risen rapidly, as people (including many Americans) connected with the oil firms have moved into the Aberdeen area.

(iii) The amount of traffic using Aberdeen harbour, chiefly service vessels for the North Sea oil rigs, has enormously increased. Harbour dues have grown in consequence. Quays have been reconstructed and oil storage depots built to service the new traffic.

(iv) Dyce airport has expanded, with numbers of passengers increasing from 135 000 in 1970 to 1 400 000 in 1980–1. The airport handles the helicopter services to the oil rigs, changing the crews, and taking in provisions.

Similar effects to these have been felt in other Scottish towns such as Lerwick (Shetlands), Inverness, Peterhead and Dundee. Flotta terminal, Orkney, employs 300 people, for example.

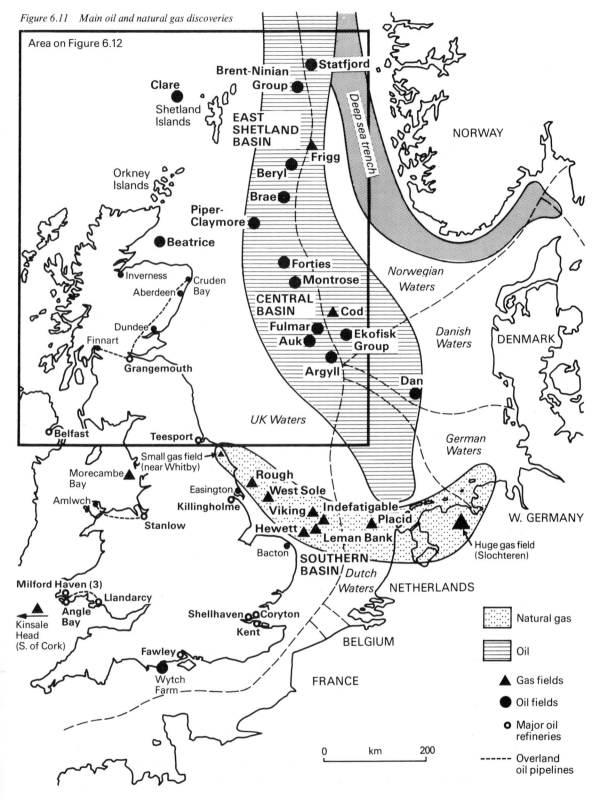

Figure 6.11   Main oil and natural gas discoveries

Area on Figure 6.12

Statfjord

Brent-Ninian Group

Clare

Shetland Islands

Deep sea trench

NORWAY

EAST SHETLAND BASIN

Frigg

Orkney Islands

Beryl

Brae

Piper-Claymore

Beatrice

Inverness

Cruden Bay

Aberdeen

Forties

Montrose

Norwegian Waters

Dundee

CENTRAL BASIN

Cod

Finnart

Fulmar

Auk

Ekofisk Group

Danish Waters

DENMARK

Grangemouth

Argyll

Dan

Belfast

UK Waters

German Waters

Teesport

Small gas field (near Whitby)

Morecambe Bay

Rough

West Sole

Amlwch

Easington

Killingholme

Viking

Indefatigable

Placid

W. GERMANY

Stanlow

Hewett

Leman Bank

Huge gas field (Slochteren)

Bacton

SOUTHERN BASIN

Dutch Waters

NETHERLANDS

Milford Haven (3)

Llandarcy

Angle Bay

Shellhaven

Coryton

Kinsale Head (S. of Cork)

Kent

BELGIUM

Fawley

Wytch Farm

FRANCE

Natural gas

Oil

▲ Gas fields

● Oil fields

○ Major oil refineries

- - - - Overland oil pipelines

0   km   200

(*d*) New petrochemical works and ancillary plants are planned for the Moray Firth, Peterhead and Firth of Forth areas.

The Problems of Exploiting North Sea Oil

Physical Problems

(*a*) The oil-bearing structures shown in Figure 6.9a and b lie below waters anything from 75 to 180 metres deep, and the drilling starts below the seabed. A whole new technology is needed to exploit undersea oil.

(*b*) There are great problems in laying pipelines across the uneven seabed to the shore. As we have seen, the deep-water trench off its shores prevents oil being taken by pipeline to Norway.

(*c*) The drilling rigs and production platforms have to be located in some of the roughest waters in the world, exposed to stormy westerly and icy northerly winds, making landing conditions very treacherous. Where tanker loading methods are used, difficulties are again created by rough weather. Much of the work of installing the drilling rigs and production platforms has to take place in the summer months.

Economic Problems

The physical difficulties raise the expense of finding and exploiting the oil to much higher levels than is the case with oil found on land. The expense is only justified by the fact that the oil finds are so large, the price of oil has increased so much in recent years, and there is a huge market for oil in Western Europe. Inflation in the 1970s has increased the cost of exploration. Small fields such as Auk and Argyll (Figure 6.12), if they had been discovered later, would probably not have been developed. In the future, smaller discoveries are unlikely to be used unless they lie near an existing pipeline to a large field, or in shallow water, such as the Beatrice field.

Another problem lies in striking a balance between the percentage of profit which goes to the government as tax, and the percentage retained by the oil companies to finance further exploration. Too large a rate of tax would certainly mean that the small fields would not be used. The idea is therefore to tax the smaller fields at a lower rate, to try to ensure that the oil companies exploit them.

Plate 6.11   Sullom Voe oil terminal

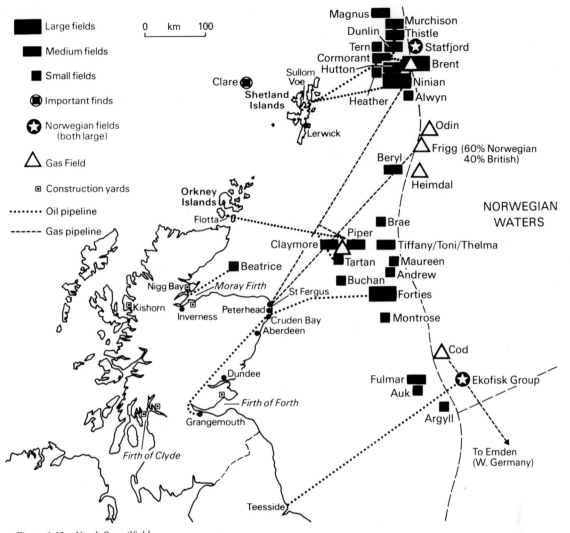

Figure 6.12   North Sea oilfields

Conservation and Environmental Problems

These arise from the construction of rigs and platforms, the landing of oil and natural gas, oil leakages, the construction of petrochemical and other works, disturbance of fishing grounds, and the general impact of new technology and population influx on what may be unspoiled stretches of coast.

Thus the Nigg Bay and Loch Kishorn construction yards lie in areas of great natural beauty along the Scottish coast (Figure 6.12). Plate 6.12 shows the enormous size of the concrete base being built for a production platform on the Ninian field. After the preliminary stages, the giant structure was floated out on to the deep sheltered waters of Loch Kishorn. Temporary buildings were put up to house the construction workers, brought into a sparsely populated area.

One of the difficulties of exploiting the Beatrice field in the Moray Firth is that it lies over an important local fishing ground. Fishing and the exploitation of oil do not mix, as trawl nets can damage pipelines, and oil spillages can destroy fishing grounds. The hazards present were dramatically illustrated in April 1977, when a 'blow-out' on one of the Ekofisk wells resulted in thousands of tonnes of oil spilling into the North Sea; and even more tragically in March 1980 when over 130 died as a result of the Norwegian 'oil-rig hotel' (or 'floatel'), *Alexander L. Keilland*, turning upside down during a storm, again in the Ekofisk sector.

Plate 6.12   An oil production platform under construction at Loch Kishorn

Exercises

British Gas boasts two new discoveries

**By Rod Chapman,
Energy Correspondent**

British Gas has made two further natural gas finds off the Lancashire Coast, when it began a new drilling programme in January. Its chairman, Sir Denis Rooke, said yesterday that preliminary testing had shown that discoveries would provide gas in commercial quantities from wells which are separate from the new Morecambe field and also from each other.

The corporation has been drilling three holes in Blocks 110/7, 110/8 and 113/26 of the Irish Sea, which is close enough to the coast to make most finds–since the waters are also shallow–commercially viable. The latest discoveries will boost its production from the Lancashire Coast area in the latter half of the decade.

(*The Guardian*, 11 May 1982)

12. Read the newspaper extract. Why are the Irish Sea gas finds important?

13. Suggest reasons why the major oil companies have combined together in the search for oil in the North Sea.
14. Try to find out more about the advantages and possible disadvantages to north-east England and north-east Scotland of the North Sea oil finds.

Oil Refining

As Figure 6.13 indicates, Britain's oil refineries are located on deep-water estuaries, or are within relatively short pipeline distance of a deep-water terminal. The major refineries are therefore on Milford Haven, the Thames, Southampton Water, the Mersey, the Tees, the Humber and the Firth of Forth. Some of the oil landed at Milford Haven is sent by pipeline to Llandarcy refinery near Swansea; oil from the Forties field is also brought by pipeline, to Grangemouth; while another pipeline connects Stanlow refinery with Shell's deep-water terminal on Anglesey.

Teesport Refinery

Teesport (Plate 6.13) came into operation in 1968. Tankers of up to 110 000 tonnes bring in crude oil along the River Tees, which is shown in the background of the photograph. After processing, the refined oil products are sent out by rail (shown in the foreground), road or coastal tanker. In Britain as a whole, about 40% of refined products are transported by road; 24% by

Figure 6.13 Major oil refineries in Britain

coastal tanker; approximately 18% by pipeline; 14% by rail; and 4% by inland waterway.

The reasons why Teesport was chosen as a refinery site illustrate well the general factors which lead to the growth of refineries. First, as in other parts of Britain, there has been a tremendous increase in north-east England in the demand for oil products, but in this area there was no existing major oil refinery to act as a local source of supply.

Secondly, Teesside itself is a major industrial zone, with huge steel works and chemical works (at Billingham and Wilton: Figure 6.14). Much of the material used in the construction of the refinery was available from the steel and engineering industries of the north-east.

Thirdly, Teesport itself was located lower down the estuary to take advantage of the deep-water channel of the River Tees, which has been dredged and deepened to take large tankers. Although the Tees cannot take the largest ocean-going tankers, this is less important than it was in the past, as a result of the North Sea oil discoveries, which have made Britain much less dependent on imported supplies, although some types of petroleum, not found in the North Sea, still have to be imported.

Plate 6.13 Teesport Refinery

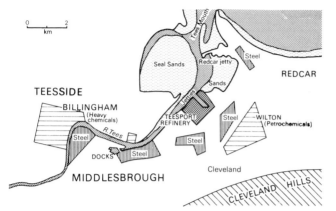

Figure 6.14   *Oil refining, chemicals and steel on Teesside*

A further advantage is the large area of flat land present on the banks of the Tees (Plate 6.13) while further cheap land has been made available through the reclamation of sandbanks and mudflats. Teesport was built on such land, and the reclamation was helped by the use of waste slag from the local blast furnaces. Plate 6.13 shows how an oil refinery takes up a large area of land for its oil tanks and processing plant. In addition, along the south bank of the Tees was an old-established rail and road system, built to serve, among other things, the many steel plants of the area (Figure 6.14). This system could be used for the transport of petroleum products.

Teesport refinery, although not one of the largest in Britain, is very highly automated, and much of it is run by computer. In contrast with other major industries, oil refineries employ relatively few people. Industries which employ a lot of people are known as *labour-intensive*. Oil refining is a good example of a *capital-intensive* industry: one which employs relatively few people, but on which an enormous amount of money has to be spent on processing equipment. Some of the complicated plant of Teesport refinery is shown on Plate 6.13. In this plant the crude oil is 'split' into its various 'fractions', which range from, (i) gases, stored in the spheres and 'bullets' on the left; through (ii) the lighter liquids such as *petrol*, *kerosene* (for jet engines) and *diesel oil*; to (iii) the heavier *fuel oils* (for electricity generation, as at Fawley). In addition, (iv) *feedstock* is produced for use in the petrochemical industry, which manufactures various plastics, as at Wilton (Figure 6.14).

Exercises

15. With the help of Plate 6.11, Figure 6.12, and information in the text, explain why the remote location in Britain of Sullom Voe was chosen for a major oil terminal.

16. Refer to Figure 6.13.
(*a*)   Make a list of estuaries and linked oil refineries.
(*b*)   Why are there pipelines from Anglesey to Stanlow; Finnart to Grangemouth; and Milford Haven to Llandarcy?
(*c*)   Account for the distribution shown on the map.
17. From other sources, find information to compare Milford Haven with the Thames estuary as locations for oil refineries.

ELECTRICITY

The supply of electricity has to be flexible to meet variations in demand. These demands change *daily*, with more electricity consumed during the day and evening than during the night, with peaks for example, on Sunday at lunch time. The demands also change *seasonally*, with more consumed in winter than in summer (Figure 6.15); and *yearly*, with, for example, increasing demands in the sixties and early seventies, when consumption rose from 265 million tonnes coal equivalent in 1960 to a peak of 346 million in 1973. Since then there has been a tendency to decline, although with isolated peaks in very cold winters such as 1979. These variations have very important consequences for the electricity supply industry.

Exercises

18. What effects are the following likely to have on the electricity industry and its consumers: (*a*) a mild winter; (*b*) a summer strike of electricity workers; (*c*) television transmissions of an important national event; (*d*) a rise in oil prices?

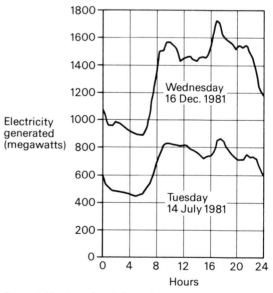

Figure 6.15   *Day of peak demand and typical summer day*

19. (a) Draw three pie graphs (divided circles) to show the information contained in Table 6.7.

(b) Why are coal-fired power stations the most important source of electricity in Britain?

(c) Try to explain the changes in coal-fired and oil-fired electricity generation between 1970 and 1980–1.

Table 6.7 Output of electricity generated by the different types of power station (%)

Type	1970	1975	1980–1
Coal-fired power stations	79	71	82.3*
Oil-fired power stations	10	16	7.0
Nuclear power stations	7	6	10.7
Others (including diesel, gas, hydro-electric, pumped storage)	4	7	<0.1

* Some stations can now use coal or oil.

The Location of Power Stations

Figures 6.16 and 6.17 are maps showing the location of the main areas of power-station development in Britain. It is clear that the locations of different types of power station vary considerably.

Coal-fired Power Stations

As we noted in the earlier chapter on coalmining, coal-fired power stations are generally found (a) on or near the coalfields, where in fact in a few cases (for example, Agecroft, near Manchester) the coal is fed direct via conveyor belt from a mine to an adjoining power station; (b) on a major river not far from a coalfield, with rail, road or canal transport available to carry the coal to the power station. The choice of a riverside location largely results from the need for huge supplies of cooling water. Perhaps the greatest concentration of coal-fired power stations in Britain is along the River Trent, a river within striking distance of a series of coalfields in the Midlands, Nottinghamshire and Derbyshire (Figure 6.16), and in Yorkshire (see pages 77–8). The most dominating feature of these stations, particularly noticeable in the generally flat landscape, is the series of associated cooling towers, such as those at Cottam in Nottinghamshire (Plate 6.14); (c) some coal-fired power stations are located at some distance from the coalfields, and supply a nearby large market with electric power. Good examples are the power stations along the Thames, as at West Thurrock and Tilbury, built to supply London. Here the major locating factor was the cheap seaborne transport of coal, particularly from the north-east. The Thames-side power stations do not, however, go far towards meeting London's needs,

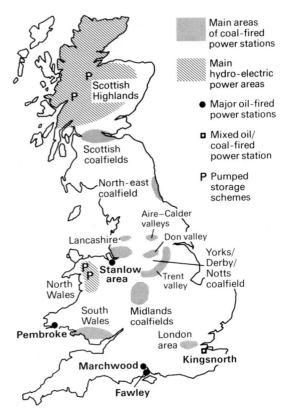

Figure 6.16 Coal-fired and oil-fired power stations; main hydro-electricity and pumped storage schemes in Britain

which are supplied largely from more distant stations via the electricity grid system. Some of the small power stations along the Thames, such as Battersea, have been closed down.

Oil-fired Power Stations

The main oil-fired power stations in Britain are located near the oil refineries which, as we saw in the previous chapter, are usually found on deep-water inlets. In this case the oil left over after refining the crude oil is the source of fuel. Such stations include Marchwood and Fawley on Southampton Water; Pembroke on Milford Haven; Grain on the Medway; and Ince (near Stanlow refinery) on the Mersey. The increasing price of oil has made this type of generation less economic and some stations, such as Kingsnorth, can now switch from oil to coal to suit the circumstances.

Nuclear Power Stations

Figure 6.17 shows the location and dates of opening of Britain's nuclear power stations. In several important ways the factors which affect the siting of nuclear power

Plate 6.14   *Cottam power station (coal-fired), Trent valley*

stations differ from those affecting the location of other types.

Nuclear power stations are *not* located near the source of fuel supply, which in this case is uranium. In other types of power station, large quantities of bulky 'fuel material', whether coal, oil or water, are required, but only tiny amounts of uranium are needed for the generation of nuclear energy. Hence transport costs are much lower than for coal and oil.

A far more vital locating factor is the presence of vast supplies of cooling water, particularly in the older types of nuclear power stations. In the newer ones, demands for water are still high, but no greater than in conventional power stations. As the demands for cooling water were so great in the 'first generation' of stations, and the rivers of Britain so much over-used, nuclear power stations have all been located at the coast, often along estuaries, with Trawsfynydd in North Wales the only exception to date (Figure 6.17).

For safety reasons, a nuclear reactor has to be encased in concrete, which results in a building of tremendous weight. Hence a firm foundation is needed. This might be provided by tough bedrock, as at Wylfa in Anglesey (Plate 6.15) with its massive twin reactor building.

Again for safety reasons, it was for a long time felt that nuclear power stations should be located well away from large towns, even though the risk of a radioactive leakage was very slight indeed. At first, all the stations built were placed in fairly isolated parts of Britain. After many years of safe operation, it is now thought that new stations might be built near urban areas without risk. Hence two of a later generation of nuclear power stations, at Hartlepool and Heysham (Figure 6.17), are in urban areas.

Figure 6.17   *Nuclear power stations in Britain*

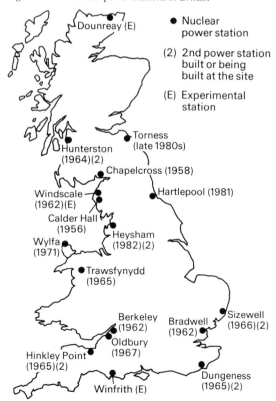

90

Plate 6.15   Wylfa nuclear power station, Anglesey

Hydro-electric Power Stations

Hydro-electricity is not very significant in Britain as a whole, as Table 6.7 suggested, but in mountainous areas of the country, and most especially in the Scottish Highlands and North Wales (Figure 6.16) it attains considerable importance. In these highland areas, the advantages for hydro-electric power production include: (*a*) the heavy rainfall, often over 2000 mm per annum, which is reliable (in the sense that prolonged drought periods are rare) and provides the source of water for generating power; (*b*) the large volumes and steep gradients, by British standards, of the rivers, which give substantial *heads* of water, supplying the energy to drive the turbines; (*c*) narrow valleys with firm rock floors which provide the sites for dams, in situations where artificial reservoirs are needed; (*d*) an absence of other local sources of power, particularly coal and oil, which are in any case expensive to transport into isolated highland valleys.

Pumped Storage Schemes

Pumped storage schemes have become more important in recent years. The largest of these is at Dinorwic in North Wales (Figure 6.16). In pumped storage schemes, cheap electricity, generated in off-peak periods, is used to pump water to high-level reservoirs, from which it descends to drive turbines, for use at peak periods, or to meet sudden surges in demand.

Exercises

20. Compare coal-fired and nuclear power stations in terms of (*a*) their locations; (*b*) their effect on the landscape.

21. On a large sheet of paper, draw an imaginary island country, with a deeply-indented coast, a central range of highlands from which valleys radiate, and wide coastal plains on one side of the island. The island is densely populated, with a major coalfield, and a good railway system. The government decides it will build a coal-fired, an oil-fired, a nuclear and a hydro-electric power station. Select a suitable site for each on your map, giving reasons in each case for your choice.

22. (*a*) Make a careful comparison, illustrated by specific examples, of the methods used to transport the different forms of energy.

(*b*) Outline the impact of the various forms of energy transport on the landscape.

7 TRANSPORT

ROADS

Motorways of the Southwest: M5 and M4

Plate 7.1 shows the A38 road on the outskirts of Tewkesbury, congested as it often was in the days before the M5 by-passed the town. Today, through-traffic normally uses the M5, and Tewkesbury town centre, though still busy, has in the main only to cope with local traffic. Motorways are built to connect large centres of population, often long distances apart. They speed up journeys between towns by (*a*) providing at least two, and usually three, lanes in each direction, to carry large flows of traffic travelling at different speeds; (*b*) having a limited number of access points to the motorway, with underpasses and overpasses for other cross routes; (*c*) by-passing the towns and villages which once formed bottlenecks *en route*, as in the case of Tewkesbury.

The effect of a motorway therefore is not to change distance on the ground, but to shorten the distance in *time* between two places.

Plate 7.2 shows Almondsbury interchange, where the M5 and M4 join. Opened in 1966, it is a four-level flyover. The M5 can be seen running from the bottom to the top of Plate 7.2 while the M4 runs from right to left on its way to the Severn where it crosses the estuary by the Severn Bridge (also completed in 1966). At one time

the *lowest bridging point* on the River Severn was at Gloucester. People wishing to cross the river further south (apart from rail travellers using the tunnel) had to use ferries. Hence the new Severn Bridge has shifted the lowest bridging point downriver (Figure 7.1).

The map (Figure 7.2) shows the routes followed by the M4 and M5. The whole length of the M4 in England was finally opened in December 1971. It look twelve years to complete, and cost £140 million. It links London with Bristol and South Wales (Figure 7.1). The M5 was completed in 1977 connecting Birmingham and Exeter, in turn joining Exeter directly to the M6, and providing about 560 kilometres of continuous north–south motorway between Exeter and Carlisle.

Exercises

1. (*a*) Draw a labelled sketch-map, using an actual example, to show what is meant by a by-pass.
(*b*) How does a by-pass benefit a town? Does it have any drawbacks?
2. Explain the advantages (and any disadvantages) of motorways as against the older main roads (Plate 7.1).
3. (*a*) By reference to Figure 7.1 suggest reasons why the new Severn Bridge was built where it was, and not further upstream or downstream.

Plate 7.1   Congestion outside Tewkesbury

Plate 7.2   Aerial view of Almondsbury interchange

(b) Draw a labelled sketch-map, using an actual example, to show what is meant by the lowest bridging point on a river. Why is it important?

4. *Avoiding the bottleneck*

Imagine that you wish to travel by road between points X and Y on Figure 7.3. Five routes are available to you:

(1) passing through points A, B, C and D,
(2) passing through points E, F, C and D,
(3) passing through points E, F, G and H,
(4) passing through points J, K, G and H,
(5) passing through points J, K, L and M.

Work out the factors you would take into account in deciding which route you would take, bearing in mind the distances involved, possible road conditions according to the information given on the map, and your own personal preferences as a traveller.

The Motorways of Britain

By 1981, over 2700 kilometres of motorway had been completed. Present plans suggest that Britain will eventually have over 3200 kilometres of motorway.

Notice on Figure 7.2 how the motorway network is planned on a series of *axes*:

1. North–south (west side of Britain), from Carlisle to Exeter (M5–M6).
2. North–south (east side of Britain), from London to Leeds (M1), with a more northerly extension in Durham (A1 (M)).

Figure 7.1   Motorways in south-west England

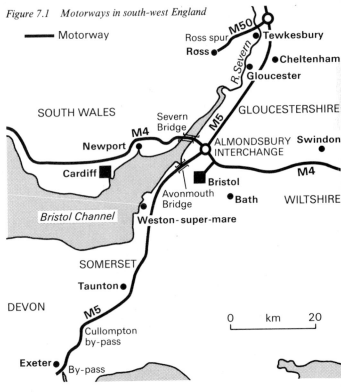

93

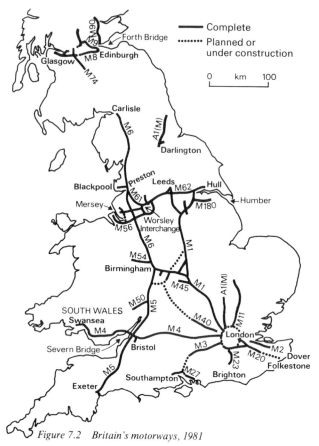

Figure 7.2 Britain's motorways, 1981

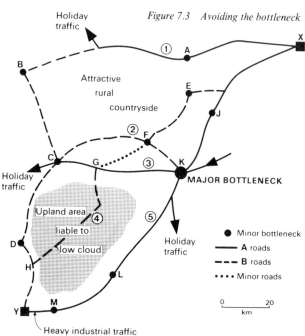

Figure 7.3 Avoiding the bottleneck

3. These are connected by cross-axes:

(*a*) M6 extension, linking the M6 with the M1 through the Midlands;

(*b*) M4, linking London with the M5, Bristol and South Wales;

(*c*) M62, linking Lancashire and Yorkshire across the Pennines, Merseyside and Humberside.

4. Several motorways form, or will form *orbital by-passes* round major urban areas. The most notable are the M25 London outer orbital, under construction, and the M63/M66 Manchester outer ring road.

5. There are also shorter motorways which link, or will link, major population centres lying fairly close together, including:

(*a*) Glasgow–Edinburgh (M8);

(*b*) London and south–coast towns (M2, M3 and M20);

(*c*) Manchester with M6 and the Preston area (M61) and with north Cheshire (M56);

(*d*) Southampton and Portsmouth (M27).

6. In addition there are various spurs from the main motorways, such as the Ross spur (M50), bringing the Midlands nearer, in terms of time, to industrial South Wales; and many motorway by-passes, such as those at Darlington and Doncaster.

Many trunk roads, about 4000 kilometres in all, are dual carriageway.

The motorways have not only changed the face of the British landscape, but also patterns of travel, as the canals and railways did in previous periods. It is now possible, for example, for motorists from the Midlands to enjoy day-trips to the Lake District. Exeter is within six hours' travelling time of Carlisle. Return journeys can be made between Leeds and London in a day. The motorways are of enormous benefit to the economy of the country, but there are many people who feel that they have not been beneficial in other ways.

Exercises

5. The motorways M61 and M62 meet at the Worsley interchange near Manchester (Figure 7.2). Assuming the motorway network was complete, work out how long it would take to travel from Worsley to each of Carlisle, Leeds, London, Birmingham, and Exeter (on the basis of average speeds of 100km/h). What benefits does the motorway system provide for industrial concerns in the Manchester area?

6. Name some of the areas of Britain not served by motorways, and suggest reasons for their absence.

7. In what ways do motorways *not* benefit the country?

8. The *detour index* (DI) between two places can be calculated by dividing the travelling distance (*x*), by the straight-line distance ('as the crow flies') (y), and multiplying the result by 100. Hence

$$DI = \frac{x}{y} \times 100$$

A high detour index is an indication of a relatively long travelling distance between two places.

(*a*) Draw two maps to show the road connections between Bristol and Cardiff (i) before and (ii) after the Severn Road Bridge and the M4 were built.

(*b*) Calculate the detour indices between Bristol and Cardiff in each case.

(*c*) To what extent has the situation been improved?

(*d*) Using the rough formula of average speed on main roads being 50 km/h and on motorways 100 km/h, work out the approximate time taken to travel between Bristol and Cardiff before and after the new developments.

Plate 7.3   *BR 125 diesel on London–Edinburgh run*

RAIL

Modernising British Rail: Inter-City Services

Plate 7.3 shows one of the Inter-City 125 expresses introduced in the late 1970s on its run between Edinburgh and London. Other 125s connect the west country and South Wales. These diesel trains attain speeds of 200 km/h and have dramatically shortened journey times. The improved services have attracted many new passengers. Thus business executives can set off from Cardiff in the early morning, take breakfast on the under two-hour journey, attend meetings in London from mid-morning, and be home by early evening. Despite the success of the diesel 125s, British Rail sees an increasing emphasis in the future on further electrification. Plate 7.4 shows an electric Inter-City express crossing the Southern Uplands of Scotland on the Glasgow–London service. Already 160 km/h electric trains operate Inter-City services between London, the West Midlands, north-west England and Glasgow.

Figure 7.4 shows the whole Inter-City system from London, with *time-distances* from the capital city to the major population centres.

Figure 7.4   *The 'Overground' of British Rail*

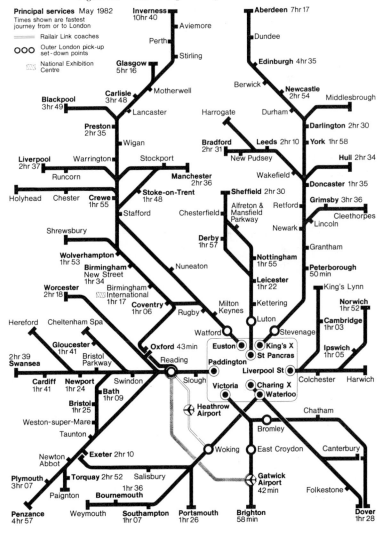

The Inter-City service has also attracted passengers who used to travel by air. Although the air journey between, say, Manchester and London, is quicker in itself than that by rail, the airports are so far away from the city centres that the time taken for the journey as a whole is little different. As Plate 7.5 shows, the London railway stations are conveniently located on the fringe of the city centre. This photograph shows three main-line stations on the north side of central London, Euston, St Pancras, and King's Cross (see also Figure 7.4).

Plate 7.4   Electric Inter-City train on London–Glasgow run

Plate 7.5   Aerial view of Euston, St Pancras and King's Cross stations

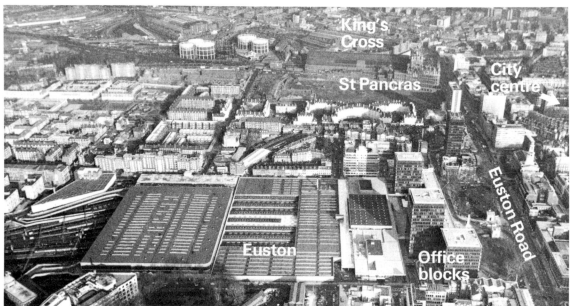

Freight Services

By running complicated cheap fare systems, British Rail has maintained Inter-City passenger traffic reasonably well, despite the recession of the late 1970s and early 1980s. Freight traffic has fared less well, declining from 170 million tonnes in 1977 to 154 million tonnes in 1981. The main items of traffic were coal/coke (95 million tonnes); iron and steel (18 million); oil and chemicals (16 million); building and constructional materials (16 million); freightliner traffic (7 million); and other traffic (2 million).

At the same time, like passenger traffic, freight traffic has been modernised, especially through the *freightliner system* (Plate 7.6), which involves the use of fast-moving

container trains on the trunk routes which connect up terminals in the main cities (Figure 7.5). The trains run at average speeds of 120 km/h in bogie wagons specially designed to carry containers. In some cases Freightliners Limited, which is owned by British Rail, arranges for a door-to-door service, using its own road vehicles to connect with the rail transport. In most instances, however, the supplier or the customer arranges the road transport to and from the rail terminal. Special handling equipment makes easy the transfer of containers from rail to road transport or, in other cases, to container ships (see Chapter 14).

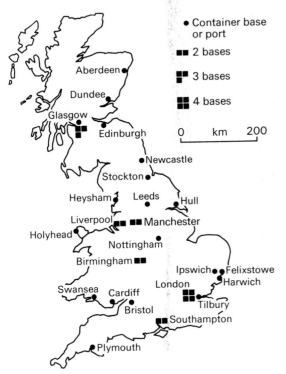

Figure 7.5   Container traffic freightliner terminals

Plate 7.6   A freightliner train

Figure 7.6   Inter-City passenger routes, 1980

Exercises

9. (*a*)   Describe the distribution of freightliner terminals shown on Figure 7.5.
(*b*)   Why does it in part reflect also areas served by motorways (Figure 7.2)?
(*c*)   Name freightliner terminals in areas not served by motorways. Why are they in these areas?
10. What are the advantages and disadvantages of having large rail terminals near the centres of cities?
11. Refer to Figure 7.6.
(*a*)   Describe the main features of the Inter-City network in England.
(*b*)   Describe the networks of Scotland, Wales and Northern Ireland, and suggest reasons why these differ from each other, and from the English network.
(*c*)   Explain the differences between Figure 7.6 and Figure 7.4.

A Railway Junction: Crewe

The railway system of Britain grew mainly in the nineteenth century. Just over 100 years ago the landscape of the whole area shown on Plate 7.7 resembled that seen in the left background of the picture. This lowland region is part of a major gap between the uplands of Wales and the Pennines, known as the Midland Gate (Figure 7.7), which provided a natural focus for the railways running between the Midlands and the north-west.

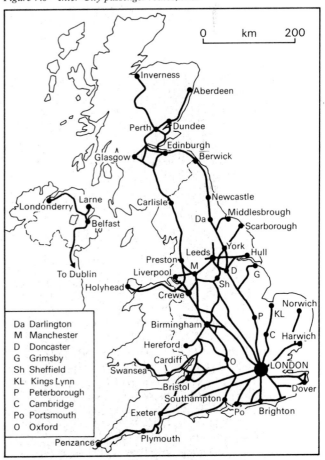

Da Darlington
M Manchester
D Doncaster
G Grimsby
Sh Sheffield
KL Kings Lynn
P Peterborough
C Cambridge
Po Portsmouth
O Oxford

W. Midlands, London

Stoke, Derby

Shrewsbury, S. Wales

Marshalling yard

Crewe station

Football ground

Manchester

Liverpool, Scotland

Chester, N. Wales

Plate 7.7   Crewe

In the early nineteenth century, Crewe, the town shown on Plate 7.7, did not exist. At this time Nantwich was the main town of the region, an important market centre and road junction, with salt and tanning industries. It seems strange that this existing town was not chosen as the new rail focus. One reason was probably the fact that Nantwich was a canal town, and the canal companies here, as elsewhere, feared the competition of the railways. They tried to persuade the local landowners not to sell their land to the railway companies. The new-fangled locomotive was described to the local farmers as 'a most frightful machine, emitting a breath as poisonous as the fabled dragon of old'. Another reason may have been that land in old-established towns such as Nantwich was expensive to buy, and the railway companies preferred to purchase cheaper rural land. On this they built the railway junction of Crewe. Plate 7.7 illustrates the effect which the decision to build Crewe has had on the landscape of this part of south Cheshire.

Apart from the station, extensive workshops and marshalling yards and homes for the railway workers had to be created. Railway lines spread out in all directions. The first line to run through Crewe, opened in 1837, linked Birmingham with Warrington, and indirectly with Liverpool and Manchester (Figure 7.7). Later lines connected Crewe with Chester and Birkenhead; Stoke and Derby; Shrewsbury; and directly with Manchester and Liverpool.

Apart from acting as a major rail junction (as distinct from a terminus), Crewe became an important locomotive building and repairing centre. Although it was situated at some distance from sources of coal and iron, such materials could easily be brought in by the rail links from the Lancashire, north Staffordshire and the Midlands industrial regions. The relatively cheap rural land was also helpful to Crewe's growth, for large areas were needed for the extensive workshops and marshalling yards (Plate 7.7).

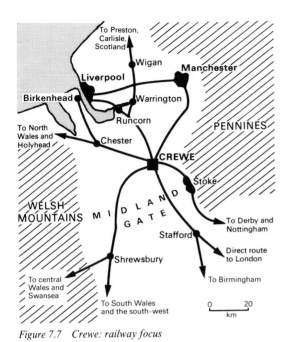

Figure 7.7   Crewe: railway focus

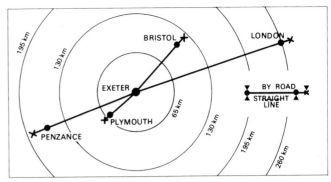

Figure 7.8a   Spatial distances from Exeter
Figure 7.8b   Time-distances from Exeter

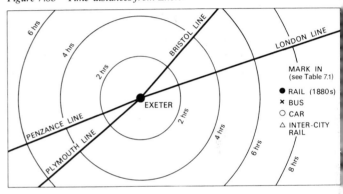

Exercises

12. Lay a sheet of tracing paper over Plate 7.7 and on the tracing outline and label housing areas; the railway station; the marshalling yards and any industrial buildings you can see; and areas of agricultural landscape. With the help of Plate 7.7 and Figure 7.7 mark in the approximate line of the railway tracks which connect Crewe with other towns. Where the lines run off the tracing, mark by arrows and names the towns they are running to. Note that the camera was pointing approximately south when Plate 7.7 was taken.

13. (*a*) Distinguish carefully between a railway junction and a railway terminus, giving examples of each.
(*b*) Describe and explain briefly the growth of Crewe as a railway town. Choose another rail junction, preferably one near your home, and find out about its growth, comparing it with that of Crewe.
(*c*) Other major railway towns in Britain include Darlington, Doncaster and Swindon (Figure 7.6). Choose one of these and compare its location and the reason for its growth with those of Crewe.

14. Refer to Figure 7.8a and b. Figure 7.8a shows, by the position of the crosses and dots on the route lines, that straight-line distance and road distance are not the same.

(*a*) Work out the detour indices (see page 94) between Exeter and the other four towns. Which is the least directly connected to Exeter by road?
(*b*) Figure 7.8b should be copied out and filled in to show how *time-distance* differs according to the means of transport between places. Using the symbols given, mark in the time-distances between Exeter and the other four towns for the different means of transport (excluding stagecoach) shown on Table 7.1, along the route lines drawn in for you on the map.
(*c*) Work out the costs for one person travelling by train, bus and private car between your home town and any two other towns. Find out the train and bus costs from British Rail and the local bus company and for car costs use a calculation such as 20p per kilometre (which would not take into account, however, such factors as depreciation). Then draw a diagram similar to Figure 7.8b to show how cost distances vary according to the method of transport used. The arcs of the circles will of course represent 'costs' instead of 'hours'.

Table 7.1 Travelling times from Exeter (fastest available service in each case)

Exeter to	Road distance	Stagecoach (at 12 km/h)	Rail (1880s)	Twentieth century		
				Bus	Car (50 km/h)	Inter-City Rail
London	270 km	18 hours	4 hr 45 min	7 hr 45 min	5 hr 40 min	2 hr 10 min
Plymouth	67 km	5 hr 15 min	1 hr 45 min	1 hr 50 min	1 hr 25 min	55 min
Penzance	180 km	14 hours	4 hr 55 min	4 hr 35 min	3 hr 45 min	2 hr 45 min
Bristol	104 km	9 hr 25 min	1 hr 55 min	3 hr 25 min	2 hr 30 min	59 min

AIR

Heathrow Airport

Heathrow Airport, shown on Plate 7.8, is London's major airport, by far the largest in Britain, and the most important international airport in the world. With Gatwick (Plate 7.9), it serves the needs of the Greater London area, and the south-east of England (Figure 7.9).

After London's two airports, the third main international airport in Britain is Manchester Ringway, that is if *scheduled flights* only are taken into consideration. There are also *charter flights*, and if these are counted Luton handles more international passengers than Manchester.

Heathrow Airport (Plate 7.8) is an enormous enterprise. As the photograph indicates, it covers a very large area, and in addition employs nearly 53 000 people. Seventy-six international airlines use Heathrow.

Apart from handling passengers, Heathrow is a major *cargo* airport. Tonnage shipped is small compared with that of a seaport because aircraft can only be used economically to carry goods of low bulk but high value. The passengers at Heathrow pass through the terminal buildings, placed in the central area of the airport (A).

Figure 7.9   The main airports of Britain

These are approached by a road tunnel from the north side, which runs under the main landing runway (see Plate 7.8) and connects with the M4.

Plate 7.8   Heathrow Airport

Plate 7.9   Gatwick Airport

Terminal 1 (B), completed in 1968, handles the domestic and European services of British Airways. It is linked with a multi-storey short-term car park, for the convenience of passengers and their friends and relatives. Terminal 1 can handle 5050 passengers per hour.

Terminal 2 (C), completed in 1955, handles the short-haul services of foreign airlines, such as those from Europe. The spectators' viewing area is on the roof of this and an adjoining building.

Terminal 3 (D), completed in 1961, is used by long-haul, inter-continental airlines, such as British Airways, TWA, Pan-Am, Qantas (Australia), Air Canada, and many others. It has been extended to accommodate the huge 'jumbo jets' (Boeing 747s), which can carry over 350 passengers each.

In the central area of Heathrow is the control tower, from which all aircraft movements are directed, by radar and other modern landing aids. There are also office buildings, roadways, a bus station, taxi ranks, and a London Underground station connected by pedestrian subways with each of the passenger terminals.

London's Third Airport?

By the mid-1950s it was clear that Heathrow by itself could not cope with the increased demands for air transport. Gatwick, 40 kilometres south of London (see Figure 7.9), already used for flying purposes, was chosen as London's second international airport, and was reconstructed and opened in 1958. Though further from central London than Heathrow, Gatwick has the advantage of being adjacent to the main London–Brighton railway and road (Plate 7.9). By 1981, with nearly 10 million *international* passengers, it had become the fourth busiest international airport in the world.

Even two international airports have since proved insufficient. In the late 1960s it became evident that London needed a third airport. Heathrow handled over 14 million and Gatwick over 3 million passengers in 1970, and 27 million and nearly 10 million respectively in 1980–1. Table 7.2 shows the anticipated demand for passenger traffic in 1985.

101

Table 7.2 Millions of Passengers anticipated, 1985

Heathrow	30–38*	Prestwick	1
Gatwick	16–25*	Liverpool	3
Manchester	8	Luton	5
Glasgow	5	Leeds–Bradford	2
Belfast	6	Southend *or* Stansted	2
Edinburgh	3		

* with new terminals.

The total number of passengers using British airports in 1970 was 29 million. The London area alone will probably need facilities to take about 60 million in 1985. This frightening picture led to the government establishing a Commission to look into the problem.

The Roskill Commission

The Roskill Commission was charged with the task of finding the best possible site for London's third airport. Eventually, after rejecting *Stansted*, the Commission concentrated its attention on four sites.

Three were *inland* sites:

(1) *Cublington*, near Leighton Buzzard, in Buckinghamshire,

(2) *Thurleigh*, north of Bedford,

(3) *Nuthampstead*, north-west of Stansted.

The fourth site was *coastal*:

(4) *Foulness*, on reclaimed land of the Maplin Sands, off the Essex coast, near Southend.

The Roskill Report was published in January 1971. The majority of members of the Commission chose *Cublington*, but a minority, led by Professor Colin Buchanan, chose *Foulness*, since increasingly referred to as *Maplin*. Professor Buchanan referred to Foulness as 'an environmental loss', and to Cublington as 'an environmental disaster', meaning that he thought Foulness was the lesser of two evils. 169 MPs of all political parties opposed the Commission's majority choice of Cublington. In April 1971 the government rejected Cublington and opted for Maplin, but this in turn was rejected. In the late 1970s Stansted was returned to as a likely candidate, well placed for motorway connections, and involving the extension of an existing airport rather than building a new one. But Stansted lies in peaceful countryside and local pressure groups have resisted the development on environmental, economic (taking over fertile agricultural land) and amenity grounds. The most likely outcome of the discussions still going on in 1982 would seem to be the building of a fourth terminal at Heathrow and a second one at Gatwick. It is hoped the latter will be open.by 1985, catering for an additional 8 million passengers per annum (Table 7.2).

Locating Airports

Factors

Site Factors

(a) An international airport requires a *vast area of land*, as Plate 7.8 indicates. A four-runway airport needs well over 3000 hectares of land. The latest jet airliners require ideally 3600–4200 metres of runway. The largest runways at Heathrow are approximately 2800 metres and 3600 metres, both shown on Plate 7.8. The runways should preferably be aligned in the direction of the prevailing wind, in Britain approximately from south-west to north-east.

(b) The land should be *flat*, with gradients of not more than 1 in 200 on the runways. The approaches to the airport should also be clear (Plate 7.8): high land should not be present to block the view. Airports are clearly more difficult to locate and less safe to use in mountain areas.

Heathrow, as Plate 7.8 shows, has the advantages of a large area of open flat land, on the river terraces of the Thames, to the west of London.

Weather

The most important factor here is *good visibility*, although radar and other modern landing aids have helped the situation in this respect. None the less, it is undesirable that an airport should be located in an area very liable to *fog*, as in certain cases of low-lying land in hollows, or *smog*, which is common in low-lying parts of industrial areas. Heathrow and Manchester Ringway (Figure 7.10) are both placed well away from old industrial areas, but are by no means free from fog.

Air Congestion

Airports such as Heathrow handle so many flights each day that congestion in the air has become a major problem. Strict controls are enforced. *Flight corridors* have been established, which must be used by aircraft approaching the airport. These corridors, particularly the heavily used ones, should preferably not pass over large cities. Those most heavily used by flights to and from London are from the south-east and west. Fewest planes come in from the north, north-east and east, and therefore the situations of Heathrow and Gatwick are very suitable, being to the south-west and south of London respectively.

While waiting to land, aircraft have to *stack* at certain points. In periods of bad weather at ground level this stacking process may take a long time, while the aircraft

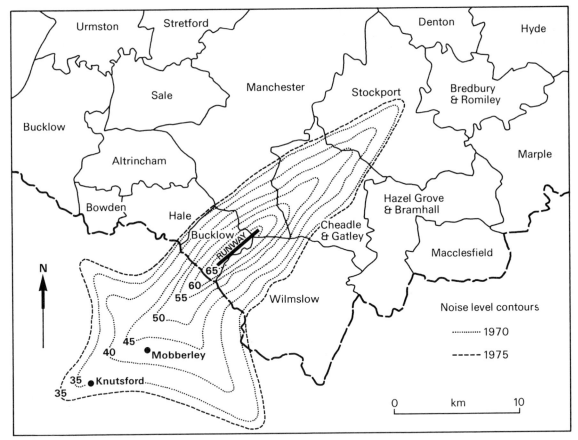

Figure 7.10   Ringway Airport: day-time noise contours, 1970 (and 1975)

await permission to land. The main stacking points for Heathrow are over Epsom (south-west London) and Watford (to the north-west). The problem of congestion is of course lessened if more than one airport is available.

Access: Questions of Economics

Airports cannot be sited in the centres of large cities. Apart from the question of the danger of crashes in a densely populated area, and the problem of smog, there is also the matter of the high cost of land near a city centre. It is, however, an advantage if the airport can be as near the city centre as possible. Heathrow's main disadvantage is that it is located 24 kilometres from the centre of London. The road links are liable to congestion, especially in peak periods of the day. There is now, however, an underground rail link from central London to Heathrow.

But on short air routes, as between London and Manchester (where Ringway is also a long journey from the city centre: see Figure 7.10), the time taken in travelling on the ground between the city centre and the airport may be longer than the actual time in the air between the two cities. It is not surprising that the airlines have suffered from the competition of the Inter-City expresses, which can run the journey between Manchester (or Liverpool) and London in two and a half hours (see page 95).

Amenity Factors: Interfering with the Environment

Few human-made creations have a greater nuisance-value in the environment than a large airport. The noise of jet aircraft taking off and landing, particularly at night, makes life almost intolerable for people living near the airport. The 'contours of noise' extend along the alignment of the flight path, as Figure 7.10 shows for Ringway Airport, Manchester. In addition, airports take up a vast amount of land, which may be of value for other purposes, as noted in the case of Stansted.

Table 7.3
Total passengers (millions)
at main British airports
1980–1

Heathrow	27.2
Gatwick	9.8
Ringway	4.3
Glasgow	2.3
Luton	2.1
Birmingham	1.6
Belfast	1.5
Aberdeen*	1.4
Edinburgh	1.2
Newcastle	1.0
E. Midlands	0.7
Liverpool	0.4
Prestwick	0.4
Ronaldsway	0.3
Standsted	0.3
Yeadon	0.3

* including helicopters

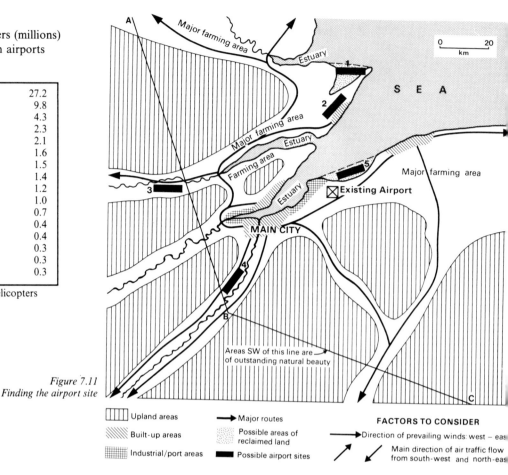

Figure 7.11
Finding the airport site

Upland areas   Major routes   **FACTORS TO CONSIDER**

Built-up areas   Possible areas of reclaimed land   Direction of prevailing winds: west – eas

Industrial/port areas   Possible airport sites   Main direction of air traffic flow from south-west and north-eas

Exercises

15. (a) Refer to Table 7.3 and Figure 7.9. On an outline map of the British Isles mark by a small dot the position of each of the sixteen main British airports, and for each draw a bar graph, proportional to the number of passengers handled in 1980–1.

(b) Suggest reasons why Heathrow is so overwhelmingly important among British airports.

16. Refer to Plate 7.8.

(a) Describe and explain the distribution of hotels (H) on the photograph.

(b) Why are the multi-storey car parks in the central part of the airport complex on the inside of the terminals?

(c) Why are there extensive areas of ground between the runways and the terminals?

17. Compare Heathrow with Gatwick (Plate 7.9) in terms of (a) scale; (b) layout; (c) land transport connections.

18. Refer to Figure 7.10.

(a) Why is the area covered by the noise contours longer than it is wide?

(b) Which administrative area is most affected by noise pollution?

(c) With the help of a map of the built-up area of the conurbation, state which densely populated districts (rather than rural) are most seriously affected by noise.

19. Refer to Figure 7.11. With the help of information in the text, examine the pros and cons of each of sites 1 to 5 as a location for a new airport to supplement the existing one. Choose which you think is the most advantageous (or perhaps least disadvantageous), giving your reasons in detail.

20. Read the following quotation:

'It appears to me too much to be borne with that (railway) lines coming only eight or nine miles are to cut up the suburbs and the town by their separate rails and termini, and have the liberty to take down property . . . and annoy the public beyond their value. It strikes me we have been a little railway mad, as if everything was to give way to railways; there is an immense mass of the public to be considered, hundreds and thousands, who have nothing to do with railways and never will have . . .'

(written in the 1840s, when the new railways were coming into large cities)

(a) With hindsight, do you think this criticism of the coming of the railways was justified?

(b) Is it in any way applicable to the coming of large airports in this century?

8 MANUFACTURING INDUSTRY

The invention of the steam engine in the eighteenth century led to the transformation of manufacturing industry from its former *domestic* state, that is, carried on in the home, to its concentration in larger and larger *factories*, often located on coalfields. This change has been termed the *industrial revolution*. Although many industries remained in towns and cities away from the coalfields, such as London, Bristol and Norwich, the most striking feature of nineteenth-century development was the growth of large-scale industry in *coalfield locations*. The transport of raw materials and finished products was made possible by the growth of canal and railway systems.

The twentieth century has also seen dramatic changes. A second industrial revolution has occurred. The switch from coal to oil and electricity as major sources of power has meant that manufacturing industry is no longer dependent on a coalfield location.

In the first section of this chapter we are going to study the coal-based industries which sprang into prominence in the nineteenth century, first by making a detailed case study of the glass industry at St Helens, and then by shorter studies of the textile, iron and steel and chemical industries, and shipbuilding. The second section will consider the changes which have taken place in this century, with special reference to car manufacturing and other consumer goods industries.

COALFIELD-BASED INDUSTRIES

Glass Manufacturing at St Helens

St Helens is a large nineteenth-century industrial town on the south Lancashire coalfield, and the main glass manufacturing centre in Britain. One of the large glass works of its most famous firm, Pilkington Brothers, can be seen in the right background of Plate 8.1. A canal divides it from the central business district of the town, in the centre of the photograph, while terraced industrial housing can be seen in the foreground.

Plate 8.1   Aerial view of the centre of St Helens

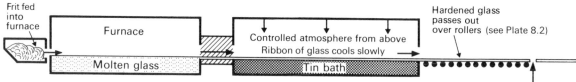

Figure 8.1   The float glass process

Glass is manufactured from sand, limestone and soda ash (made from salt). Figure 8.1 shows how, in the float glass process, these materials (known as the frit) are fed into the furnace to make molten glass. The molten glass is then passed into another tank where it gradually cools and hardens. At this stage, a molten tin bath below and controlled atmosphere from above ensure that both surfaces of the glass are free from blemishes. Plate 8.2 shows a ribbon of float glass passing out of the tank on padded rollers before being cut automatically.

Other factories in St Helens manufacture glass bottles and containers, safety glass for car windows, and glass fibre for insulation. The importance of the glass industry to St Helens is shown by the following selection from the employment figures for 1981.

Table 8.1

Total insured population of St Helens Metropolitan District	65 000
Total employed in manufacturing and coalmining	26 000
Total employed in glass manufacturing	12 000
Total employed in coalmining	500
Total employed in engineering and metalworking	2500
Total employed in brickmaking	250

Plate 8.2   Float glass leaving the production line

Recession has hit St Helens as elsewhere, and this and modernisation have reduced numbers in, for example, glass manufacturing, from over 19 000 in 1971 to about 12 000 by 1981. In 1981, over 10 500 people, nearly 17% of the insured population of the St Helens area, were unemployed.

Exercises

1. Refer to Plate 8.1. Lay a sheet of tracing paper over it and outline and label the following: the canal; important roads; the glass works; the central business district; nineteenth-century terraced housing; derelict land.

2. Using the figures given in Table 8.1, draw a pie graph to illustrate the employment situation in St Helens as follows:

(a) Draw a large circle to represent the total numbers *employed*. The 360° of the circle thus represents 65 000 people.

(b) Work out how many degrees will represent the other figures given.

(c) Divide the circle into correctly-sized segments representing glass manufacture; coalmining; metalworking; brickmaking; others employed in manufacturing; and those employed in non-manufacturing occupations. Colour and label each segment.

(d) What proportion of the numbers employed in St Helens are engaged in (i) glass manufacturing; (ii) coalmining?

(e) Name as many different types of occupation as you can think of which would be placed in the non-manufacturing group of occupations.

The Growth of St Helens

Two hundred years ago, the landscape of the St Helens area was largely rural, broken by a few small collieries, glass works, and the villages that were later to be swallowed up in the growth of St Helens. Table 8.2 shows the increase in population in the St Helens area after 1750.

Table 8.2 Population of St Helens (thousands)

1750	1800	1850	1900	1951	1971	1981
0.2	7.5	25	90	110	104	99

The story of St Helens is largely the story of the development of its main industries: glass manufacture, coalmining, brickmaking and metalworking; and of two

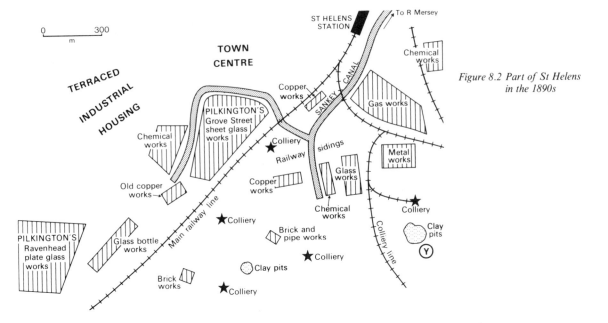

Figure 8.2 Part of St Helens
in the 1890s

industries no longer present today, heavy chemical
manufacture and copper smelting. Figure 8.2 shows an
area near the centre of St Helens in the 1890s, in which
all these industries were found.

The rapid expansion of manufacturing after 1750
was the result of the presence in the area of a power
supply, many raw materials, and an improving transport system. In addition, there were human factors and
decisions which promoted industrial development.

Power

Coal was used increasingly after 1750 as a source of
power in the foundries and in the glass, copper, chemical
and brick works. The shallow coal pits of the early days
were later replaced by deeper shafts. Scores of small
collieries were established in the St Helens area, a few of
which can be picked out on Figure 8.2. Today oil and
electricity have largely replaced coal as sources of fuel in
the glass industry.

Raw Materials

The nearest raw material was the clay used in the
brickmaking industry, and some of the St Helens clay
pits are shown on Figure 8.2. Glass sands were found
to the north-west of St Helens on the south-west
Lancashire plain (Plate 3.4). The other main materials
for glassmaking, soda ash (from salt) and limestone, are
obtained from Cheshire (the Northwich area) and
Derbyshire (the Buxton area) respectively. Supplies of
salt were also needed for the chemical industry, which
was important in the St Helens area until early in this

century. The copper for the smelting works was brought
in from Anglesey, via the Mersey estuary and the
Sankey Canal (Figure 8.2).

Transport Facilities

Coal, salt and sand are *bulky* materials. They are heavy
in weight and take up a lot of space, and are therefore
expensive to transport. In the middle of the eighteenth
century the transport facilities of the St Helens area,
even after the recent opening of the turnpike road to
Liverpool (exercise 6), were incapable of handling the
large quantities of coal needed in the expanding Merseyside region. Improvements were essential if progress was
to be made. Because of this situation the *Sankey Canal*
was built from St Helens to the River Mersey, following
the valley of Sankey Brook. In the same period, the
Weaver navigation, which connected the Mersey with
the Cheshire salt field, was improved. From this time,
large quantities of coal and salt could be carried between
the collieries of the St Helens area and the salt mines of
Cheshire.

In the nineteenth century, *railways* replaced canals as
the main means of transport. St Helens was connected
with the Liverpool–Manchester line, and with the main
north–south line from Preston to Crewe (at Wigan).

Today, *roads* have replaced railways as the most
important method of transporting goods. St Helens has
an advantageous position in relation to modern roads,
including the East Lancashire Road, the M6, M57, and
the M62.

The growth of these transport facilities was important not only for bringing in raw materials, but also for taking manufactured goods to customers. Densely populated areas such as south Lancashire have the largest proportion of such customers. St Helens' glass, for example, finds a ready market in the north-west and in Britain as a whole, and much is exported as well. The presence of an easily accessible port at Liverpool was therefore another advantage to St Helens.

Labour Supply

The skills developed in the small glassblowing concerns and collieries were an asset to St Helens when larger factories and coalmines were established. Many families in St Helens have been associated with the glass industry or coalmining for generations. Apart from the need for skilled labour, there was also a huge demand for unskilled labour as industry expanded in the nineteenth century. This was satisfied in part by the influx of Irish people, who came into the area by way of the port of Liverpool.

Management

The Pilkington family began to make glass in St Helens in 1826. The concern is still owned by descendants of the founders and in 1970 became a public company. Over the years, the firm has pioneered a number of important inventions, of which the most recent is the float glass process. This has been licensed to thirty-one overseas manufacturers in twenty-one countries including the USA, the Soviet Union, and Japan. Hence a tradition of successful management as well as of skilled labour has long been present in St Helens.

Plate 8.3   Industrial landscape in the St Helens area

Exercises

3. (*a*) With the help of graph paper and the figures given in Table 8.2, draw a line graph to show the growth of population in St Helens from 1750 to the present day. Population growth should form the vertical axis, and the passage of time the horizontal.
(*b*) At what period was growth most rapid? Suggest reasons for this.
(*c*) Describe and try to explain the population trends in the twentieth century.
4. Refer to Figure 8.2.
(*a*) State the types of industry shown on the map, giving details of the size and location of the different types of factory.
(*b*) Give at least four reasons shown on the map for the growth of industries.
(*c*) Which of these industries are no longer present in St Helens?
5. Find out the advantages and disadvantages of each of (*a*) canal, (*b*) railways, and (*c*) modern roads, for the transport of manufactured goods and raw materials.
6. (*a*) With the help of maps of south-west Lancashire, show the location of St Helens in relation to Liverpool and the Mersey estuary, marking in the Sankey Canal, the Liverpool–St Helens–Bolton road (the old turnpike road); the East Lancashire Road; the M6, M57 and M62; and the main railways.
(*b*) Outline the advantages of these, at different stages, to St Helens.

Industrial Pollution in St Helens

Derelict Land and Buildings

Plate 8.3 is a view of part of St Helens today, taken from approximately the position Y which is marked on Figure 8.2 with the camera pointing almost due north. No houses can be seen, for the land is occupied either by industrial buildings or is unfit for housing construction. In the foreground are the remains of old clay pits, partly filled in by coal waste. Beyond that are old factories and the former Ravenhead colliery. Mining under the built-up area of St Helens has meant that buildings are liable to subsidence. In the distance, the skyline is dominated by the gas works and factories. Apart from the coal spoil heaps, and the old clay workings, the former chemical industry also left large dumps of waste.

Atmospheric Pollution

Figure 8.3 is a map of England and Wales showing the parts of these countries which have the highest death rates from bronchitis. Notice that St Helens lies in the heart of one of the largest areas, the south Lancashire industrial region. The smoke from factory and domestic chimneys pollutes the atmosphere. Under foggy conditions this can cause smog, which is known to be harmful, and in some cases deadly, to people who suffer from bronchial complaints.

Figure 8.3 *England and Wales: areas with the highest death rate from bronchitis*

Plate 8.4 *Factory Row, St Helens, a Victorian industrial terrace*

River Pollution

The peaceful Sankey Brook of 1700 is now perhaps the most polluted stream in Lancashire, running past old waste heaps on the eastern side of St Helens. The smell from its polluted waters has on occasions been so unpleasant that it has caused local householders to complain to their Town Council. Such polluted streams are also a danger to health. Many factories pump their waste products, known as *effluent*, into ponds, rivers and canals, making them unfit for water supply and for fish to live in. In some cases, untreated sewage is fed into rivers.

Slum Housing

As the factories developed, rows of terraced dwellings were built to house the workers, such as that shown in Plate 8.4, which is named Factory Row, and lies near the Ravenhead glass works. A date plaque shows its year of construction (1854). We have seen that early housing in particular was built as quickly and cheaply as possible, and has deteriorated over the years. Although cheaper in the short term, this policy has left a grave problem for today. By modern standards, many of these old dwellings are unfit for human occupation and are described as *slums*. Like many other old industrial towns, St Helens has had the major task of clearing large areas of them.

Iron and Steel Manufacturing

Figure 8.4 shows the distribution of the main integrated iron and steel works in Britain today. Notice that some of these works relate and others do not relate to the coalfields (Figure 8.5). Iron and steel is a classic example of a *heavy* and formerly *coal-based* industry. In the case of iron and steel, of course, a product equally as bulky as coal is needed, namely iron ore. In Britain, three main types of ore have been used:

(a) *haematite*, found in Carboniferous strata in the Cumberland and Barrow-in-Furness area (now part of Cumbria), and also in South Wales, giving rise to iron and steel works in these areas;

(b) *black band* (*Coal Measure*) *ores* are also found in Carboniferous rocks, as in the Scottish, Lancashire and Yorkshire, and north and south Staffordshire coalfields;

(c) *Jurassic ores*, found in the Jurassic limestone of the Cleveland Hills, the Scunthorpe area of Lincolnshire, the Corby area of Northamptonshire, and in Oxfordshire.

In addition to differences of type, there have been striking production changes over the years: in the nineteenth century a shift from black band to haematite ores; and in this century a shift from haematite mining to opencast extraction of the Jurassic ores. Overall, production has declined. Before 1914, Britain was producing about 16 million tonnes of ore per annum, and importing only 8 million. In the early 1970s, domestic

109

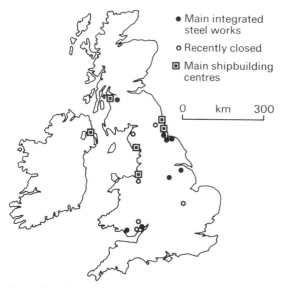

● Main integrated steel works
○ Recently closed
▣ Main shipbuilding centres

0　　km　　300

Figure 8.4　Steel and shipbuilding

Figure 8.5　The main industrial areas of Britain based on coalfields

▥ Major coalfields
(NOT National Coal Board Areas)

0　　km　　200

CENTRAL SCOTLAND
Iron and steel
Shipbuilding

NORTH-EAST ENGLAND
Iron and steel
Shipbuilding
Chemicals

CUMBRIA
Iron and steel

LANCASHIRE
Cotton
Glass
Chemicals

YORKS, DERBY, NOTTS
Woollens
Iron and steel
Varied

NORTH WALES
Iron and steel

EAST MIDLANDS
Varied

NORTH STAFFS
Pottery

WEST MIDLANDS
(BLACK COUNTRY)
Metal goods

SOUTH WALES
Iron and steel
Tin plating

production was only 9 million, and 22 million tonnes were imported. By 1981, less than 1 million tonnes were produced at home and about 8.5 million tonnes imported.

Locations of the Iron and Steel Industry

Figure 8.6 shows the processes involved in the production of steel. The raw materials, coal, limestone and iron ore are all bulky products, and there is a clear *cost advantage* to the firm if it can locate its works near the producing area of one or more of these resources. Such conditions existed more in the past than they do today, and one of the considerations in the following section is to examine *changes over time* in iron and steel production, through the examination of a very old-established steel centre, Sheffield, and a newer one, Scunthorpe.

Sheffield
Sheffield remains one of the greatest as well as one of the oldest steel manufacturing centres in Britain. It developed at a castle site overlooking the confluence of the rivers Don and Sheaf (Figure 8.7), and the local relief, geology and water supplies of the area had a considerable influence on its development.

(*a*) *Before 1800*　In its early days, the iron industry was a domestic industry. The local black band ore was extracted in shallow *bell-pits*. Timber was abundant on the hillsides, and *charcoal* was used for smelting. The industry became concentrated along tributary valleys of the Don and Sheaf, such as the Porter Brook (Figure 8.7), using *water power* to turn the grindstones that made the cutlery and other metal goods. The grindstones were made from the coarse Millstone Grit rocks of the Pennines (page 8). The reputation of Sheffield as a cutlery centre is thus based on centuries of tradition.

(*b*) *The nineteenth century*　In the nineteenth century, local raw materials and power supplies continued to dominate. The main change was the increasing use of *coal* for smelting, using *blast furnaces*. The Coal Measures supplied both black band ore and coal for this purpose. Many collieries developed in the city, though all are now closed down. Limestone flux (see Figure 8.6) could be brought from Derbyshire. In addition to the traditional cutlery industry, much of which became concentrated in quarters adjacent to the city centre, a heavy iron and steel industry grew in much larger factories, concentrated in the Don valley, requiring the level land of the valley for large plant, and using the river

Figure 8.6   *The processes in steelmaking*

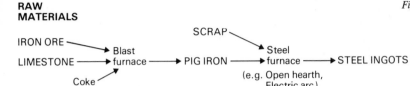

RAW
MATERIALS

for water supply and disposal of waste. Plate 8.5, although taken between the wars, shows a typical 'nineteenth-century' urban scene of the Don valley, with steel works concentrated by the river, and workers' terraced houses adjacent. Notice too that the gas works, also dependent on coal, needed the flat land of the valley floor as well.

(c) The twentieth century   In the course of this century, Sheffield has lost many of these advantages. The black band ore is worked out and coalmining has moved eastwards to the Doncaster area. Sheffield remains an important steel centre, however. But as iron ore has to be brought in, Sheffield no longer smelts it. It relies now on pig-iron made elsewhere, and also on iron and steel scrap. Some of the older, smaller steel works have been closed, as can be seen by comparing Plates 8.5 and 8.6.

The continuation of the steel industry in the Sheffield area reflects the ability of local industrialists to *adapt* to these changed circumstances. One of the most effective ways of doing this has been to concentrate on the production of high-quality specialised steels, making full use of the skilled traditions of the Sheffield area. Sheffield therefore remains important for *cutlery* and for special steels such as *alloy steels*, which have great toughness and resistance to different types of erosion. It

makes about two-thirds of the nation's alloy steel. The long tradition of metallurgical research in the city helps to keep Sheffield abreast or ahead of its competitors.

The situation in which a place maintains its traditional industries, even though the initial advantages which allowed the industry to grow in that place have gone, is known as *industrial inertia*.

Scunthorpe
Unlike Sheffield, Scunthorpe is not located on a coalfield. It developed as an iron and steel centre only at the end of the nineteenth century. Its great advantage was its location on the Jurassic limestone of north Lincolnshire (Figures 1.6 (page 9) and 8.8) which contains thick beds of the Frodingham ironstone. This was mined opencast. Evidence of opencast mining can be found by looking carefully at Plate 8.7. This is a view of the great Appleby–Frodingham steel works at Scunthorpe, with the very recent Anchor development in the right middle and foreground, which makes this one of the largest integrated steel works in Britain.

Figure 8.7   *Sheffield*

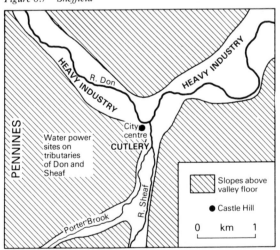

Figure 8.8   *Scunthorpe*

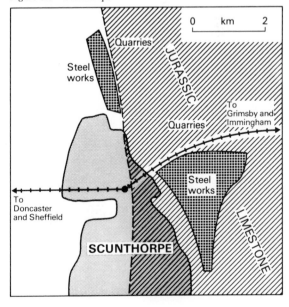

111

Plate 8.5   *Nineteenth-century urban scene in the Don valley (Sheffield)*

Plate 8.6   *Twentieth-century Sheffield*

Scunthorpe makes pig-iron as well as steel, and for its blast furnaces (Figure 8.6), coking coal is brought from Yorkshire and Nottinghamshire, and the South Wales and Durham coalfields. In addition to the low-grade local ore, high-grade iron ore is imported by bulk carriers of up to 100 000 tonnes, which come into Immingham (Chapter 14), from where the ore is brought by rail to Scunthorpe (Figure 8.8). A small amount of Scunthorpe's pig-iron is sent to Sheffield, but most is consumed locally in its great steel works.

Coastal Locations

In this century, and particularly since the Second World War, the trend has been to locate the new steel developments at the coast, reflecting the increasing use of imported ores. Some steel plants were already sited at the coast. One of the best examples is Teesside, where the steel industry grew round Middlesbrough to use Cleveland ores and Durham coking coal. The Cleveland ores are now worked out, but the steel works are well placed to import foreign ores (Figure 6.14 (page 88)). Perhaps the two most important post-war integrated steel works have been in South Wales, on flat coastal sites at Port Talbot and Newport (Llanwern).

Markets

The main outlets for the major integrated works are other manufacturing industries, including (*a*) *sheet steel*, for the car and tin-plating industries, and (*b*) *constructional steel*, for the building of bridges, oil rigs and production platforms, and girders for buildings. Teesside tends to concentrate on constructional steel, and South Wales on sheet steel. South Wales is Britain's most important tin-plating area, while it is well placed for supplying sheet steel to the car industry of the Midlands and the south-east (see pages 121–4).

The Decline of the Steel Industry

Figure 8.9a illustrates the drastic decline of the British steel industry during the 1970s. From a production of about 28 million tonnes in 1965, there followed a series of fluctuations, but an overall fall to about 20 million tonnes in the late 1970s, then plummeting to little over 12 million in 1980. The decline has been in part a result of world recession, and an international glut of steel through over-production. But it has also been due to inefficiency in the British steel industry compared with

Plate 8.7 The Appleby–Frodingham steel works at Scunthorpe

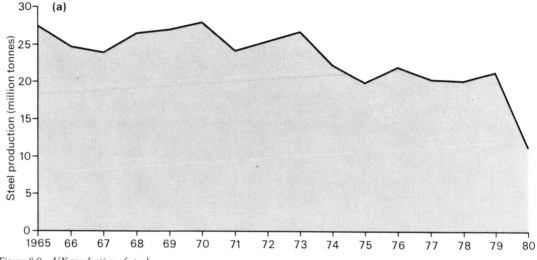

Figure 8.9 *UK production of steel*

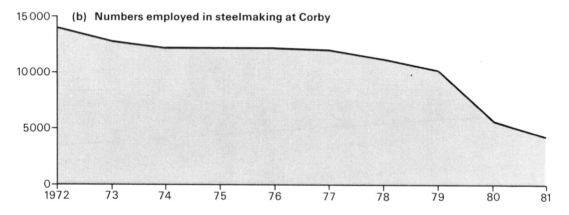

overseas competitors; in 1976 only 131 tonnes of steel per worker per year were produced compared with 225 in West Germany, 274 in USA, and 372 in Japan.

The Situation in Corby

Figure 8.9b shows the impact of this general decline in one steelmaking town, Corby, which developed to make use of the Northamptonshire Jurassic ores, opencast mining of which has scarred the countryside around the town. The closure of the steel works in 1980 threw over 5000 people on the labour market. British Steel kept open its tube-making works, which still employs about 4500.

The closure was part of the British Steel Corporation's policy to close uneconomic plants and concentrate production at huge integrated works on or near the coast. Because of the energy needed to smelt low-grade Jurassic ores, the Corporation prefers to import high-grade ores, and turn these into steel at coastal plants such as Redcar on Teesside (Figure 6.14), then transporting the steel by rail to the tube works at Corby.

In so small a town, the loss of so many jobs, with potentially over 20% unemployed, could have been devastating. To combat this situation, Corby has been made a Development Area (see pages 124–5) and certain parts of the town have been designated 'Enterprise Zones'. As Figure 8.10 shows, there are three of these in Corby, at Weldon North, Weldon South, and Earlstrees (Plate 8.8), the latter being an existing industrial estate to which the Enterprise Zone has been added, shown in the foreground of the photograph. In an Enterprise Zone, firms are exempted from many taxes and rates, and planning permission is easily and quickly granted.

The presence of new industrial estates is *diversifying* the employment structure of Corby. Among the 'light industries' (see page 121) of Corby are the manufacture of raincoats, cosmetics, plastic packaging materials,

114

Plate 8.8   Earlstrees Extension Area Enterprise Zone, Corby

Figure 8.10   Industrial change in Corby

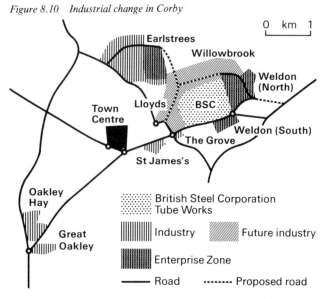

potato crisps, and tobacco. These industries are all helped by the central location of Corby in the East Midlands, close to the junction of M1 to M6, as it will be to the M1–A1 link road, which will by-pass the town to the south.

Exercises

7. (*a*)   Give reasons for the continuance of Teesside and the decline of Corby as a steelmaking centre.
(*b*)   With the help of Figure 8.10 and Plate 8.8 and information in the text outline changes in manufacturing industry in Corby.
8. Refer to Plates 8.5 and 8.6.
(*a*)   Outline the advantages for steel production shown on the photograph. What advantages did Sheffield have which are not shown on the photograph?
(*b*)   Describe and discuss the changes in land use shown on the two photographs, one taken before the Second World War and one recently.
9. Compare the layout and extent of the steel works shown on Plates 8.5 and 8.7.

115

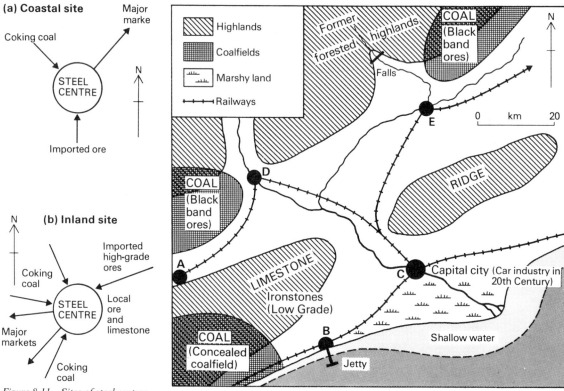

(a) Coastal site

Coking coal → STEEL CENTRE → Major marke[t]

Imported ore ↑ STEEL CENTRE

N ↑

(b) Inland site

N ↑

Coking coal → STEEL CENTRE

Imported high-grade ores

Local ore and limestone

Major markets

Coking coal

Figure 8.11   Sites of steel centres

Highlands
Coalfields
Marshy land
Railways

Former forested highlands

COAL (Black band ores)

Falls

N ↑

0   km   20

E

D

COAL (Black band ores)

RIDGE

A

LIMESTONE

Ironstones (Low Grade)

C   Capital city (Car industry in 20th Century)

B

Shallow water

COAL (Concealed coalfield)

Jetty

Figure 8.12   Locating the steel works

10. Refer to Figure 8.11a and b.
Which of the following are the two steel centres represented on the sketches: Motherwell (Clyde valley); Port Talbot; Scunthorpe; Sheffield; Teesside? Give reasons for your choice in each case.
11. Refer to Figure 8.12, a map of an imaginary area in which conditions approximate to those in the Sheffield–Scunthorpe–Immingham transect. Choose which of the areas A to E on the map was likely to be the best site for iron and steelmaking in (a) a pre-nineteenth century period; (b) the nineteenth century; (c) the twentieth century. Give reasons for your choices.

The Shipbuilding Industry

Figure 8.4 shows the distribution of Britain's main shipbuilding centres. The most important are Clydeside, Tyneside and Wearside, all near coalfields and steel manufacturing areas. Other shipbuilding centres have grown away from the coalfields, such as Barrow and Birkenhead in north-west England. These are less important than the other three areas mentioned, and tend to rely on government contracts for naval vessels. We shall concentrate here on the case of Belfast, in an area with no resources of coal or steel plate.

The Harland and Wolff Shipyards at Belfast

The key factor in the location of a shipyard must be the presence of water. The larger the ships to be launched, the deeper and more extensive the area of water has to be. While local supplies of coal and iron and steel would be helpful, they could be brought in by sea, the cheapest method of transport.

In the middle of the nineteenth century the initiative of Harland promoted the development of an existing shipyard on Queen's Island, an artificial island in Belfast Lough. He chose as his partner a man named Wolff, an engineer. It was their combined energy and abilities, rather than local raw materials, that led to the shipyard prospering. Coal had to be brought in by sea from the Ayrshire and Cumberland coalfields, and steel plate from the steel works of the Clyde valley. But they had the advantages of plenty of flat land to build the large works needed, and sheltered Belfast Lough and its feeders into which to launch and test ships.

The Harland and Wolff shipyards have been modernised and can now build tankers of a quarter of a million tonnes. Like other British shipbuilders, they have suffered from the intensity of overseas competition, especially from Japan, and from the recession in world demand for ships. Closure would be disastrous for the 9000 workers employed there, as there is no other employment on this scale in Northern Ireland. The Belfast shipyards, like others in Britain, can only survive through highly skilled management backed up by government subsidy.

Exercises

12. With the help of an atlas, draw a map to show Belfast's location in relation to its suppliers of basic materials in Scotland and northern England.

13. Find out why (a) the shipyards of Clydeside and north-eastern England are more important than those of north-western England and Northern Ireland; (b) there has been a recession in the world demand for ships since the 1970s.

The Heavy Chemical Industry

The term 'heavy chemicals' covers a wide variety of products, including fertilisers and pesticides for agricultural use, dyestuffs, and chlorine, caustic soda, soda ash and alkalis, widely used in such industries as textile, paper, glass and soap manufacture. The main heavy chemical regions in Britain (Figure 8.13) are the Mersey Basin (Figure 8.14) and Teesside (Figure 6.14).

Essential raw materials for the heavy chemical industry include salt and limestone. The traditional source of energy is coal, becoming more popular again with the rise in price of oil. The Mersey Basin chemical industry (Figure 8.14) has always been well placed for the salt of Cheshire, the limestone of Derbyshire, and coal from the south Lancashire coalfield. Teesside similarly has

Figure 8.13 Heavy chemicals and traditional textile manufacturing areas

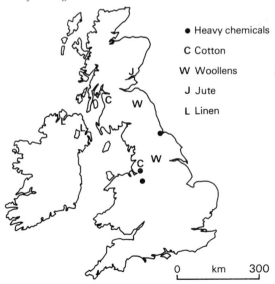

- Heavy chemicals
- C Cotton
- W Woollens
- J Jute
- L Linen

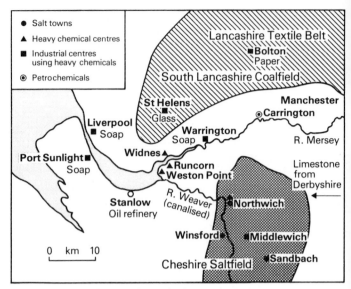

Figure 8.14 Mersey Basin chemical industry

access to the salt (and also gypsum and anhydrite) deposits and coal of south Durham, and limestone from the upper Tees valley.

These raw materials and the finished chemical products are bulky to transport. The Mersey Basin industry was helped by the canalisation of the River Weaver. Now much salt is transported in the form of brine by pipeline from the Northwich area to Runcorn (Figure 8.14). Markets for the chemical products are again very accessible. The alkalis are used in the glassmaking industry of St Helens (page 106); the soap-making industries of Warrington and Merseyside; and the papermaking industries of Lancashire. Chloride has long been used as a bleaching agent by the textile industries of Lancashire, but is now largely produced as a by-product of the petrochemicals industry. Another heavy chemical, sulphuric acid, an important material for the fertiliser industry, is manufactured at Widnes, Runcorn and St Helens. The main centres of the alkali industry remain Northwich and Runcorn (Weston Point).

Petrochemicals

Though not in any direct way a 'branch' of the heavy chemical industry, this modern section of the industry has grown in recent times, often in the traditional heavy chemical areas. As the name implies, its raw material comes from petroleum. Naphtha is extracted from crude petroleum and forms the 'feedstock' for the petrochemical industry. Thus naphtha is taken by pipeline from the Shell refinery at Stanlow to the petrochemical works at Carrington (Figure 8.14). The

117

main petrochemical plant on Teesside is at Wilton (Figure 6.14). Industrialists value the extensive areas of relatively cheap flat land of the lower Mersey and Tees valleys.

The petrochemical industry is the basic source of plastics, used today in an amazing variety of ways, and also of such products as detergents, solvents, anti-freeze, and many others.

Conservation

Few industries can be more noxious than heavy chemicals, a notorious pollutant in the past of both the air and rivers. Widnes and St Helens have been subject to particularly bad pollution. Figure 8.2 shows that St Helens once had a number of chemical works. One writer of the 1840s told of the 'strange compound of smells' proceeding from the chemical works near the station. When the chemical industry left St Helens, gigantic heaps of chemical waste were left, to add to the spoil heaps of the coalmines (Plate 8.3).

A different sort of problem was left by older methods of salt mining in Cheshire. In the nineteenth century, the process of 'wild brine' pumping led to alarming subsidence, for example in the Northwich area (Plate 8.9). Since the 1920s, however, a process of 'controlled brine pumping' has been introduced, which has much reduced the subsidence problem.

Although we have concentrated on the Mersey Basin and Teesside areas, it must be emphasised that the

Plate 8.9   Subsidence caused by wild brine pumping, Northwich

industries using these chemical raw materials have a very widespread distribution. While the basic industries are raw material orientated, the industries they supply are mostly consumer goods industries, with many locations in the market areas of large centres of population. Thus the London area is an important centre of the drugs, dye, paint and varnish, and detergent industries.

Textile Manufacturing

Figure 8.13 shows the main concentrations of textile manufacturing in Britain, though the map leaves out a wide distribution of smaller centres, particularly those to do with artificial fibres and clothing. We are going to concentrate here on the two main coal-based regions, the cotton region of Lancashire and the woollen worsted region of the former West Riding. These were the classic areas of the localisation of the textile industry in the industrial revolution period. *Within* these areas there developed the phenomenon of *specialisation* by area.

In Lancashire, for example, *spinning* towns tended to be concentrated on the *south* side of the Rossendale Upland (as at Bolton, Bury, Rochdale and Oldham), and *weaving* on the *north* side (as at Blackburn, Accrington, Burnley and Nelson). *Dyeing and bleaching* were found in many of these towns, but also in small industrial villages in the Rossendale Upland, tapping the pure water supply needed for these processes. *Clothing* and *marketing* were concentrated in Manchester.

These divisions were not clear-cut, however. Thus the photograph of Bolton (Plate 8.10) shows in the left foreground a 'combined' mill, which once undertook both spinning (the several-storeyed rectangular buildings), and weaving (the single-storey 'sheds' with north-facing windows).

In Yorkshire, similar divisions developed, but by separate products rather than separate processes (the system in Lancashire). *Woollens* were widespread over the West Riding, but Huddersfield and other towns of the *south-east* were major centres. *Worsteds* (of more tightly woven cloth than woollens) were rather more focussed in towns of the *north-west* of the region, in the Bradford, Halifax and Keighley areas. *Shoddy*, made up from old knitted goods, was a speciality of the Dewsbury–Batley area. Bradford became the main *marketing* centre for the industry, and Leeds the great *clothing* centre.

Like the iron and steel industry, both the cotton and woollen/worsted industries have passed through three main stages, enjoying many advantages and suffering many disadvantages in common.

118

Plate 8.10 Urban landscape, Bolton

The Cottage (Domestic) Industry Stage: Pre-1780

There was a domestic woollen (and in Lancashire also linen) industry on both sides of the Pennines at this stage, using wool from the upland sheep. The industries were carried on in stone cottages as part of a *dual economy*: farming and the making of cloth. The soft-water streams of these Millstone Grit areas were used to wash the greasy wool. The cloth was then taken down to markets in upland fringe towns such as Bolton and Halifax.

The Industrial Revolution and the Nineteenth Century

The cotton industry was the first to be concentrated in factories, as a result of a series of important *inventions*, such as Kay's 'flying shuttle' and Hargreaves' 'spinning jenny'. These and other inventions were later taken up in the West Riding. The cheap cloth they produced led to the decline and extinction of handloom weaving.

The early machines were driven by water wheels, which necessitated *riverside location*. But by the mid-nineteenth century most of the factories were steam powered. Thus the mills of both Lancashire and York-shire *moved* in many cases from the rivers *to the coalfields*, a major change in industrial location. The large new mills drove the domestic industry of the uplands out of existence.

Both industrial regions were well served by *canal* (the Leeds and Liverpool for example), and later by *rail*. The Lancashire textile belt and the West Riding were thus connected to *ports* such as Liverpool and Hull, which imported raw cotton and wool and exported the finished cloth. During the nineteenth century there were large export markets for these products. Many *ancillary industries* developed, such as the manufacture of engines and other machinery for textile factories.

119

Figure 8.15   Map of part of Bolton   Scale 1:10 560

The impact of the nineteenth century on the industrial landscape is still apparent, as shown in the photograph and map of part of Bolton (Plate 8.10 and Figure 8.15). Though urban renewal is taking place, the landscape is still dotted with the blocks of mills, rows of terraced cottages, and railway sidings (often now derelict) which served the mills. Similar scenes can be found in the West Yorkshire conurbation.

Twentieth-Century Changes

Since the late nineteenth century, the British textile industry has had to compete with the rapidly developing industries of other countries, particularly in Asia. Britain's industry has been severely handicapped by the continued use of out-of-date machinery. Decline had set in before the Second World War, but has been much more dramatic since, especially in the cotton industry. In Bolton, for example, the number of cotton mills dropped from 122 in the town in 1934 to only 20 in 1974. Not all these mills have been demolished. Many have been converted to other uses, which has helped to keep up employment.

Government grants were used to compensate firms going out of business and to help the larger mills to become more efficient. Another important change has been the switch from natural to artificial fibres. Lancashire's textile industry is no longer really a cotton industry; the cotton is usually mixed with artificial fibres such as Terylene. Today oil or electricity rather than coal are the main sources of energy. There is little difference now between the former specialist 'spinning' and 'weaving' towns. A second industrial revolution has thus taken place.

Changes have been less dramatic in West Yorkshire, although there has been a similar tendency for smaller firms to be taken over by larger companies. A striking feature has been the increased use of immigrant labour, especially in the Bradford area, which now has a huge Asian community (see Chapter 9), helping the mills to work round the clock on a shift system, unpopular with many British workers. Round the clock working is vital to make the most economic use of expensive modern machinery.

Both Lancashire and West Yorkshire have benefited from new motorway links: the M6, M61 and M62 in Lancashire and the M1 and M62 in Yorkshire providing major north–south and east–west axes of development. Thus more accessible cotton towns such as Bolton have had more success than less accessible ones such as Burnley in attracting new industries to disused cotton mills and industrial estates. Similarly, the south-east of West Yorkshire has an access advantage over the north-west.

Exercises

14. With the help of Figure 8.14 and the text, outline the industrial links between Lancashire and Cheshire.

15. With the help of an atlas, draw a map or maps of the south Lancashire and West Yorkshire textile towns, to show by symbols how specialisation occurred at an earlier stage of their industrial growth. Thus the Lancashire spinning towns should have a different symbol from the weaving towns, for example. Mark and name the coalfields, canal connections, and railways to the ports.

16. Refer to Plate 8.10.

(*a*)   Five letters A–E are labelled. Distinguish those marking nineteenth-century and twentieth-century land use.

(*b*)   Suggest the influences which have led to the development of, and change in, this industrial landscape.

(*c*)   Describe the general layout of the urban landscape as shown in this photograph and the OS map extract (Figure 8.15).

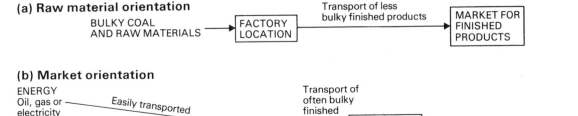

(a) Raw material orientation

BULKY COAL AND RAW MATERIALS → FACTORY LOCATION → Transport of less bulky finished products → MARKET FOR FINISHED PRODUCTS

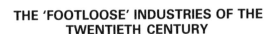

(b) Market orientation

ENERGY Oil, gas or electricity — Easily transported

VARIETY OF RAW MATERIALS AND MANUFACTURED COMPONENTS → FACTORY LOCATION → Transport of often bulky finished products → MARKET FOR FINISHED PRODUCTS

Figure 8.16   Market orientation

THE 'FOOTLOOSE' INDUSTRIES OF THE TWENTIETH CENTURY

The manufacturing industries which have come to the fore in this century in many cases existed in the nineteenth, although the car and aircraft industries are exceptions. As we have seen, typical nineteenth-century industries have continued, often as a result of industrial inertia, into this century, adapting as best they could to its changed circumstances. It is, however, possible to identify characteristics that distinguish the growth industries of this century from the dominant industries of the nineteenth.

(1) They reflect the increasing affluence of western society, particularly since the Second World War, which has resulted in an enormously increased demand for *consumer goods*. There is therefore today a much wider variety of industries, and an increase in importance of so-called *light industries*, such as food processing, electrical goods, plastics, and many others.

(2) As they tend to rely not so much on basic raw materials as on other manufactured goods, and on roads for transport, they are less tied down to distinct sources of raw materials. Roads provide flexible transport facilities, and the goods being transported are not generally as bulky as those associated with heavy industries.

(3) Similarly, they are not tied to coal as a source of power, using rather electricity, oil or gas, all easier to transport.

These industries can thus be termed *footloose*, being less localised in particular areas than those we have so far considered. Managers can afford to pick and choose sites more freely. But they do depend on a large consumer market, and the orientation is not so frequently to raw materials or fuel supplies as to *markets*. Thus the London area, having lost some of its importance for manufacturing in the nineteenth century because it was well away from the coalfields, has regained it in this century.

The differences just described are illustrated on Figure 8.16a and b. The first diagram relates to the older coalfield/raw material-based industries, such as iron and steel. Another industry of this type is sugar beet (page 60), in which the raw material is bulky, but the finished product less so. Figure 8.16b shows the market orientation of many twentieth-century industries: a variety of components is assembled to make what may be a bulkier product, such as a piece of furniture. Location near the market is therefore an advantage.

We are now going to look at perhaps the most characteristic of all twentieth-century industries, car manufacturing.

Car Manufacturing at Luton

A feature of a modern car plant is the use of *mass production* methods, by which large numbers of vehicles are produced on a series of assembly lines. Plate 8.11 shows a late stage on the assembly line at the Luton works of Vauxhall. The employees are placed at

Plate 8.11   Quality control on the assembly line, Luton

different points on each assembly line, where they repeat the same job as each car passes, perhaps hundreds of times a day. This high degree of *division of labour* is characteristic of many modern industries and is very efficient in allowing a large amount of goods to be produced fairly cheaply.

Materials and Components

Unlike the glass industry, where only a few materials are required, the vehicle industry needs thousands of components. The most important of these is sheet steel, which arrives at the works in coils and bales, which are cut and pressed into the shape of the different panels of the car, such as the roof, doors, bonnet, and so on. The complete body shell is then welded. It then goes to the paint and trim shop, where the body is first painted and sealed. In the 'trim' stage, items of 'furnishing', including seats, carpets, instruments, door panels, electrical parts and glass, are added to the body shell.

The car bodies are then lowered from the trim shop at the body-mounting station, where they meet the mechanical units, such as engines, gearboxes and axles. It is essential that the right bodies meet the right 'mechanicals' at the right time, for each vehicle has to fit a particular order. One for export will need a left-hand drive, for example. Hence all the operations are carefully synchronised. On the final assembly line there are many 'quality control' points (Plate 8.11), where the earlier assembly work is examined. When the car is driven off the assembly line it goes through a further

series of tests before being sent out for sale to other parts of Britain or abroad.

In addition to the partly processed materials, a car plant has to bring in components made by other firms. Vauxhall buys about 28 000 different components from 900 other companies, a sign of how complex the car-manufacturing process has become. Mass production methods also require a considerable amount of factory space, and the large size of the Vauxhall plant at Luton can be seen on Plate 8.12, where it occupies the whole of the right centre of the photograph.

The main areas of Britain supplying raw materials and components to the Vauxhall works in Luton are indicated in Table 8.3.

Table 8.3

Area	Main materials
The Midlands	Very varied, including tyres and electrical parts, castings and forgings
The London region	Similar to the Midlands
The North-west (Lancashire, Cheshire)	Includes electrical parts and springs
South Wales	Particularly sheet steel and alloys
Yorkshire (a) Sheffield area	(a) Castings Forgings Alloy steels
(b) West Yorkshire conurbation	(b) Upholstery and carpeting

Plate 8.12   Aerial view of the Vauxhall plant at Luton

The Growth of Luton

At the time the car industry came to Luton in the early years of this century, Luton had a population of about 40 000 people. Until about 1800, when its population was 3000, Luton was merely a small market town near the junction of the route through the gap in the Chilterns with the ancient route (Icknield Way) which ran along the foot of the escarpment through nearby Dunstable (Figure 8.17).

As with other market centres, Luton had its local industries, such as brewing and flour-milling, based on agricultural produce from the surrounding countryside. In addition, there was a straw plait industry, using wheat straws, introduced into the Luton area in the seventeenth century.

In this century, Luton has expanded enormously, largely as a result of the growth of car manufacturing. By 1951 the population had reached over 110 000 and in 1981 over 160 000.

The Introduction of the Car Industry

The Vauxhall Company was founded in 1857, and manufactured marine engines for river craft. It started to make motor cars as a sideline in 1903. Soon after this, its lease in London ran out, making it necessary to move to a new location. The company chose Luton. In the early 1900s a 'New Industries Committee' had been set up in Luton to attract industry to the town. Factory sites were offered at low prices and low rates. In addition, Luton was one of the first Local Authorities to build a municipal power station, providing cheap electricity for industry. Also present was a supply of skilled labour, with experience of employment in the engineering trades. Such labour was needed by the car industry, which at that time was very small in size and did not use mass production methods. Another advantage of the Luton area was that lower rates of pay prevailed than in London, reducing labour costs for the Vauxhall Company.

Unlike the glass industry of St Helens, however, the location of the car industry in Luton had a strong element of chance about it. While Luton had certain advantages, as we have seen, a location in almost any of the towns surrounding London might have been chosen. Another example of this was the choice of Cowley (Oxford) (see Figure 8.18) by Lord Nuffield for the manufacture of Morris cars (now British Leyland).

Luton Today

The importance of car manufacturing to Luton today is shown in Table 8.4 which gives employment figures up

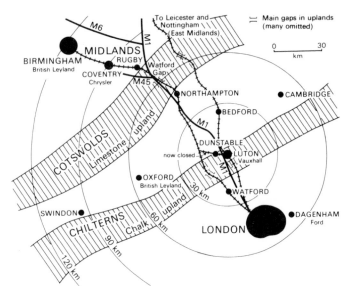

Figure 8.17 The situation of Luton

to 1978 (to the nearest 1000) which can be compared with those for 1971, 1951 and 1939. Rapid growth began in the late 1920s when the huge General Motors concern of the USA took over the Vauxhall Company, which from then on concentrated on mass production of cars for the popular market. In contrast, the old staple industry of Luton, hatmaking, has declined, as fashions in headwear have changed.

Table 8.4

	1939	1951	1971	1978
Total employed population	48 000	60 000	81 000	80 000
in manufacturing	30 000	43 000	46 000	40 000
in car manufacturing	10 000	14 000	21 000	9 000
in other engineering	10 000	14 000	15 000	14 000
in hatmaking	12 000	5 000	2 000	1 000

Luton's strategic location between the London and the Birmingham areas (Figure 8.17), astride major *lines of communication* out of London, has been of considerable benefit to its industrial growth. In fact a number of the towns shown on Figure 8.17 have similarly advantageous locations. The names of the important car-manufacturing firms in the map area are marked, and it can be seen that Luton and Dunstable lie in the heart of this prosperous vehicle-manufacturing belt. In addition, most of the towns marked on the map supply parts for the vehicle industry.

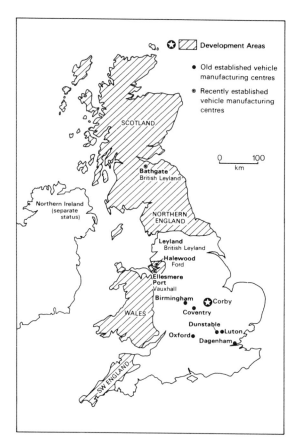

Figure 8.18 The Development Areas and car manufacturing centres of Britain

Exercises

17. What differences are there in the factors which led to the growth of the car-manufacturing industry in Luton and glass-manufacturing in St Helens?
18. Compare the employment figures of St Helens (Table 8.1) with those of Luton (Table 8.4). What are the major similarities and differences revealed?
19. Compare the urban scene shown on Plate 8.12 with that of Plate 8.6. Why are they so different?

Growth Areas in Decline

The *light consumer goods* industries we have been discussing are market orientated (page 121) and thus are ideally located in former growth areas, which until the 1970s were areas of increasing population and of increasing affluence. In this century, such growth areas have tended to be away from the northern coalfields, and more in the south-east of England and the Midlands. The main growth axis runs from London, north-west through Birmingham towards Liverpool and Manchester. Another runs through the East Midlands to Yorkshire, and a third one west towards the Severn estuary. These growth axes are all served by motorways (Figure 7.2).

But the recession of the late 1970s and early 1980s has seen decline setting in, even in the former growth areas, and the southward spread of unemployment (Figure 8.19). Unemployment is no longer confined to the fringes of Britain. The 5–10% unemployment figure considered bad in 1972, is now only to be found in the most favoured region, the south-east. All other areas have over 10%. Unemployment is also no longer confined to unskilled or unqualified workers. Neither is it any longer a short-term problem. It is the key economic and social issue of our time.

Before the recent recession, some of the areas in economic decline had gained the benefit of being designated *Development Areas* (Figure 8.18). These still exist. Industrialists establishing factories in such areas gain benefits such as 15% grants for new buildings and plants, tax concessions, and favourable loan conditions. In addition, such areas qualify for cheap loans from the European Community budget, whose objective is to try to iron out differences in economic wealth between different regions in Western Europe.

As we have seen in Corby (page 114), which is not one of the 'traditional' areas of economic decline (Figure 8.19), *Enterprise Zones* are being established in areas hit by serious economic decline and social problems, which qualify for even greater help than is

The improvement in road links provided by the motorway system is particularly useful to the Vauxhall Company, as its plants at Luton and Ellesmere Port make not only cars, but also components that they each use. Gearboxes, for example, are manufactured at Ellesmere Port, and delivered by road to Luton. A fleet of articulated lorries makes daily journeys between the two factories. Road transport has now almost completely taken over from rail in transporting Vauxhall products, and the link of the M56, M6 and M1 (Figure 8.17) has made the journey between Ellesmere Port and Luton a much faster one.

The rapid growth of industry and population in Luton, particularly marked since the Second World War, has resulted in a wide expansion of the built-up area. Large new housing estates have been built, some of which can be seen on Plate 8.12. In general, Luton has fewer slum areas than old industrial towns such as St Helens, because its main growth has been in this century and not in the previous one.

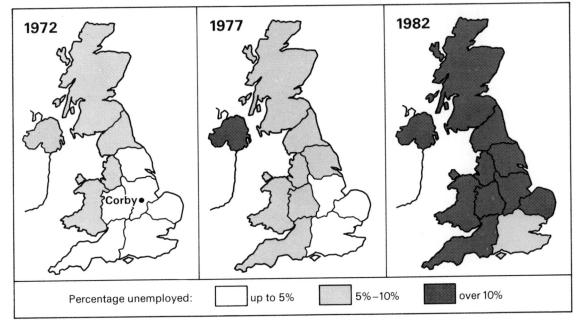

Figure 8.19   *The southward spread of unemployment*

available in Development Areas. Here *advance factories* may be built, waiting to be taken over, while services such as roads, drainage and sewage are all laid on in advance. In addition to government and EEC incentives, Local Authorities also help, sometimes providing rent-free or cheap-rent buildings, for example.

The Effects of Government Policy on the Car Industry

When firms such as Vauxhall wished to expand in the south-east and the Midlands in the 1950s, they were not permitted to do so. Instead they were given a list of Development Areas in which new building could take place. Unable to extend its plants in Luton and Dunstable, Vauxhall chose to go to Ellesmere Port on Merseyside, building a large plant on the site of an old airfield. Similarly, other British car manufacturers built factories in the 1960s in Development Areas (Figure 8.18), including British Leyland at Speke (Merseyside) and Bathgate (near Edinburgh); Ford at

Halewood (Merseyside); and Chrysler (now Talbot) at Linwood (near Glasgow). In the early 1980s, Speke and Linwood were closed because of economic recession.

In the post-war period, *Government decision* became one of the key factors in selecting sites for industrial development.

Exercises

20. Refer to Figure 8.18.
(*a*)   What were the main car-manufacturing areas of Britain before 1960?
(*b*)   What regions have been added since then?
(*c*)   Which is the most important of the new areas? Try to find out why.
21. (*a*)   Make lists of the main industries of (i) the coalfield areas of Britain, and (ii) south-east England.
(*b*)   How and why do the two lists vary?
(*c*)   Distinguish between (i) growth and declining industries and (ii) tied and footloose industries, giving examples of each.
22. Try to discover the reasons why an important light industry or Development Area was established in your home area. Compare the reasons for its development with those which led to the growth of *either* the glass industry *or* the car industry.

9 POPULATION

THE GROWTH OF URBAN POPULATION

The nineteenth century experienced an enormous growth in towns and cities, and nowhere was this process more marked than in Britain. As one writer put it: 'In England the cities are most monstrous, and bleak and disorganised... These aggregations are something new in the history of things, to which no former time can furnish any precedent or parallel' (Plate 9.1). This represented a general view that the unchecked growth of cities had led to serious social and environmental problems.

The population of England and Wales had risen from 9 million in 1801 to 32 million in 1901. It was increasingly concentrated in the towns: about one-third in 1801; half in 1851; and over three-quarters in 1901. The new phenomenon of the *conurbation* (Chapter 12) arrived in this century. The transformation of the people from a rural to an urban state, through a drift to the towns, has continued in this century. Looking back at Figure 5.1 (page 49), we see that there has been a shift from a state in which farmscape, wildscape, and farmscape-wildscape (marginal) fringe predominated, to one in which large areas are overwhelmed by townscape and townscape-farmscape (sometimes called *rurban*) fringe.

There have been population changes other than migration to the towns, however. In this century, a *decline in death rates* through medical advances has resulted in an increase in the population, and particularly in the number of old people in the population. In addition, after a long period of *increasing birth rates* in the nineteenth century, this century has seen a gradual decline. After a rise between the early 1950s and early 1960s, a steep decline in the birth rate has set in, as a result of married couples having smaller families in a

Plate 9.1   Birmingham in the 1880s

period of increased female employment and wider use of birth control methods. As a result, for the first time in the nineteenth and twentieth centuries, there was hardly any population growth in the United Kingdom between 1971 and 1981, the population rising by 0.5% only, from 55.7 to 55.9 million.

Exercises

1. Refer to Plate 9.1.
(a) Describe in detail the scene depicted.
(b) The Birmingham you see on the photograph was one its citizens were proud of. How is the prosperity suggested?
(c) Outline similarities and differences from a similar large city scene of today (see Plate 12.1, page 150).
2. Refer to the population figures for the UK, 1901–1978, in Table 9.1.
(a) Draw graphs to show the trends of these figures.
(b) What is likely to be the effect of the following population changes on the economy: (i) an increasing number of old people; (ii) an increasing number of children; (iii) a decreasing number of people of working age?

Table 9.1 Birth and death rates (per thousand)

Year	Birth rate	Death rate
1901	28.6	17.3
1911	24.6	14.1
1921	23.1	12.7
1931	16.3	12.2
1941	not available	
1951	15.8	12.6
1961	17.8	12.0
1971	16.2	11.6
1978	12.2	11.9

THE CHANGING DISTRIBUTION OF POPULATION

Figure 9.1 shows the distribution of population in the United Kingdom in 1981. Notice the great concentrations on the coalfield areas (Figure 6.7, page 79) and in the Greater London region, and also the spread of population along the 'coasts of retirement' in southern England, North Wales, and Lancashire.

The trend towards increasing concentration in conurbations, which was so marked a feature of the nineteenth and early twentieth centuries, has now gone into reverse, with people moving out of the central parts of the conurbations into smaller towns and overspill districts, resulting in 'erosion' of the countryside as housing estates spread. Figure 9.2 illustrates population changes over England and Wales between 1971 and 1981, and indicates clearly how all the major conurbations are losing people, with over a 5% decrease in

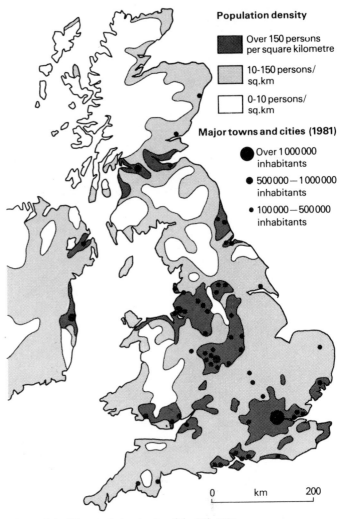

Population density

- Over 150 persons per square kilometre
- 10–150 persons/ sq.km
- 0–10 persons/ sq.km

Major towns and cities (1981)

- Over 1 000 000 inhabitants
- 500 000 – 1 000 000 inhabitants
- 100 000 – 500 000 inhabitants

Figure 9.1   The population density of the UK, 1981

Greater London, West Midlands, Merseyside and Tyneside. Birmingham dropped below 1 million people, and Sheffield, Leeds and Manchester below ½ million. On the other hand, rural areas in East Anglia, the Welsh borders and the south gained population. Some of this is related to New Town growth, as at Telford (Shropshire) and Milton Keynes (Buckinghamshire), and expanded towns such as Northampton and Peterborough.

The changes shown on Figure 9.2 are the result of natural change, or migration, or a combination of the two. As we have seen, the movement is away from the city centres, but much of this is of more well-to-do people, leaving a concentration of poorer people in the inner city.

127

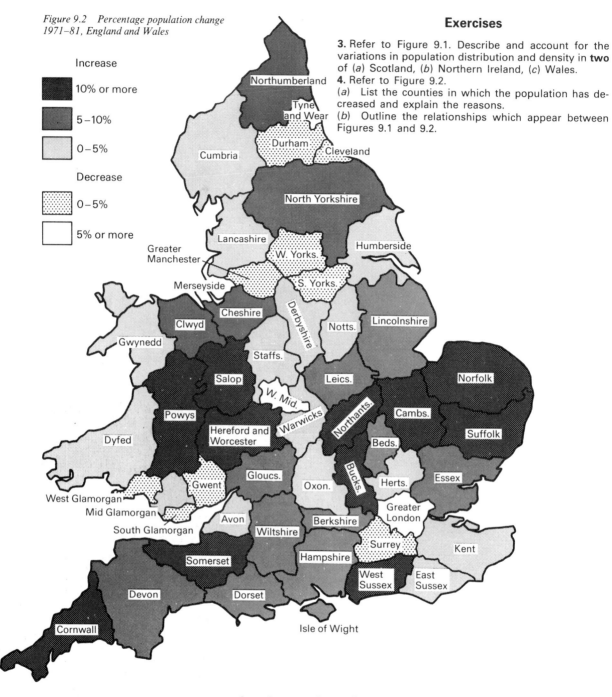

Figure 9.2 Percentage population change 1971–81, England and Wales

Increase

- 10% or more
- 5–10%
- 0–5%

Decrease

- 0–5%
- 5% or more

Exercises

3. Refer to Figure 9.1. Describe and account for the variations in population distribution and density in **two** of (*a*) Scotland, (*b*) Northern Ireland, (*c*) Wales.

4. Refer to Figure 9.2.

(*a*) List the counties in which the population has decreased and explain the reasons.

(*b*) Outline the relationships which appear between Figures 9.1 and 9.2.

Immigrants from Overseas

The post-war period has seen three major phases of immigration into Britain.

(1) In 1945–55 there were large numbers of European refugees, especially from Poland.

(2) In 1955–62 there were large numbers of coloured immigrants from Commonwealth countries, attracted by the employment opportunities created by an increasingly affluent post-war society. This led to a net inward migration (i.e. after emigrants had been subtracted from immigrants) of 480 000 people in the 1955–62 period.

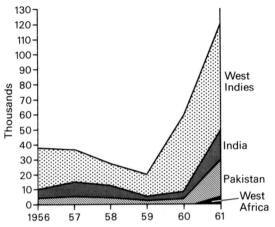

Figure 9.3   Immigration from selected Commonwealth countries to the UK, 1956–61

In 1962 the influx was restricted by the Commonwealth Immigrants Act, after particularly rapid increases between 1959 and 1961 (Figure 9.3).

(3)   Since 1962, immigration from the so-called 'New Commonwealth' has been restricted to (a) dependants of workers already here; (b) a group of British passport holders of Asian origin who have been forced to leave (i.e. been deported from) East Africa.

The total estimated population of overseas-born people (not only coloured people) was 3.1 million in 1971, or 5.8% of the population. Of this it is estimated just over 1 million is coloured. This overall total is quite small, but conceals the fact that certainly the coloured immigrant groups are concentrated in particular urban areas, as Table 9.2 indicates.

Table 9.2   Percentage of total 'New Commonwealth' immigrants in England and Wales living in six conurbations, 1971

	Percentage of total 'New Commonwealth' immigrants in conurbation	Conurbation population as percentage of total population
Tyneside	0.4	1.7
West Yorkshire	6.4	3.6
Selnec*	4.7	4.9
Merseyside	0.5	2.6
West Midlands	14.5	4.9
Greater London	40.5	15.2
Total for the six conurbations	66.8	32.9
Rest of England/Wales	33.2	67.1

* Selnec is the south-east Lancashire–north-east Cheshire conurbation.

While the conurbations together have about one-third of the total population of England and Wales, they contain about two-thirds of the coloured immigrant groups from the 'New Commonwealth'. Greater London, the West Midlands and West Yorkshire have far above the average percentages of such immigrants, while others have much less. Merseyside's low figure, even though it has a considerable coloured population, probably reflects the fact that many of its members came in at an earlier period, and were born in the area, not overseas.

Even more than this, within the conurbations, the coloured groups tend to be concentrated, or 'segregated' in their own communities, particularly in inner city areas (Plate 9.2). They have been forced to live in the 'blighted zone' (page 146). This happened in the nineteenth century when Irish and Jewish immigrants were forced into these 'ghetto' areas. The present-day situation is well illustrated in Birmingham. Figure 9.4 shows the percentage of heads of households born in Pakistan or 'New Commonwealth' countries in the different wards of Birmingham's *Special Area* at the time of the 1981 census. Such Special Areas were set up in 1978 in Liverpool, Manchester–Salford, Birmingham, Newcastle–Gateshead, and three areas of London, and given financial help with a view to arresting and reversing urban decay and social distress. Notice how in Birmingham's Special Area, the coloured population is concentrated in the 'blighted zone' surrounding the CBD (see Chapter 11), with the highest percentage, over 70, in Soho Ward, and over 50 in four other wards. Merseyside has a similar concentration of overseas-born heads of household, although the general percentages are much lower. In contrast to 11% in the West Midlands conurbation as a whole, Merseyside as a whole has only 1%, but this average covers a range from 11.2% in Granby Ward in the inner city, to negligible percentages on the outskirts. The variations between the conurbations are of course reflected in Table 9.2.

The social problems of inner city areas are not only caused by racial tension, otherwise Liverpool's social problems would be much less than those of Birmingham, which is not the case. In these inner city areas, a linked series of social problems is to be found, not only questions of colour prejudice, but also cultural differences, multi-occupation of houses, educational disadvantage and unemployment. In times of boom, unskilled coloured workers 'fill in the gaps'. In times of recession, they are the first to be made redundant. It is probably the combination of unemployment, poverty, racial tension, as well as a dislike of the police, who logically concentrate their attentions on the inner city areas where crime rates are high, but are viewed as being prejudiced against coloured people, that has led to riots in recent times in St Paul's (Bristol), Brixton (London), Moss Side (Manchester) and Toxteth (Liverpool).

These riots have reinforced the need for the *Inner City Partnership Programmes*, started in the late 1970s and designed to put new life and confidence into the blighted areas of such cities as Birmingham and Liverpool. These combine the resources and skills of different authorities. The Birmingham Inner City Partnership is made up of the government, the City of Birmingham, the West Midlands County Council, and Birmingham Area Health Authority, combining in a ten-year programme.

Exercises

5. Find out which countries make up the 'New Commonwealth'. Which Commonwealth countries do not belong to this group? What are the main differences between the two groups?

6. Look into the reasons for the migration of 'New Commonwealth' people into Britain from the 1950s, in terms of the factors pushing them out of their own countries and pulling them into Britain.

7. Refer to Table 9.2.

(*a*) Describe the variations in the distribution of 'New Commonwealth' immigrants in the conurbations of England and Wales.

(*b*) Try to find reasons why this variation has occurred.

(*c*) What are the main problems facing such immigrants when they come to settle in British cities?

8. (*a*) Describe the pattern of the distribution of heads of households born in Pakistan or 'New Commonwealth' countries shown on Figure 9.4.

(*b*) Try to explain why the distribution has taken this form.

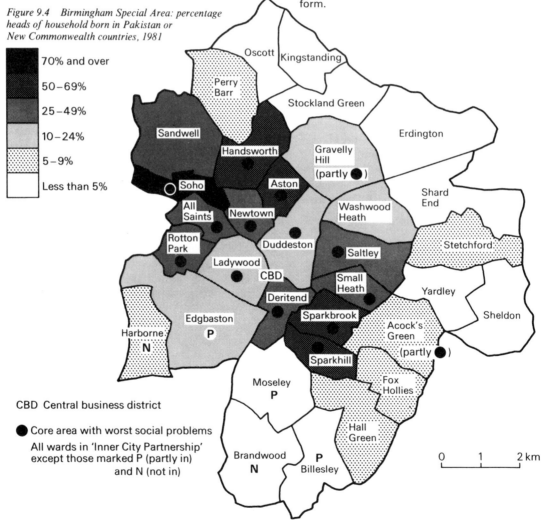

Figure 9.4 Birmingham Special Area: percentage heads of household born in Pakistan or New Commonwealth countries, 1981

70% and over

50–69%

25–49%

10–24%

5–9%

Less than 5%

CBD Central business district

● Core area with worst social problems

All wards in 'Inner City Partnership' except those marked P (partly in) and N (not in)

130

Plate 9.2   Mixed racial group in Wolverhampton

10 MARKET TOWNS AND SPHERES OF INFLUENCE

The Rural Settlement Hierarchy

Figure 10.1 is a map of settlements in Lincolnshire in 1861 which had a population of about 2000 and over. The symbols in the key show an order of size, forming a settlement hierarchy. At this time, Lincoln and Boston, at the top of the hierarchy, had populations of over 15 000. Six towns had between 5000 and 15 000 people and eleven between 2000 and 5000. There were many more places with less than two thousand. The number of settlements is thus approximately in inverse proportion to size.

The full settlement hierarchy ranges from the individual farm, the hamlet and the village, through a whole range of sizes of town to the largest conurbation. In this section, however, we are going to concentrate on the *rural settlement hierarchy*, at the apex of which is the regional capital, with below this a series of *market towns* of different size. Many of the settlements shown on Figure 10.1 ranked as market towns, places where people met to exchange goods. Many were granted rights by the Crown to have a market as long ago as the Middle Ages. With the exception of the south-east, the spread of towns on Figure 10.1 is fairly even. The reason why a historical map has been chosen is to demonstrate the situation before nineteenth-century industrialisation disturbed the traditional settlement pattern.

Moving away from Lincolnshire, let us imagine a theoretical county with an entirely level area, the same sort of soils, and no coastline or mineral deposits. In these 'ideal' circumstances a quite even spread of settlement can be envisaged, as shown on Figure 10.2, showing just one segment of such a region. At its heart is the regional centre. Regional centres of equivalent importance (not shown on the diagram) might be, say, 40 kilometres away. The importance of the centre is related to the size (and prosperity) of the population it can draw upon. The major regional centre provides a very wide range of shopping, entertainment and other services. A densely populated region will support more of such centres.

Within the market areas of these large regional capitals will be smaller market towns, such as those marked on Figure 10.1. Each of these centres will have in its market area smaller centres. We shall see later in this chapter that people are prepared to travel further to the larger centres in the hierarchy to enable them to benefit from the wider range of services they offer (pages 136–7).

Of course, in reality, things are not as neat and tidy as Figure 10.2 would indicate. As Figure 1.6 (page 9) showed, Lincolnshire is not a level county but is broken up by limestone and chalk uplands. Figure 1.8 (page 11) indicated that villages have not developed in an even grouping round market centres, but along spring lines at the foot of the uplands, and at dry points above the marshy lowlands, giving in some areas a *linear* arrangement of villages. The presence of a coastline, with harbours, as at Boston, is an added complication.

Much greater complexity in the pattern has arisen since the nineteenth century. Thus three of the largest towns in the historic county of Lincolnshire, Grimsby (92 000 population in 1981), Scunthorpe (66 000) and Cleethorpes (36 000), were relatively unimportant or hardly existed in 1861 (Figure 10.1). Their growth is a result of nineteenth-century industrialisation, creating in these cases a great demand for fish (leading to the growth of Grimsby), iron and steel (Scunthorpe) and holiday facilities (Cleethorpes), with all three centres helped by the coming of the railways.

Figure 10.1 Settlements in Lincolnshire, 1861

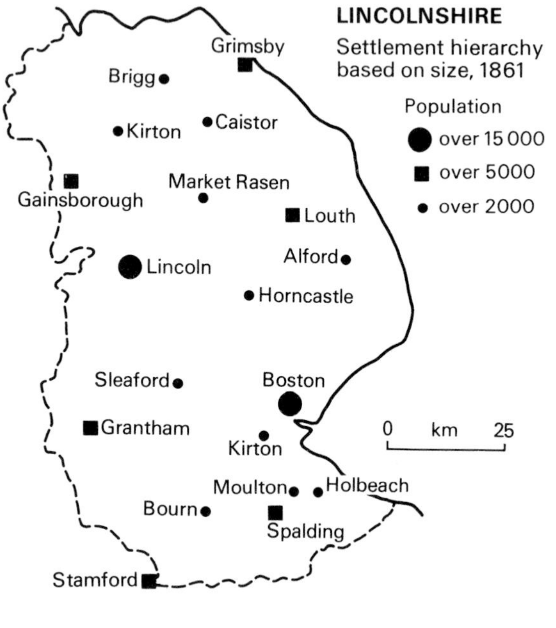

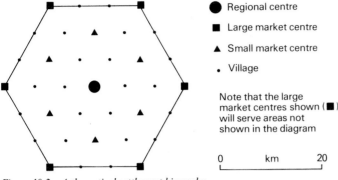

● Regional centre

■ Large market centre

▲ Small market centre

• Village

Note that the large market centres shown (■) will serve areas not shown in the diagram

0   km   20

Figure 10.2   A theoretical settlement hierarchy

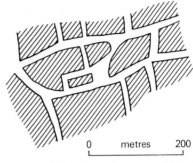

0   metres   200

Figure 10.3   The market centre of Louth

Only the traditional regional centre of Lincolnshire, *Lincoln* itself, today retains the high position it had in the mid-nineteenth-century hierarchy. This reflects the excellence of its situation in the county (Figure 1.6, page 9) at the most important *gap* in the Lincoln Edge. It was at the meeting point of two great Roman roads, Ermine Street, connecting London and York, and running along the crest of Lincoln Edge; and Fosse Way, coming from the south-west and Midlands via Leicester.

Louth: A Lincolnshire Market Town

Figure 10.3 is a map of the centre of Louth (Figure 10.1), showing its market square, the place where livestock and crops were brought in from the surrounding country and sold, or exchanged for other produce, including the produce of the town. Such market squares often lie at the heart of the present-day shopping centre.

Plate 10.1 is an aerial photograph of Louth; Figure 10.4 is a map showing its situation in relation to surrounding areas, as also does the OS 1:50 000 map extract (Figure 10.5). The photograph shows its street pattern and its setting in a rural landscape. The map indicates its location near the junction of the chalk dip slope and coastal marshes (Figure 1.6, page 9), and at the meeting point of routes running along the edge of the dip slope, and down the valleys and gentle spurs of the chalk dip slope.

Louth was thus very well placed for marketing the goods produced in the chalk uplands, and those of the coastal areas, not to mention the materials it produced itself. It remains a centre for the agricultural produce of its region. In Chapter 5 we noted it as one of the centres in which Mr Parker marketed his produce. It has agricultural processing industries such as flour-milling and retains its livestock market. Note on Figure 10.4 and the OS map extract, that apart from road it has also rail freight connections, and a link with the sea, the Louth Navigation. At one time it was also a rail junction, as the OS map shows.

Exercises

1. Table 10.1 shows the populations of Lincolnshire towns with over 5000 people in 1981.

Table 10.1

Grimsby*	92 000	Stamford	15 000
Lincoln	77 000	Skegness	14 000
Scunthorpe	66 000	Louth	12 000
Cleethorpes*	36 000	Sleaford	8 000
Grantham	30 000	Barton*	8 000
Boston	26 000	Bourne	8 000
Gainsborough	19 000	Mablethorpe	7 000
Spalding	17 000	Brigg*	5 000

* Now in Humberside (see Figure 12.10, page 160)

(*a*)   Group these towns into order of size and, using a different symbol for each group, with the help of an atlas draw a map similar to Figure 10.1.
(*b*)   Describe and try to explain the similarities and differences between the two maps. ((*c*) is on page 136.)

Figure 10.4   The situation of Louth

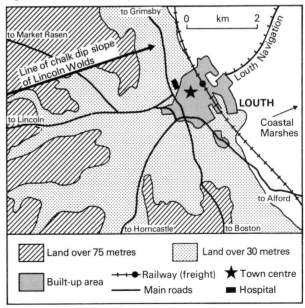

▨ Land over 75 metres	░ Land over 30 metres
▦ Built-up area	+●+ Railway (freight) ★ Town centre
	— Main roads ■ Hospital

Plate 10.1   Aerial view of Louth

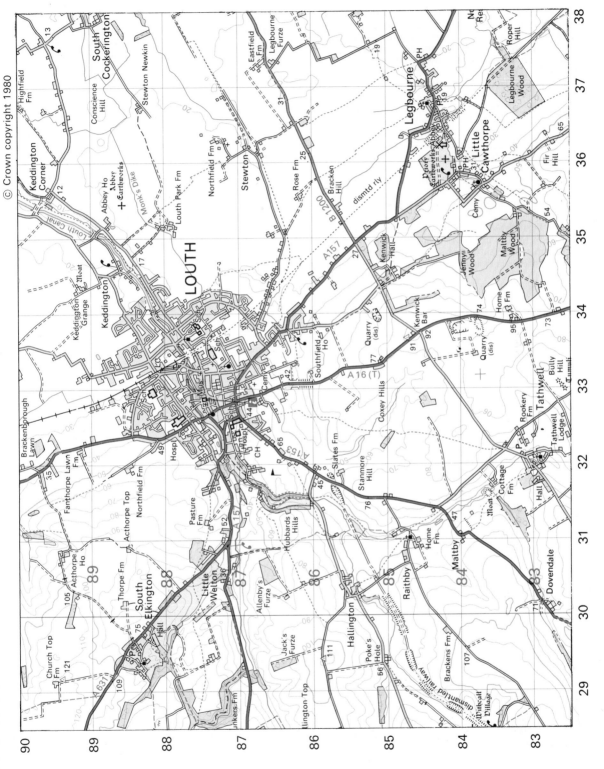

© Crown copyright 1980

Figure 10.5   OS map extract of Louth

(c) Imagine you lived in Horncastle (Figure 10.1), a market centre of about 4000 people, with a cattle market and some agricultural service industries, and a small shopping centre round the market square. For what reasons do you think you might travel regularly into Lincoln?

2. Lay a sheet of tracing paper over Plate 10.1, and with the help of the OS map extract mark and label the main roads, the railway, the built-up area, the town centre and market place, older housing areas and newer housing. Note that the photograph was taken looking towards the east.

3. Refer to the OS 1 : 50 000 map extract of Louth (Figure 10.5).

(a) Outline differences in the relief east and west of the town.

(b)· Contrast the pattern of A and B roads shown on the map.

(c) Indicate how communications have been and still are important to Louth as a market centre.

4. Use this and other information to account for Louth's importance as a market town.

Journeys for Shopping and Entertainment

In answer to question 1(c) you will probably have worked out that people will travel regularly into Lincoln to work, for certain shopping purposes, for entertainment, and for visiting friends and relatives. One of the ways in which it is possible to assess the importance of a place is to see how effectively it draws people into it, as measured by such things as numbers of people coming in, the distance they are prepared to travel, and the frequency of their visits.

We shall be looking later (Chapter 12) at journeys to work. Here we shall consider journeys for shopping and for entertainment. In terms of shopping, for example, the people of a small village may only enjoy the services of a general store. A larger village, and certainly a small market town, will have more specialist shops such as grocers and newsagents, although these might well be combined with, say, a post office, or the sale of greengroceries. A small market centre will also have clothes and shoe shops.

For other services, such as the buying of furniture or going to the dentist, people would have to travel further afield, unless they actually lived in a larger town. A place like Louth has a wide range of services, and it would only be necessary for its people to travel into Lincoln if, say, they wished to have a wide choice of furniture stores, or go to a League football match.

Hence different goods and services are associated with different-sized catchment areas, or *spheres of influence*. Figure 10.6 shows that grocers' shops have smaller spheres of influence than furniture shops. This is because furniture, an expensive item, is needed and bought less frequently than groceries. Thus a small centre would be unlikely to have a furniture shop as it would not attract enough customers frequently enough to pay its way. On the other hand, people buy groceries often, so many villages have a store selling groceries.

Similar factors operate with entertainment. These days it is often necessary to travel to quite large towns to find a cinema, and even to a major city to go to a theatre. Before the television era, when going to the cinema and theatre was more popular, even small market centres would have a cinema. A rough measure of the importance of places over the country as a whole comes from a study of the distribution of teams in the Football League. Clearly other factors have here to be considered (such as the quality of managers and directors of football clubs!). Figure 10.7 shows the general distribution of Football League clubs in 1981–2. Notice how

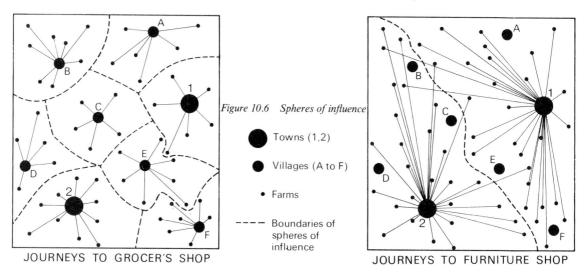

Figure 10.6   Spheres of influence

● Towns (1,2)

● Villages (A to F)

• Farms

- - - Boundaries of spheres of influence

JOURNEYS TO GROCER'S SHOP

JOURNEYS TO FURNITURE SHOP

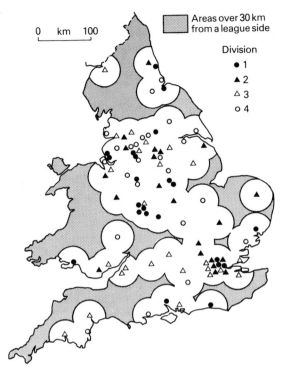

Areas over 30 km from a league side

0 km 100

Division
● 1
▲ 2
△ 3
○ 4

Figure 10.7   Location of teams in the English Football League, 1981–2

they tend to relate to the map of population distribution, and also to axes of communication centred on London.

Study of the League tables will show a rough hierarchical correlation between status in the League and urban size. Thus First Division clubs tend to be concentrated in large cities. Towards the end of the 1981–2 season, for example, seven of the top ten clubs in the First Division, such as Liverpool (Plate 10.2) came from the major conurbations. These are areas in which greatest support can be achieved. Note the different sizes of grounds at Liverpool (Plate 10.2) and Crewe (Plate 7.7), in the First and Fourth Divisions respectively in 1981–2, representing the top and bottom of the whole Football League. Successful teams to a large extent reflect bigger gate receipts, which allow the purchase of the best managers, coaching staff and players. The large population of young people in major cities provides a local reservoir of players. In contrast, the three clubs of the historic county of Lincolnshire, Grimsby, Lincoln and Scunthorpe, all medium-sized towns, but the three largest in the county, were respectively in the Second, Third and Fourth Divisions.

Plate 10.2   Anfield Football Ground, Liverpool

It must be stressed, of course, that size in the urban hierarchy does not *determine* the success of a football club. It can merely provide more favourable conditions for success. Thus in the 1981–2 season one of the Sheffield clubs was in the Fourth Division, as was one of the Bristol clubs in 1982–3, and these are respectively the fourth and seventh largest cities in England.

Bus Services

One important purpose of bus services is to link regional centres such as Exeter with smaller towns and villages in the surrounding area, as shown on Figure 10.8. Notice that the thickest flow lines on the map, denoting most bus services, join Exeter with relatively small places nearby. The buses bring in people who wish to use the services and facilities which an important town such as Exeter provides, including department stores and other shopping facilities, various types of offices and entertainments, surgeries, and educational institutions, which may not be found in their own smaller towns and villages.

The plotting of bus services, as on Figure 10.8, is another approximate measure of the *sphere of influence* of a town. Hence a line joining the end points of the thicker flow lines on the map shows roughly Exeter's sphere of influence. The longer thinner flow lines are those linking up towns of similar importance to Exeter. For these more distant connections, more comfortable coach services are often provided. These are frequently express services, as most of the passengers using them wish to travel as quickly as possible between the two towns concerned. The local bus services may well be more frequent, but they are also slower, picking up passengers at each stop on their route into town.

These more distant towns have their own spheres of influence. Where large towns are fairly close together, as in the cases of Exeter, Taunton, Plymouth and Torbay, their spheres of influence are likely to overlap. Many small places are in the sphere of influence of more than one town, and in such areas of overlap the different towns compete for trade. In many cases the people in them will choose a shopping centre purely as a personal preference, and not necessarily because it is the nearest.

The mapping of bus routes is not, of course, an ideal way (nor is it the only way) of plotting spheres of influence, because so many people now journey to shopping centres by car.

Exercises

5. Refer to Figure 10.6.
(a) Describe and explain the differences between the two shopping patterns.
(b) Why do none of the farmers travel into the villages to buy furniture?
(c) Why do the spheres of influence on the second map overlap?
(d) Assume that these two maps were made at a time when people had to travel to shop by horse and cart. What might be the effect of the introduction of a bus route, running through villages A, C and F and town 2, on shopping patterns?
6. (a) Can you think of any ways other than the plotting of bus routes to work out the sphere of influence of a town?
(b) Your own school has a sphere of influence. How could it be measured? Draw a map to show it.
(c) Outline the likely differences in catchment areas between (i) a primary school; (ii) a comprehensive school; (iii) a selective grammar school; (iv) a residential independent school. Try to explain these differences.
7. Discuss the extent to which the factors influencing a successful football club also influence the success of a large department store.
8. (a) With the help of Figure 10.7
(i) name a conurbation with each of: five, three, two and one First Division football clubs in it;
(ii) describe and explain the distribution of areas over 30 kilometres from a Football League ground.
(b) For your own area, find the nearest First Division, Second Division and Third/Fourth Division football clubs. Do these match up to the size and importance of the centres in which they are found? Examine the effects of local competition and transport services on the success of the club. If these factors do not provide a valid explanation, speculate on those which, in your opinion, do.
(c) With reference to Plate 10.2, describe the urban landscape in which the Anfield football ground is set. In what ways does it differ from that of Louth (Plate 10.1)?

Figure 10.8 Flow map of bus service to Exeter

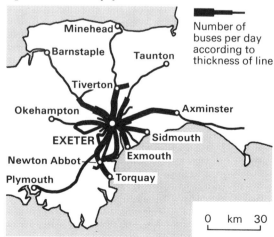

11 THE GROWTH OF A CITY: EDINBURGH

As we have seen, location of settlements can be looked at in two ways: (*a*) site, which refers to the ground on which the settlement stands, and (*b*) situation, which is the general position of the settlement in relation to other settlements and connecting routes.

The Site of Edinburgh Castle

Plate 11.1 shows Edinburgh Castle standing on a steep-sided rocky crag. The crag is a natural defensive site. Behind it the land slopes away gently, forming a 'tail' to the castle crag. The tail was important in giving well-drained land on which the oldest part of Edinburgh grew, under the protection of the castle. Many of the ancient buildings of the town can be seen in the background of the picture.

The Formation of the 'Crag and Tail'
(see also pages 19–21)

Tens of thousands of years ago, huge ice sheets approached the site of Edinburgh from the west. When the ice reached the crag, which is made of tough rocks, it was diverted to either side, as the arrows on the photograph indicate. The surrounding weaker rocks were more easily worn away, except for those protected behind the crag. They remain and form the gentle slope of the tail.

On either side of the tail, the rocks were gouged out by the ice to form valleys. These are shown in the section (Figure 11.1), which is drawn almost at right angles to the tail. Part of the line of the section is marked on Plate 11.1.

The valley formed on the north side of the tail was at one time filled by a lake named the Nor' Loch.

Plate 11.1   The site of Edinburgh

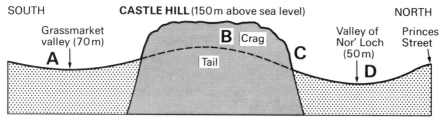

SOUTH   CASTLE HILL (150 m above sea level)   NORTH

Grassmarket valley (70 m)

B Crag

A

Tail

C

Valley of Nor' Loch (50 m)

Princes Street

D

Figure 11.1 Section to show the effects of glaciation in the Edinburgh Castle area

(Movement of ice towards the viewer)

Exercise

1. (a) From the evidence given on Plate 11.1 explain why the crag forms a natural defensive site.
(b) Draw a simple section from west to east (that is with the castle on the left) to show the 'crag and tail' at Edinburgh. Describe briefly how the feature has been used by people.

The Situation of Edinburgh Castle

Figure 11.2 shows the situation of Edinburgh and its castle in relation to lowland routeways. Many natural defensive sites were not of course used as castle sites. Castles were only built where they were needed, usually at strategic locations where important routeways could be controlled from a defensive position. Edinburgh Castle lies about 3 kilometres south of the Firth of Forth. Between the Firth and the Pentland Hills is a low-lying coastal plain, which formed a convenient route, followed in the past by invading Highlanders from the north-west and English from the south.

Edinburgh as a Route Centre

The routes shown on Figure 11.2 are those used at the present day. The well-chosen situation of Edinburgh showed its value as time went on. The city came to

Figure 11.2 Edinburgh as a route centre

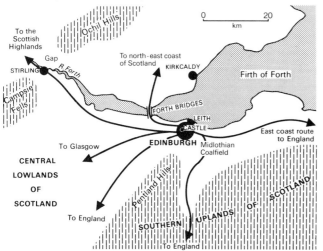

control not only the coastal routes, but also those which crossed the Central Lowlands of Scotland to Glasgow, and went south to England through gaps and valleys in the Southern Uplands (see exercise 2(c)). As the population grew in the Central Lowlands, so did Edinburgh's importance as a major route centre. A disadvantage of Edinburgh's location lay in its poor links immediately to the north, interrupted by the wide Firth of Forth. Figure 11.2 shows the nearest bridging point, well to the west of Edinburgh. Here the old ferry has been replaced by two great bridges, the railway bridge being completed in the late nineteenth century and the road bridge, carrying a motorway, in 1964.

Exercise

2. Refer to Figure 11.2.
(a) Calculate the distance in kilometres from Edinburgh to Kirkcaldy (i) via Stirling, (ii) via the Forth bridges. What distance has been saved by the bridges?
(b) With reference to Stirling, explain what is meant by 'lowest bridging point'. When did Stirling cease to be the lowest bridging point of the Forth? State one advantage and one disadvantage to Stirling of the construction of the Forth Road Bridge.
(c) With the help of an atlas, name
(i) two large towns north of Edinburgh on the east coast of Scotland which have benefited from the building of the Forth bridges;
(ii) the estuary reached by the route to Glasgow;
(iii) two towns just over the English border, reached by routes from Edinburgh;
(iv) the sea of which the Firth of Forth is an inlet;
(v) two countries facing Scotland across that sea;
(vi) Draw a sketch map to show the location of Edinburgh *in relation to the places mentioned in answers to parts (i)–(v) of this question.*

Other Castle Locations in Britain

Sites

The castle crag at Edinburgh is a good example of a *hill-top* defensive site. Figure 11.3a is a map of another site of this type, at Corfe in Dorset.

In some cases, *spurs* of high land extend into a lower-lying area, and these often provided sites for castles,

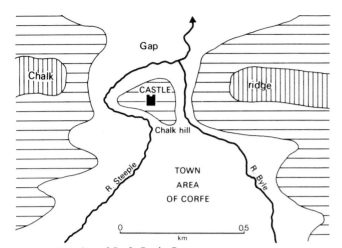

Figure 11.3a   Site of Corfe Castle, Dorset

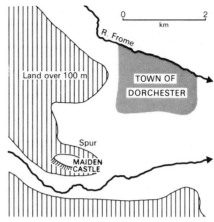

Figure 11.3b   Site of Maiden Castle, Dorset

as at Maiden Castle in Dorset (Figure 11.3b). Here an ancient earthwork was built, much older than Edinburgh and Corfe castles. In this case, the neighbouring town of Dorchester grew later, at a route focus in the Frome valley.

At Durham (Figure 11.3c) the winding River Wear has worn down the land to leave a steep-sided *incised meander*. Durham Castle was built on the 'neck' of this meander, protecting the old town behind. As the map shows, the river formed a natural moat on three sides (see page 26).

Criccieth Castle (Plate 11.2) was built on a *headland*, protected on the seaward side by steep cliffs which plunge down to Tremadoc Bay, part of which can be seen behind the castle.

In lower-lying areas, where no natural defensive site was present, castles had to have artificial protection, partly provided by their own tall and thick stone walls, and partly by a surrounding moat.

Another essential feature of castle sites was the presence of a water supply on the spot, either from a spring or well in the grounds. In some cases hundreds of metres of hard rock were bored through to reach water.

Situations

We have seen that Edinburgh was a good example of a castle controlling a *coastal plain* route. During the thirteenth century, an English king built a series of castles along the coast of North Wales, including Conwy (Plate 11.3), Caernarfon, Beaumaris, Criccieth and Harlech, to defend the coastal route against the people of the Welsh highlands who were hostile to him. These coastal castles could be supplied with provisions and arms by sea.

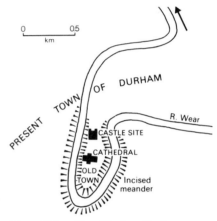

Figure 11.3c   Site of Durham Castle

Plate 11.2   Criccieth Castle, North Wales

Plate 11.3   Conwy Castle, North Wales

Another important situation lay in the control of a *gap* in a ridge, as at Corfe; or where an upland and a lowland zone joined, at the *outlet* of a valley. Stirling Castle (Figures 1.15, page 15; and 11.2) controlled both a gap in the hills, and a valley route leading from the Scottish Highlands. Lincoln Cathedral (page 9) lies similarly in a commanding position overlooking the Witham Gap.

Figure 11.4   Exercise on castle locations

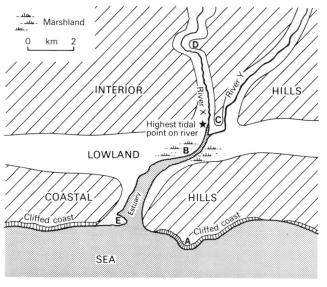

Exercises

3. (*a*)   With the help of your atlas (consulting the index if necessary) locate the position in Britain of each castle named in the text.
(*b*)   Compare and contrast Plates 11.1 and 11.2, referring to the sites and states of repair of the two castles.
(*c*)   Compare the advantages of (i) Corfe and Durham, and (ii) Maiden Castle and Criccieth as defensive sites.
4. With the help of an atlas, draw a sketch map to show the coastline and mountains of North Wales. On it mark and name the main castle towns. Describe briefly the situation of each castle, stating whether it controlled any particular sea area, inlet or strait, or the outlet of any valley.
5. Imagine that at some time in the past you were asked to choose a castle site to defend the area shown on Figure 11.4 against an enemy who could attack by land or sea, or both. You came to the conclusion that the five locations marked A to E on Figure 11.4 were all possible sites for your castle.
(*a*)   Describe the relief of the five locations shown.
(*b*)   List the advantages and disadvantages of (i) site and (ii) situation of each of the locations, and arrange them in an order of preference.
(*c*)   Trace out the map into your exercise book, and mark in a possible route system, in relation to your chosen preference of castle site.
(*d*)   A class discussion might then follow, to come to some conclusion as to which was the best possible site for a castle in the first place, and which site had the best prospects for the later growth of a town.

The Growth of Edinburgh

The usually compact original sites of towns are not always easy to recognise in the sprawling urban landscapes of today. Yet the characteristics of the early site may still affect the present layout of roads and buildings in towns. Edinburgh has expanded from its original cramped site on the crag and tail to occupy almost all the coastal plain between the Pentland Hills and the Firth of Forth. Some of the city is shown on the Ordnance Survey map extract on the scale 1:25 000 (Figure 11.5) and on the aerial photograph (Plate 11.4). The photograph was taken with the camera pointing approximately north-eastwards.

The Castle and the 'Old Town'

Under the protection of the castle, Edinburgh grew from the fourteenth century onwards. Notice the street (letter A on Plate 11.4) running down the tail behind the castle. It ends at Holyrood Palace (see OS map extract, Figure 11.5), the home of the former kings and queens of Scotland. The distance between the castle and the palace is about one mile, and the street is known as the 'Royal Mile'. It is lined by ancient buildings, including St Giles Cathedral (B).

Plate 11.4   Aerial view of Edinburgh

The early growth of Edinburgh was helped by its position on the east coast, with trading connections across the North Sea to the countries of Europe. One of these was France, with whom Scotland had for many years an alliance against England. Leith developed as the port of Edinburgh. Many rich merchants, as well as ordinary people, lived along the Royal Mile. Some of

their houses still stand, but few are used for domestic purposes today.

At an early date, the 'Old Town' spread from the tail into the Grassmarket area (C). This was the site of the old market, where agricultural produce from the surrounding country was sold. Growing towns soon established trading connections with the neighbouring

143

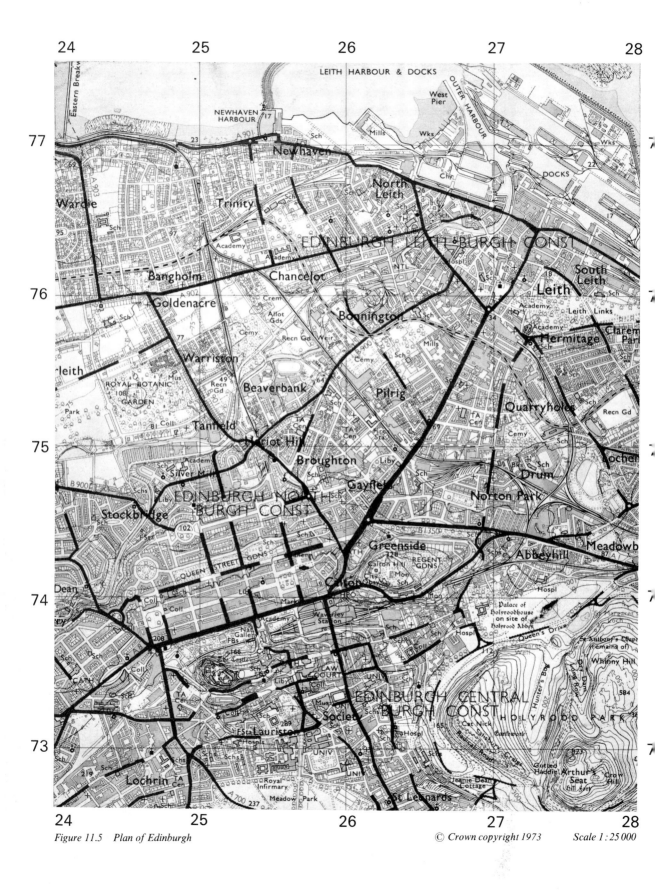

Figure 11.5   Plan of Edinburgh

© *Crown copyright 1973*   *Scale 1 : 25 000*

countryside, exchanging food produce for goods made in the town. Edinburgh thus became a major market centre as well as a route centre. The fact that the city was the capital of Scotland, an independent country at the time, was a continual stimulus to growth. From an early stage of urban growth the 'Old Town' was short of space. Hence buildings were made high to accommodate as many people as possible.

The 'New Town'

Congestion had become so bad by the middle of the eighteenth century that Edinburgh was forced to expand outwards. It was decided to build a 'New Town' on the land to the north of the Nor' Loch. Like the New Towns of today, it was carefully planned. In place of the crowded, winding and insanitary streets of the 'Old Town', wide streets and crescents were laid out, lined by elegant buildings as can be seen behind and in front of the trees on the left of Plate 11.4 (D). Plate 11.5 shows Royal Circus, built during this period, which can be located on the OS map extract at GR 248745. Well-to-do people moved their homes from the 'Old Town' into areas such as this. The finest of all the new streets was Princes Street (E on Plate 11.4) with its magnificent view

across the valley to the castle and the picturesque buildings of the 'Old Town'. It is now the main shopping street of Edinburgh and one of the most attractive thoroughfares in Britain.

The city also expanded southwards from the tail. Adjoining marshy areas were drained to provide building land. In this district a great educational and medical quarter developed in the second half of the eighteenth and first half of the nineteenth century. Edinburgh had long had a famous university. During this period it became one of the great cultural and scientific centres of Europe. The town continued as a major route and market centre. It also remained the capital of Scotland, although the country by now was no longer independent of England. By 1800, Edinburgh's population had reached about 100 000.

Exercises

6. Refer to the OS map extract (Figure 11.5) and Plate 11.4.

(*a*) Name and give the grid references of the points marked F and G on the photograph.

(*b*) Contrast the pattern of the streets in the 'New Town' with that in the 'Old Town'. Name two streets in each, using information in the text.

Plate 11.5   Royal Circus, Edinburgh

Plate 11.6   Jamaica Street, Edinburgh (now demolished)

7. Lay a large sheet of tracing paper over Plate 11.4. On it outline:
(a)   the area covered by the 'Old Town' of Edinburgh, naming the Castle Crag, the Royal Mile, the Grassmarket, and St Giles Cathedral;
(b)   the site of the Nor' Loch, Princes Street, George Street, Calton Hill, Princes Street Gardens, and the approximate boundary of the part of the 'New Town' present on the photograph.
(c)   Explain why the bridges marked by the letter H had to be built.

The Nineteenth Century

Look now at Plate 11.6. It shows a street of tall, terraced stone-built tenements, constructed later than Royal Circus, but not to such high building standards, and looking far more decrepit. Many streets like this are still present in the industrial zones of Edinburgh, which grew up in the nineteenth century to the north-east and south-west of the city centre. Parts of these areas can be seen at I and J respectively on Plate 11.4. Today, they are probably the most dismal districts of Edinburgh; 'blighted zones' of factory buildings, railway sidings, and terraced slum tenements.

Like other towns of Britain, Edinburgh became increasingly industrialised in the nineteenth century. The Midlothian coalfield, to the east of the city (Figure 11.2), supplied power to the newly developing factories. Edinburgh already had old-established industries, based on its agricultural surroundings (flour-milling and brewing), on trade, or on its own needs (such as paper for the governmental and educational bodies in the city). To these were added the manufacture of rubber, chemical and engineering products, among others.

Some of the early factories were sited along streams running north to the Firth of Forth, which supplied water for power and for processing, One of these streams was the Water of Leith, which runs across the map from Dean Bridge (244740) to Leith Docks. Later, factories grew where transport facilities were available, such as (a) along the Union Canal, the terminus of which is shown at Lochrin (246728); and (b) along the railways, a number of which concentrated on Leith and the area to the south-west of the former Princes Street Station (246735). The trade of the port of Leith (K on Plate 11.4) grew rapidly with this industrial development.

By the end of the nineteenth century, Edinburgh's population had reached 400 000.

The Twentieth Century

The population of Edinburgh has continued to grow, though less rapidly, in this century, and is now over 500 000. New housing estates have been built on the outskirts of the city (as at L on Plate 11.4) to accommodate the increased numbers of people, and also the people displaced from more central areas such as that shown on Plate 11.4. These people are being rehoused in new housing estates on the fringes of the city, such as that shown on Plate 11.7.

Edinburgh remains an important administrative (government offices), cultural, (art galleries (M), museums, and concert halls (N)), industrial, and route and market centre. Perhaps the most rapid growth in recent years has been in the tourist industry. Large hotels, such as that by Waverley Railway Station (O), accommodate the many tourists who come to see Princes Street, the Royal Mile and Holyrood Palace (see Figure 11.5). Overlooking all is the castle, which attracts 400 000 visitors each year, many of whom come at the time of the Edinburgh Festival.

Plate 11.7   Edinburgh: new housing estate

Exercises

8. Refer to Plates 11.5, 11.6 and 11.7, and compare their layouts and relative advantages and disadvantages as areas to live in.

9. Refer to Plate 11.4 and the OS map extract (Figure 11.5).

(*a*) Add to your tracing of Edinburgh; Waverley Railway Station and the railway line running into it, and any industrial feature you can pick out on the photograph.

(*b*) Show how the course of the railway which runs from the west into Waverley Station has been affected by features of the site of Edinburgh. Can this line be seen from Princes Street? Give reasons for your answer.

(*c*) What features shown on the OS map extract (Figure 11.5) suggest that Leith is an important port? Try to find out why it is not so important a port as Glasgow.

10. Copy Figure 11.6 into your exercise book. Make your copy twice as big as Figure 11.6. The thick lines mark the approximate boundaries of the various 'zones' of Edinburgh. One of these (a nineteenth-century residential zone) is already marked in for you. With the help of the text, the OS map extract (Figure 11.5) and Plate 11.4 complete this 'growth map' of part of Edinburgh by labelling the following (not given in the correct order) in

the places marked 1 to 9 on Figure 11.6: Royal Mile; 'Old Town'; 'New Town'; Princes Street; dock zone; two other industrial zones; Waverley Station; the educational and medical zone (universities, colleges and hospitals).

11. Figure 11.7 is a simplified model of the growth structure of a 'theoretical' town. Models are artificial frameworks which do not exist in reality, but which may help to 'explain' reality. Our model is basically a *concentric* one, containing four circular zones: (i) a central core; (ii) a 'blighted zone'; (iii) an inner residential zone; and (iv) an outer residential zone. These circular zones are, however, often broken up into smaller zones or *sectors*. In some cases, for example, high-class residential sectors developed on one side of a town, or an industrial sector developed along a canal or railway (see below).

Various factors may have helped to interfere with the straightforward development of such patterns, including:

(1) *the form of the land*, perhaps location in a narrow valley, or at the coast, neither of which would allow a full concentric pattern to develop;

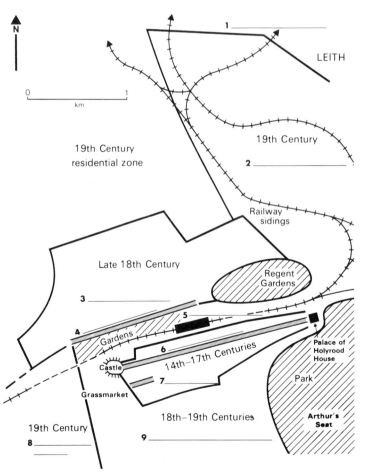

Figure 11.6   The growth of Edinburgh

(2) *lines of communication*, which tend to *radiate out* from the town centre. As already noted, many nineteenth-century industrial zones developed alongside canals (page 107) and railways. More recently, ribbon development has taken place along roads running out from the central core;

(3) *growth of nearby towns*: in many industrialised areas of Britain, towns have grown too close together to allow such simple concentric patterns to develop. Even so, in such areas as Birmingham (see Chapter 12) many of the features described here are present.

It is useful to test the model we have described against your own town or one near you.

(*a*) With the help of the growth map you have made for your own town, and with the advice of your teacher, try to construct a simplified model of the town.

(*b*) Indicate ways in which it is similar and ways in which it differs from Figure 11.7.

(*c*) What features in Edinburgh (OS map extract, Figure 11.5) would tend to interfere with a concentric pattern of growth? Which zones in the model (Figure 11.7) are not shown on Figure 11.6?

(*d*) Describe briefly features found in the central core and the 'blighted zone' (if there is one) of your town.

Figure 11.7   A simplified model of the growth of a town

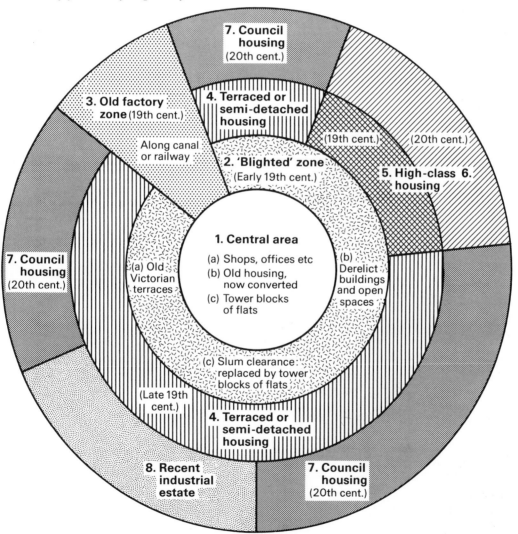

12 CONURBATIONS

BIRMINGHAM AND THE WEST MIDLANDS

Birmingham is the major centre of the West Midlands conurbation, one of the seven great conurbations of Great Britain (Figure 12.11). Returning to the idea of hierarchies introduced in Chapter 10, Birmingham is near the pinnacle of the hierarchy of settlement in Britain, ranking with a group of other large cities first behind London. It is the most important shopping and entertainment centre in the Midlands.

The Bull Ring, Birmingham

The Bull Ring scheme, marked A on the right of Plate 12.1, provides Birmingham with one of the most up-to-date shopping centres in Britain. Opened in 1964, it cost £8 million to build. Apart from the shopping precincts, it includes a tall office block, the Rotunda (B), an open-air retail market (C), and gardens (D). It adjoins New

Plate 12.1   Aerial view of central Birmingham

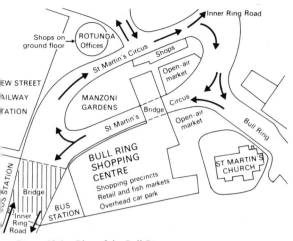

Figure 12.1   Plan of the Bull Ring

Street railway station (E), and the city's main bus station (F), and stands where the Inner Ring Road (G) meets roads leading out to Stratford, Warwick and Coventry. Figure 12.1 is a plan of the Bull Ring scheme and shows how people and traffic are separated by arranging the shops along pedestrian precincts, connected across the Inner Ring Road by enclosed bridges

(H), and served by overhead car parks, thus reducing congestion and increasing safety.

The City Centre

The place where many of the services of a town or city are concentrated is in the central area, referred to as the *central business district* (CBD).

The CBD of a town is by far the most important shopping centre, but it is by no means the only one. Towns also have a number of suburban shopping centres, which can be quite large in a big city. Some of these may be strung out along main roads radiating out of the town. Others, more compact, may be based on an old village centre which has been engulfed in the growth of the town. In addition, there are minor 'street corner' suburban shopping centres, containing just a few shops. Each of these types of shopping centre performs a different type of service, and the whole system forms a hierarchy within the built-up area, an arrangement in order of importance, with the CBD at the top, and the 'street corner' shopping centre at the bottom. Similarly, the larger the town, the more important its CBD tends to be.

Table 12.1 shows the main characteristics of shopping centres within a town.

Table 12.1

Type of centre	Position in hierarchy	Number of shops	Contains	Serves
The CBD (the only one in the town)	Most important (most central)	Hundreds (number varies with the size of town)	Multiple and chain stores. Several supermarkets. Luxury shops and a wide variety of other shops. Local headquarters of banks. Many offices.	*The whole town* and surrounding smaller settlements.
Major suburban shopping centres (number varies with the size of the town)	Less important than CBD (less central) though vary between themselves in importance according to size.	Up to 200 in a very large city. From 10 to 80 in a medium-sized town.	One or two supermarkets. Rarely multiple stores, except in very large centres. A variety of shops. A small number of banks. Occasionally offices.	*The major suburbs of* a town. In a large city these may be equivalent to a medium-sized town.
Street corner suburban shopping centres (or perhaps small rows of shops) (large numbers in old towns)	Least important	Usually less than 10.	Limited number of types of shop. Include general stores, grocers, greengrocers, hairdresser, newsagents, laundrettes, fish and chip shops, etc.	Only *the local neighbourhood*, which may be similar in size to a village. 'Street corner' shops are more typical of older built-up areas, and may merely occupy the front room of a house.

Exercises

1. With the help of Plate 12.1 and Figure 12.1, work out the advantages for shoppers of the Bull Ring scheme compared with normal shopping streets. Are there disadvantages?
2. If you live in a town, make out the following questionnaire for homework. Ask adults from three or four different families (your own, relatives and friends) to answer the questions. The person answering the questions should give you the name of the street concerned. It is your job to locate the street and place a tick in the appropriate column to the right on the table.

If the place visited was in another town, write the name of that town in the CBD column.

Key: CBD Central business district
      SSC Major suburban shopping centre
      CSC Corner shopping centre

Questions	Name of street	CBD	SSC	CSC
(1) Where did you last buy bread?				
(2) Where did you last go to a chemist?				
(3) Where did you last buy shoes?				
(4) Where did you last buy furniture?				
(5) Where did you last go to a bank?				
(6) Where did you last go to a cinema?				
(7) Where did you last go to a theatre?				

(a) From your own questionnaire, total up the number of ticks for each of (1) to (7) in each column (CBD, SSC, and CSC).

(b) The class as a whole should then make a grand total of ticks from all the questionnaires for each of (1) to (7) in each column.

(c) Which of the services mentioned in (1) to (7) are found in the CBD; the SSCs; the CSCs; or only in a larger town centre than your own?

(d) What is the proportion of each type, compared with the CBD, in the two separate types of suburban shopping centre?

(e) Explain why different types of shops are found in different types of centre. Why are people prepared to travel into a town centre, or even into another town, for certain types of goods and services? Name such goods and services.

The Growth of Birmingham

By 1930 Birmingham had become the second English 'million city'. The population had roughly doubled itself in the twenty years from 1910 and there was an enormous growth of the built-up area, so that practically all the land inside the city boundary was taken up.

Although Birmingham had long been an important centre of a wide variety of metalworking industries, of guns, toys, buttons, jewellery making and many other small-scale goods, as a focus of the canal and rail systems of England, it was rather different from many other towns of the coalfield areas. They grew most rapidly in the nineteenth century, whereas Birmingham's greatest expansion was still to come.

One important reason for the rapid growth in population was the development of the motor car industry, which itself took up large areas of land on the city outskirts, particularly at Longbridge in south-west Birmingham, where the Austin Motor Company developed its works. The Birmingham–Coventry area became the most important vehicle-manufacturing region in the country. One important advantage was the presence of suitably skilled labour in the old-established metalworking and engineering industries of the area. In its early days, more skilled workers were needed than under the mass production methods of today. The many independent car firms of the early days have increasingly been amalgamated, so that nowadays most of the vehicle production of the Midlands is under the control of two giant organisations: British Leyland and Talbot.

The car industry brought with it a whole series of other manufacturers, required to provide materials, parts and accessories. Among many possible examples are the tyre-manufacturing firms of Dunlop (at Birmingham) and Goodyear (at Wolverhampton). These and other growing industries attracted large numbers of people to the West Midlands from other parts of Britain, such as South Wales and north-east England, often in a state of depression and unemployment in the inter-war period. Since the war, there has been a continuing need for an increased labour supply, and this has been met by an influx of immigrants from former British colonies overseas (pages 128–31).

Birmingham and the West Midlands thus combine the features of the older manufacturing districts, built up on the coalfields, and the newer industrial developments of the twentieth century, which we also examined in Chapter 8.

The West Midlands has been one of the most important and prosperous manufacturing regions of Britian though, like most other areas of the country, it has been seriously affected by economic recession, especially in the motor car industry.

Exercises

3. (*a*) With the help of an atlas or other map showing the British canal network, work out approximately how far Birmingham was by canal from the ports of (i) the Thames, (ii) the Severn, (iii) the Mersey, and (iv) the Humber estuaries. Assuming that the canal boats travelled at 6 kilometres per hour on average, work out how long it would have taken to transport a cargo of goods from the canal-side factory to each exporting port. The information should be marked on a table, based on the one below, with the name of the main port on each of the four estuaries placed in the left-hand column:

(*b*) What clues does your table give to account for the nineteenth-century growth of Birmingham?

Birmingham to		Kilometres from Birmingham	Time taken by canal
Ports	(a)		
	(b)		
	(c)		
	(d)		

4. Outline ways in which the nineteenth-century and twentieth-century growth of Birmingham has differed from (*a*) West Yorkshire; (*b*) the London area.

Problems of Central Birmingham

Traffic Problems

We have seen that one of the reasons for the continuing prosperity of Birmingham has been its location at the centre of Britain's transport networks. In the last ten years, the number of motor vehicles in the country has doubled, and this has created serious congestion on the roads, particularly in large cities such as Birmingham. The following improvements have been introduced or are planned to reduce the traffic problems of the area.

General Traffic Management
This means the setting up of one-way streets; parking restrictions with various types of yellow lines alongside the pavement; bans on loading at certain times in central area streets; control of turning at certain junctions; and the establishment of parking meters.

New Car Parks
Figure 12.2 shows the location of permanent car parks in the heart of Birmingham, including multi-storey and roof-top car parks (see Figure 12.1). Such car parks are vitally important to the working of a major business and shopping centre. A number of temporary car parks on cleared sites, which provide valuable additional parking spaces, are also shown on the map.

Figure 12.2   Central Birmingham, Inner Ring Road and car parks

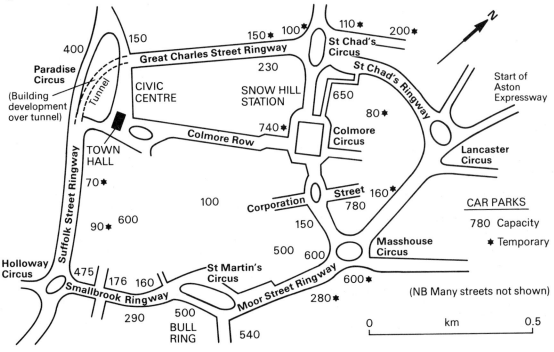

153

A New Urban Road System

Birmingham has planned one of the most elaborate urban road systems in Britain, which will take many years to complete fully.

(*a*) *The Inner Ring Road* is now completed, and can be seen in part on Plate 12.1 (letter G). Notice how it by-passes the city centre, but as Figure 12.2 shows, has links into the centre, focussing on Colmore Circus. Containing over 5 kilometres of dual carriageway, and eventually costing over £33 million, the Inner Ring Road is fronted by shops and offices, most of which have rear access for loading and unloading goods, thus reducing congestion on the road itself.

(*b*) Construction has also started on the *Middle Ring Road*, after the clearance of the five Redevelopment Areas which surround the city centre. The line of the road runs up to 2.5 kilometres from the centre. The fact that slum clearance is taking place over large areas of Britain's cities makes the planning and building of new urban motorways easier than it would otherwise be.

In addition, the public transport system has been improved. Commuter rail links in particular have been strengthened with, for example, the opening of a new rail service in 1978 from Four Oaks in the north to Longbridge in the south, passing New Street Station (Plate 12.1) in the CBD.

(*c*) *The Outer Ring Road* (Figure 12.3) is already in part in existence, as are the main roads radiating out from the centre of Birmingham (*radial roads*), marked on Figure 12.3.

These have been or are going to be widened into dual carriageways. Where the radial roads cross the ring roads, congestion is liable to occur, and flyovers or roundabouts are needed. The Hockley Flyover (located on Figure 12.3), for example, carries the main road from Wolverhampton and West Bromwich over the Middle Ring Road.

Birmingham's Wider Connections

As Figure 12.3 indicates, Birmingham is directly linked to two of Britain's motorways. The M5 and M6 are joined close to the city boundary, and the M6 runs across the northern suburbs of the city to connect with the M1. A major difficulty used to be the link between the city centre and the M6. It was realised in planning for the future that the A38 road (Figure 12.3) would not be able to take the weight of traffic that would be required. Hence a new urban motorway, the *Aston Expressway*, has been constructed. Figure 12.2 shows the point at which it leaves the centre of Birmingham, at Lancaster Circus.

Plate 12.2 shows the complications which have arisen at Gravelly Hill, on the north side of

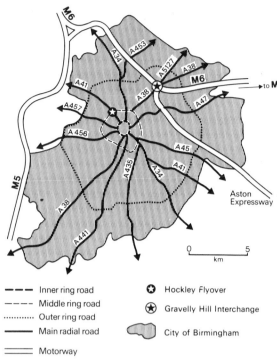

– – – Inner ring road	✪	Hockley Flyover
– – – – Middle ring road	✪	Gravelly Hill Interchange
.... Outer ring road		City of Birmingham
——— Main radial road		
═══ Motorway		

Figure 12.3 Birmingham: road systems

Birmingham, where the Aston Expressway and the A38 meet the line of the M6. This multi-level interchange, opened in May 1972, has been nicknamed 'Spaghetti Junction'. A newspaper report described it as follows: 'At ground level it looks like a concrete forest in a science fiction world with five hundred pillars supporting four miles of road' (*The Sunday Times*, 3 January 1971).

Weather conditions can create serious traffic hazards on the motorway and the interchange. High cross-winds occur on elevated roads. Fog is a problem in the Tame valley, along which the M6 runs. Icing on the roads is made worse by condensation from the cooling towers of a nearby power station. In addition, serious faults have been found in the concrete structure of the interchange, requiring expensive treatment to renovate.

Exercises

5. With the help of an AA or any other appropriate road map find the nearest towns to which the A roads on Figure 12.3 lead. Then draw a map to show the wider road connections of Birmingham.

6. Assuming an average road speed of 50 kilometres per hour on ordinary roads, and 100 kilometres per hour on motorways, with the help of road maps work out how long it now takes to reach the following by car from Birmingham, compared with the pre-motorway era: (*a*) London, (*b*) Liverpool, (*c*) Bristol.

Plate 12.2   Gravelly Hill interchange

7. (*a*)   Lay a sheet of tracing paper over Plate 12.2 and on the tracing shade in the areas occupied by (i) transport facilities; (ii) industry; (iii) housing; (iv) other uses, and comment on the proportion taken up by each.
(*b*)   How do you think the Gravelly Hill interchange will affect (i) industry, and (ii) housing, in the area shown on the photograph?

Housing Problems

As at St Helens (pages 105–9), Birmingham's rapid growth in the industrial revolution led to the development of vast areas of terraced housing, which have become today's slums, needing clearance.

Comprehensive Redevelopment Areas
To meet such problems, Birmingham set up *Comprehensive Redevelopment Areas*, which contained the worst housing remaining in the city. Five were set up in the first phase, as shown on Figure 12.4. Before redevelopment, they had in the early 1950s housed over 100 000

people. In 1971, their total population had been reduced to 36 000 (Table 12.2) and, with a continuing decline in household sizes, there has been little growth since.

Table 12.2

Area	Population before redevelopment	Population 1971
Newtown	28 000	8700
Nechells Green	19 000	8700
Ladywood	24 000	6300
Lee Bank	15 000	5200
Highgate	16 500	7200

Newtown Redevelopment Area   Newtown lies to the north-west of the centre of Birmingham and can be seen in the left background of Plate 12.1 (letter I). Figure 12.6 is a 1:2500 OS map extract, dating back to before the First World War, which shows part of the Newtown

155

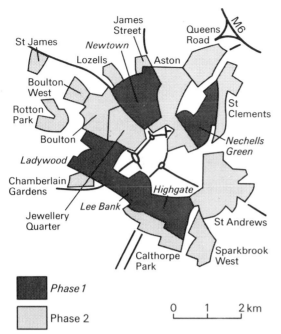

Phase 1

Phase 2

0   1   2 km

Figure 12.4 Birmingham: the Comprehensive Redevelopment Areas

area as it was. Notice the closely packed rows of houses, mixed in with industry. Something of the former character of this area can be seen in the top half of Plate 12.3 on which Webster Street and some of the other streets on the eastern edge of the map can be seen.

Figure 12.5 Layout of former housing in part of Newton

Plates 12.4 and 12.5 give an impression of the nature of the old housing, now largely cleared. Plate 12.4 is a row of terraced houses, New John Street West, just off the southern edge of the map extract. Plate 12.5, of the same street, shows three-storeyed dwellings overlooking a court. These could well have been back-to-back houses, with the entry leading to the main street, which the other half of the back-to-back fronted. Figure 12.5 is a plan of the layout of the housing which used to exist on part of New John Street West, showing both the terraced housing, and back-to-back houses arranged round a court. Under the redevelopment scheme, the particular area on Figure 12.5 is now a public open space, and is marked by a star on Figure 12.7.

Newtown, like the other Redevelopment Areas, was being planned as a comprehensive unit, with different types of land use, but with housing and industry much

Plate 12.3 Newtown precinct, Birmingham

156

Figure 12.6   Ordnance Survey map of part of Birmingham

Scale 1:2500

more separated (Figure 12.7) than in the old layout (Figure 12.6). Newtown's District Centre, shown on Plate 12.3, has a variety of shops, banks, a market hall, a roof-top car park and swimming baths. Adjoining the centre are high-rise blocks of flats, characteristic of the Redevelopment Areas.

Notice that there are far fewer 'through roads' on Figure 12.7 than on the OS map extract (Figure 12.6). The main road out of the city, Newtown Row, by-passes the residential areas of Newtown, and there are few minor roads which cross these areas. A motorist can

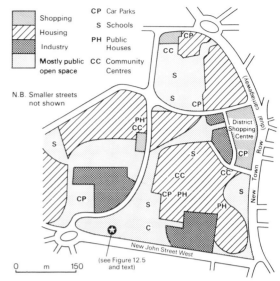

Figure 12.7 Part of Newtown Comprehensive Redevelopment Area

Plate 12.4 A Victorian terrace, New John Street West, Birmingham

Plate 12.5 A Victorian court, New John Street West, Birmingham

easily get lost in a maze of cul-de-sacs (not shown on the map), which have been built solely to service the houses and flats. The map also indicates the large areas left as open spaces. The landscape is much more spacious than in the old Newtown.

In common with other cities, Birmingham has found problems following its redevelopment schemes, particularly those associated with tower blocks of flats. These are unpopular with families with children, and in some cases there has been rapid deterioration of the fabric of these often prefabricated structures. The attempt is now being made to improve older housing, by giving Local Authority grants towards upgrading external structures (the whole cost) and for internal improvements (part of the cost).

The majority of the Victorian slums have now been cleared and the emphasis is on renovation and improvement of old houses which still have a long life, so long as they are not allowed to deteriorate further. This is cheaper than building new housing, and is also usually more popular with families, who wish to remain in their own homes.

The West Midlands Conurbation

A *conurbation* is a large continuous built-up area resulting from the growing together of nearby towns which were once separated by rural areas. The West Midlands conurbation includes Birmingham and the Black Country towns of Wolverhampton, Walsall, Dudley and West Bromwich, and Smethwick (now part of Sandwell), among others (see Figure 12.9).

Overspill Housing

The shortage of land on which to build new houses in Birmingham has also, until recent years, been true of the West Midlands as a whole. In the early 1960s there were about 100 000 slum houses remaining in the conurbation and, on top of these, 400 000 in urgent need of improvement. Many had no fixed baths and/or inside toilets. The problem has, however, been reduced by falls in the birth rate since the middle 1960s, and a consequent reduction in population. The population of the West Midlands fell from 2 777 638 in 1971 to 2 628 419 in 1981, a 5.4% decrease.

Even so, there remains a need for overspill housing, as central areas still cannot cope with the space requirements of new housing, which is nearly always of lower density than old housing. Land has been found beyond the limits of the conurbation in overspill estates in expanded towns, and in the new town of Redditch and the new city of Telford (Figure 13.1). Table 12.3 illustrates the decline in population in inner areas of the conurbation and expansion outside, typical of the national position (see Chapter 9).

Table 12.3 Population change in the West Midlands

	1971	1981	Percentage change
Inner			
Birmingham	1 088 367	996 369	−8.5
Coventry	334 180	310 216	−7.2
Sandwell	329 918	306 993	−6.9
Dudley	291 798	298 524	+2.3
Walsall	272 820	265 922	−2.5
Wolverhampton	269 990	252 462	−6.5
Solihull	190 565	197 933	+3.9
Outer			
Overspill (expanded towns) (Figure 13.1)			
Tamworth	40 285	64 315	+59.7
Lichfield	22 660	25 600	+13.0
Daventry	11 815	16 178	+36.9
Droitwich	12 748	18 073	+41.8
New Town			
Redditch	37 552	63 414	+68.9
New City			
Telford	79 451	103 664	+30.5

Local Government

Figure 12.8 shows the variety of Authorities responsible for local government which made up the West Midlands conurbation. Notice that they were divided into County Boroughs, Municipal Boroughs and Urban Districts. In addition, there were Rural Districts outside the conurbation. Each of these was part of one of three counties: Staffordshire, Warwickshire and Worcestershire. The Counties and the County Boroughs were the most important Local Authorities, carrying out a wide

Figure 12.8   West Midlands conurbation Local Authority boundaries, 1950

range of tasks. The Municipal Boroughs and Urban Districts had a smaller range of duties. In education, for example, the Counties and County Boroughs ran the system, but not in general the Municipal Boroughs and smaller Authorities, which relied on the County to provide schools.

In travelling through the West Midlands, however, there was little in the landscape to suggest that there were so many different units of local government, unless two adjoining Authorities, for example, used different street lighting systems, or maintained their roads in very different states of repair. In a conurbation, different colours of buses were also an indication that there were separate Authorities with their own transport systems.

For some time it had been widely believed that this division of local government was an expensive and

Figure 12.9   The Metropolitan County of West Midlands

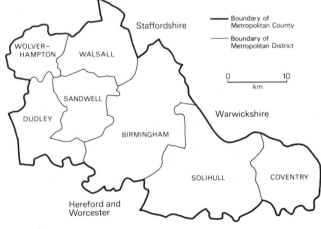

159

inefficient way of running affairs. It is generally accepted that it is more economic to run a large undertaking than a small one, as for example in the bulk purchases of materials which a big Authority can make. On the other hand, suggestions for joining together Local Authorities aroused a great deal of argument in the areas concerned, partly because of local pride, and partly because of the feeling that small areas and individual people tend to be neglected when larger units are set up.

In 1966, plans came into operation for joining together the Local Authorities of the West Midlands. Seven enlarged County Boroughs were established and

Solihull also became a County Borough. The new County Borough of Warley–West Bromwich was made up of the old County Boroughs of Smethwick and West Bromwich, together with adjoining Municipal Borough areas. This later became Sandwell (Figure 12.9). Notice the increases in population of these towns (apart from Birmingham, which did not change in size) as a result of the amalgamations.

The *Maud Report* of 1970 examined the organisation of local government. With minor changes, the recommendations of the Maud Report were accepted by the government in 1971, then further modified to produce, for England, the result shown on Figure 12.10. This

Figure 135   England: local government reorganisation, new counties

shows the new arrangement, outside London, of Counties and Metropolitan Counties. The West Midlands is one of the six Metropolitan Counties, each of which is responsible for overall planning in its own region. The Metropolitan Counties are divided into districts, which are responsible for other local affairs. There are seven such districts in the West Midlands Metropolitan County based on the County Boroughs of Birmingham, Wolverhampton, Walsall, West Bromwich–Warley (Sandwell), Solihull, Coventry and Dudley, while other parts of the conurbation have joined in with the surrounding counties of Staffordshire, Warwickshire and Hereford and Worcester. These Authorities therefore have replaced the twenty-four which existed before 1966.

THE CONURBATIONS OF BRITAIN

Figure 12.11 is a map showing the seven major conurbations of Great Britain. They include over 18 million people, about one-third of the population of Britain. All share the problems discussed in the case of the West Midlands. All are major industrial areas, which grew largely in the nineteenth century and, apart from London and Merseyside, on the coalfields. They were all able to expand through the provision of local transport systems, particularly train, tram and bus services. These allowed people to live several kilometres away from the city centre in which they worked, leading to the spread of housing and the growth of dormitory suburbs, to produce in this century an *urban sprawl*. It is in the conurbations that the main economic and social problems of today have to be faced (see pages 129–30).

Green Belts

On the edges of conurbations there exist large areas of townscape–farmscape (urban) fringe (Figure 5.1, page 49), in which there is a danger that town will completely swallow up country. In Lancashire and Cheshire, for example, there is danger of the Merseyside and Selnec conurbations joining to form a *megalopolis*, which is what Greater London is already.

To prevent unchecked urban sprawl, therefore, the government have designated *green belts*, which are girdles of open space round towns and cities, planned to be retained as farmland, recreational land, or wildscape. It is more difficult to get permission to build in these areas, although basic lines of communication still break up the countryside in them.

If space for overspill cannot be found within the conurbation, then New Towns and New Cities have to be built beyond the green belt (see Chapter 13).

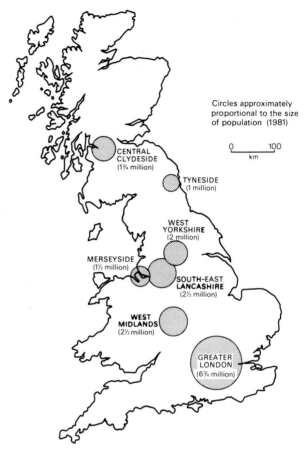

Figure 12.11 The conurbations of Great Britain: population

Exercises

8. Compare in detail the types of housing shown on Plates 12.4 and 12.5 and Figures 12.5 and 12.6 and the general setting in which they are placed. What are the disadvantages of each type of housing?

9. Refer to Table 12.3.
(*a*) Draw a map to show the locations indicated, with the help of an atlas and Figures 12.8 and 12.9.
(*b*) Describe the situation indicated by the statistics in the table.
(*c*) Outline the reasons for the movement which took place between 1971 and 1981.

10. Find out how the reorganisation of local government affected your area. Examine the arguments for and against the formation of a smaller number of larger Authorities which apply in your area. To do this properly, you will have to look into the various duties performed by different types of Local Authority.

11. Refer to Figure 12.11.
(*a*) Name the main towns associated with each of the conurbations shown.

(b) Compare this map with the maps of (i) industrial areas of the country (Figure 8.5, page 110 and Figure 8.18, page 124) (ii) the New Towns (Figure 13.4, page 169) and (iii) the map showing the new Metropolitan Counties (Figure 12.10). In what ways are the maps linked?

12. What is the nearest conurbation to your home? Try to find out how it is dealing with (a) transport problems, (b) housing problems, (c) other social problems, (d) problems of pollution.

13. What is meant by a 'green belt'? Why are green belts important to the country as a whole?

Journeys to Work

At the beginning of this section, reference was made to the importance of the growth of urban transport systems in the development of conurbations. In the nineteenth century the tramway system allowed people to move out from homes in the city centre into attractive suburbs, to live in large Victorian villas such as that shown in a present-day photograph (Plate 12.6) at Edgbaston (see Figure 9.4) where there was plenty of open space and semi-rural surroundings. The houses left in the central area tended to decay, and were subdivided among poor tenants. They quickly deteriorated into slum property. It was the tramway and the railway systems which allowed not only the development of Victorian suburbs inside the city boundary, but also dormitory towns further afield, such as Sutton Coldfield and Solihull (Figure 12.8) in the case of Birmingham, a process which has continued in this century. People travelling daily into the city centre to work are called *commuters*, and the places in which they reside are known as *dormitory centres*.

Plate 12.6   A Victorian villa in Edgbaston, Birmingham

Exercises

14. Figure 12.12 is a map of the West Midlands conurbation, together with a table showing areas of residence (marked by numbers on the map) of Birmingham's work force in 1971.
(a) Trace the map into your exercise book and draw bar graphs on it to show the sizes of Birmingham's work force residing in each area.
(b) Try to account for the differences between (i) area 1; (ii) areas 2–7; (iii) areas 8–11.

15. Indicate how *commuting* is related to the urban transport problems of Birmingham (pages 153–4).

16. Compare the journeys to work of the nearest city to which you live and Birmingham.

Figure 12.12   The working population of Birmingham

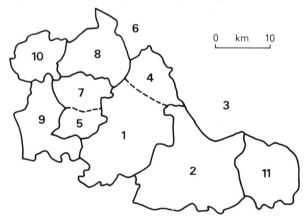

TOTAL WORKING POPULATION OF BIRMINGHAM, 1971: 580 000

Area of residence

1	Birmingham	420 000
2	Solihull	25 000
3	Meriden	23 000
4	Sutton Coldfield	19 500
5	Warley	12 500
6	Aldridge-Brownhills	10 300
7	West Bromwich	9 700
8	Walsall	3 200
9	Dudley	2 900
10	Wolverhamton	1 900
11	Coventry	1 200

NB The figures are rounded off

13 A NEW CITY: TELFORD

Location

Telford is named after the famous eighteenth-century builder of canals and bridges, Thomas Telford, who for some time was the County Surveyor of Shropshire (Salop), in which county the New City is located. Telford lies about 16 kilometres from the north-western edge of the West Midlands conurbation (Figure 13.1). The New City extends northwards from the Severn Gorge at Ironbridge, and takes in the existing towns of Wellington, Oakengates and Dawley, large villages such as Ironbridge, Coalbrookdale and Madeley (Figure 13.2) and many smaller villages.

Telford is built on a plateau which slopes gently eastwards from the edge of the Wrekin (Plate 13.1), a steep-sided ridge of ancient rocks. The plateau is made up of Coal Measure rocks, including ironstone and clay as well as coal deposits, and is cut into by the deep wooded gorges of the River Severn and its tributaries, as at Ironbridge (Plate 13.2), Coalbrookdale, and Blists Hill.

Planning and Development

It was decided in 1963 to create a New Town at Dawley, stretching from the A5 road (now M54) in the north to the Ironbridge Gorge in the south (Figure 13.2). Under

Plate 13.1 Telford New City centre with Wrekin in the background

this scheme, Dawley's population of 21 000 was to have been expanded to 90 000. It was soon realised, however, that this was not enough to meet the overspill problem of the West Midlands (pages 159–60). In 1968 the scheme was changed to cover a much larger project, Telford New City, including not only Dawley, but also the Wellington and Oakengates areas to the north.

Figure 13.1 West Midlands conurbation and overspill towns

Planning Problems

The first problem was one of *cost*. Such large schemes as Telford mean spending a lot of money, amounting to hundreds of millions of pounds, and require finance from the government.

Much of Telford has been built on ground which forms part of the long-used *Shropshire coalfield*. Although only one mine is still working in this area, there is much evidence of old workings, of subsidence and derelict land.

In other parts, slopes are *too steep* for building to be economic. This is particularly true in the Severn Gorge area, although, as Plate 13.2 shows, such slopes were used in the past in the building of Ironbridge (left centre) and Coalbrookdale (right background). In the Severn Gorge, the problem is worsened by *landslipping*. As we shall see, in the past there were good reasons for building in these gorge areas. Today it is much more economical to use the plateau areas for building. Notice the new housing on the plateau above the gorge in the right foreground of Plate 13.2.

The New City had to be fitted into a confused sprawl of old housing, derelict land and factory buildings, which has made planning a complicated process.

Plate 13.2   *Aerial view of Ironbridge, looking west towards Buildwas Power Station*

Figure 13.2   The growth of Telford

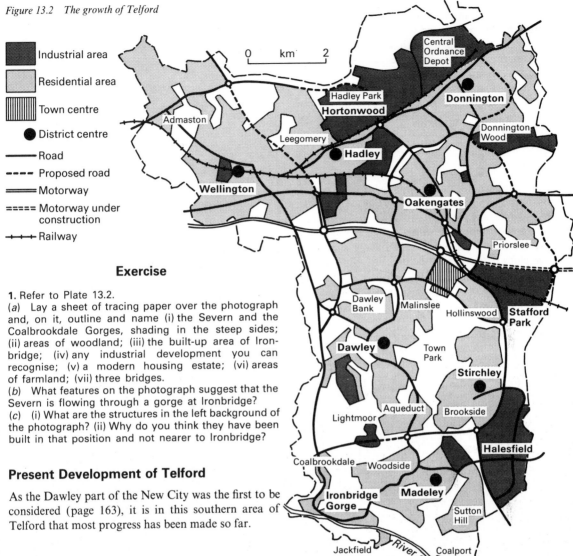

Legend:
- Industrial area
- Residential area
- Town centre
- ● District centre
- —— Road
- ---- Proposed road
- ═══ Motorway
- ===== Motorway under construction
- +—+—+ Railway

Map labels: Admaston, Leegomery, Wellington, Hadley Park, Hortonwood, Hadley, Central Ordnance Depot, Donnington, Donnington Wood, Oakengates, Priorslee, Dawley Bank, Malinslee, Hollinswood, Stafford Park, Dawley, Town Park, Stirchley, Aqueduct, Brookside, Lightmoor, Halesfield, Coalbrookdale, Woodside, Ironbridge Gorge, Madeley, Sutton Hill, Jackfield, Coalport, River Severn

Exercise

1. Refer to Plate 13.2.
(*a*) Lay a sheet of tracing paper over the photograph and, on it, outline and name (i) the Severn and the Coalbrookdale Gorges, shading in the steep sides; (ii) areas of woodland; (iii) the built-up area of Ironbridge; (iv) any industrial development you can recognise; (v) a modern housing estate; (vi) areas of farmland; (vii) three bridges.
(*b*) What features on the photograph suggest that the Severn is flowing through a gorge at Ironbridge?
(*c*) (i) What are the structures in the left background of the photograph? (ii) Why do you think they have been built in that position and not nearer to Ironbridge?

Present Development of Telford

As the Dawley part of the New City was the first to be considered (page 163), it is in this southern area of Telford that most progress has been made so far.

Housing

The earliest housing to be built was in the Madeley district in the south (Figure 13.2), largely completed by 1972. Plate 13.3 is a photograph of Sutton Hill, in the eastern part of Madeley. Note the local centre on the photograph. The next area to be developed was the Stirchley area, the first families moving in in 1972. This estate was completed in 1975. Figure 13.2 shows later developments, one of which, at Hollinswood, is shown on Plate 13.1.

The *residential units* will build up into the structure of the New City, and are planned as Figure 13.3a indicates. They are arranged in the form of a pyramid, with the city itself at the apex, and thousands of individual family units at the base (Figure 13.3b).

Industry

A variety of metalworking and engineering industries were present in the area before the new development took place. The largest of these is the GKN Sankey works at Hadley Park (Figure 13.2) which makes wheels chassis and truck bodies for the vehicle industries of Britain. Another huge works is the Central Ordnance Depot at Donnington (Figure 13.2).

As part of the New City development, there are new industrial estates, including (*a*) *Halesfield*, east of Madeley (Plate 13.3), with a variety of industries, as indicated on Table 13.1; (*b*) *Stafford Park*, where

165

prestige firms, including those engaged in the distribution of goods, are located; and (c) *Hortonwood* (Figure 13.2), where very large units, such as those concerned with the motor trade, which make use of the large expanses of level land in that area, tend to be concentrated. Many firms have strong links with the West Midlands, and so demand the access provided by good road links to the motorway system, and an advanced internal urban road network (see Plate 13.1).

Services

One of the problems facing the people who first come to live in a New Town or City is that they often find a lack of the services and amenities which they took for granted in the town from which they came. This is because it is not economic to build large shopping centres, clubs and cinemas before the New Town reaches a certain size. Table 13.2 gives examples of facilities and services which can be provided when the population of a particular district in a New City area reaches this size. At Madeley, for example, the population is big enough to justify an important 'district

Table 13.1 A selection of industries at Halesfield, 1982

Cassettes	Zinc alloys
Acoustic foams	Shock absorbers
Electronic circuits and controls	Soft toys
Diving equipment	Timber cases, crates and pal
Aluminium foil containers	Automotive seating
Saw blades	Vehicle door hinges
Ladders	Commercial vehicle bodywo
Pneumatic tools	Electrical equipment
Plastic goods	Locks
Gear motors	Pottery
Brake shoes	Garden furniture
Billiard cues	Windscreens
Fuel burners	Ice cream
Pre-cast concrete	Cranes
Coloured pigments	Louvred windows
Carpet yarns	Tractors
Propane and butane gases	Safes and security doors
Enamel cookware	Computer stationery
Iron castings	Pneumatic controls
Domestic appliances	Roof cladding
Steel fabrication	Gutters
Overalls	Dehydrated foods
Office partitions	Industrial gloves
Tubes	Duplicating papers
Spiral staircases	Soft drinks
Jeans, trousers and pyjamas	Vacuum pumps

Plate 13.3   *Aerial view of Sutton Hill and part of Halesfield Industrial Estate*

Halesfield Industrial Area

Corporation Sponsc Private Housing

Hills Lane Estate
Wrekin D.C. Housing
for rent

Sutton Hill
Corporation Housing for rent

Primary School

Local Centre

shopping centre' (Plate 13.4), and also a large comprehensive school, combined with youth club and general recreation facilities.

Table 13.2 New City facilities and services

Population	Examples of facilities
Less than 100	Toddlers' play area
Less than 1000	Equipped play area
Less than 2000	Nursery school
Less than 5000	Primary school Local shops Public house, etc.

Less than 10 000	Community centre
	Local centre (e.g. Sutton Hill):
	   Small clinic
	   Middle school (for 9–13-year-olds)
	   Small supermarket, etc.

Less than 30 000	District shopping centre (Plate 13.4)
	District centre (e.g. Madeley):
	   Comprehensive school
	   Youth club/Recreation facilities
	Old persons' home
	Doctors' group practice, etc.

Shopping Centre

The idea of a services hierarchy can well be illustrated by Telford. Three different levels in this hierarchy can be recognised:

(*a*) *Local shopping centres*, as at Sutton Hill, serving community units (Figure 13.3a and b) of up to 8000 people, and containing probably a small supermarket, a sub-post office, and some small shops which provide for everyday needs.

Figure 13.3   The city structure of Telford

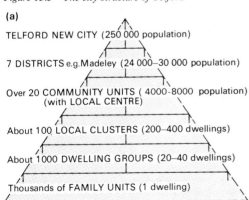

Plate 13.4   Madeley District Centre

(*b*) *District centres*, as at Madeley (Plate 13.4), providing for up to 30 000 people, and containing a much larger range of shops than local centres, with large supermarkets, offices and banks.

(*c*) *The central shopping area* (Plates 13.1 and 13.5) is at Malinslee and is closely linked with the primary ring road of the new city (Figure 13.2). It also lies near the M54, which will be connected to the M6, and the mainline railway from Wolverhampton to Shrewsbury. It can thus draw in shoppers from a wide area.

By 1981 the centre was being used by nearly 100 000 shoppers per week. It includes a Carrefour hypermarket as well as large department stores such as Debenhams. The planners have also sought to attract offices to this new CBD, by building prestige office blocks (Plate 13.6).

(b) The smallest units

(i) The dwelling group (20–40 dwellings)

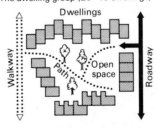

(ii) The family unit

Plate 13.5   Telford central shopping area, Malinslee

Plate 13.6   Prestige office block at Malinslee

Transportation

Regional services

The main regional road is therefore the new M54 by-passing the city centre and linking with the M6 and the West Midlands conurbation. It is also hoped that the A442 will be enlarged, linking the vehicle-producing areas of Merseyside, the Midlands and Oxford, with Telford (producing parts). These improved links will make Telford even more attractive to industrialists.

Local Services

Figure 13.2 showed how Telford is served by a *primary distributor* (ring) road, of motorway standard, by-passing the main district centres and Malinslee. This is joined by dual-carriageway *district distributors*, which connect the districts to the primary distributor. In addition, there are *local distributors* which are the most important roads serving the community units and local clusters (Plate 13.1). Figure 13.3b indicates how dwelling groups and their individual houses are linked to two systems of movement: roads and pedestrian walkways. Over large areas, pedestrians are kept completely separate from vehicles. No through-roads run through housing estates (see Plate 13.1).

The present generation of New Towns of Britain (see Figure 13.4), including Telford, Skelmersdale (Lancashire) and Cumbernauld (Scotland), are particularly well served by internal road systems. Although these take up a lot of space they make for efficiency and safety. Cumbernauld has the lowest road accident rate per person of all towns in Britain, largely as a result of these measures.

Exercises

2. (*a*)   Refer to Plate 13.3. What are the advantages and disadvantages of living in a New Town compared with (i) an old row of terraced houses; (ii) a tower block of flats, typical of redevelopment in a large city?
(*b*)   Refer to Plates 13.1 and 13.5. What are the benefits of shopping in a centre such as this? How does it compare with the Bull Ring in Birmingham (Plate 12.1 (A) and Figure 12.1)?
3. Refer to Table 13.1, which shows manufacturing at Halesfield.
(*a*)   With the help of the table draw a 'proportional rectangle' to show a classification of types of industry on the new Halesfield Industrial Estate. There are fifty-two separate industries shown. Take a piece of graph paper and use squares of side 2 centimetres to represent one firm. Classify firms into the following seven categories: (i) *engineering*, including firms making equipment for other industries; (ii) *metal goods*;

(iii) *consumer goods*, those sent to the wholesale and retail trade, and not made for other manufacturers; (iv) *plastics*, including goods supplied to the plastics industry; (v) *construction*; (vi) *non-manufacturing industries*, involving the hire or repair of vehicles and other heavy equipment; (vii) *others*.

Place each of the fifty-two industries in one of these categories. If there are say, seven industries in one category, that category will make up seven adjoining squares on your graph paper. Shade or colour in each category separately, and label it.

(*b*) Which are the two most important categories? Can you suggest why?

(*c*) Why do you think the manufacture of concrete is likely to be important in an area such as Telford?

(*d*) How do new industrial estates compare with old manufacturing areas?

(*e*) If there is an industrial estate near to your school, make a list of its industries, and classify them in the same way as you have done for Halesfield. State the similarities and differences between your industrial estate and Halefield.

Figure 13.4 *The New Towns of Britain*

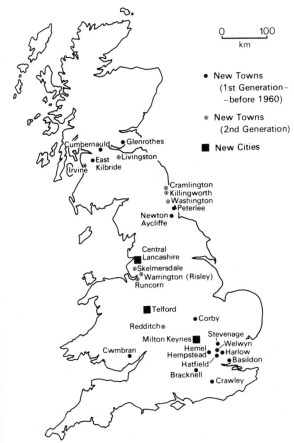

The New Towns of Britain

The New Towns of Britain came into being after the New Towns Act of 1946. As Figure 13.4 shows, the first generation of New Towns was mostly planned around London. They have all been designed to take overspill population, and to provide these people with as many local jobs as possible, to prevent them from having to commute into cities such as London. They also all provide more attractive living conditions than those from which their people originated, often in overcrowded slum areas of the great conurbations (see page 159). Practically all the first generation of New Towns have a population limit of less than 100 000.

For some time, it was thought that much larger units than this would be needed, and New Cities were planned at Telford, central Lancashire (for Manchester overspill), and Milton Keynes (for Greater London overspill), each designed originally to reach 250 000 people. Decline in the birth rate, and the fact that city centres are now losing population too fast, has led to drastic reductions in plans for New Towns and Cities. The ultimate target for Milton Keynes has been reduced to 200 000; for Telford to 150 000. By 1981, Milton Keynes's population had reached 96 000 and Telford's 103 000.

Not all New Town and New City dwellers are happy at first in their new surroundings, and the feeling of 'New Town blues' has often been described. This may be in part a natural feeling of strangeness. It may also be a result of the lack of activities provided in the early stages of New Town development, when there are not enough people to make economic the building of cinemas and clubs. In addition, the cost of living in New Towns, particularly the rent of houses, is usually greater than in the old ones, which can cause financial problems, especially for young married couples.

Exercises

4. What is the nearest New Town or New City to your school? Find out what you can about its growth and purpose, and compare it with the development of Telford.

5. Describe and account for the distribution of New Towns and New Cities shown on Figure 13.4, referring especially to links with Figure 12.11.

6. Refer to information in this and the previous chapter.

(*a*) Define carefully the following terms: *conurbation*; *green belt*; *New Town*; *urban road system*.

(*b*) Describe problems facing planners in British conurbations, and explain how these problems are being dealt with (i) within the conurbation, (ii) beyond the green belt.

14 PORTS

LONDON: A COMMERCIAL PORT

Container Traffic

Plate 14.1 is a photograph of a gantry crane, specially designed for lifting and transporting containers. Containers are large weatherproof boxes intended to enclose in one space a number of separate pieces of cargo. They are normally 2.5 metres wide, 2.5 metres high, and up to 13 metres long, being built to agreed international sizes so that they can be handled by carriers, cranes, lorries and trains all over the world. The handling machinery makes the transference of cargo from one means of transport to another (Plate 14.1) much easier than under the conventional system, where each item of cargo has to be handled separately. The place at which the goods are transferred is known as a *break of bulk* point.

Plate 14.1   A gantry crane

Plate 14.2   The container port at Tilbury

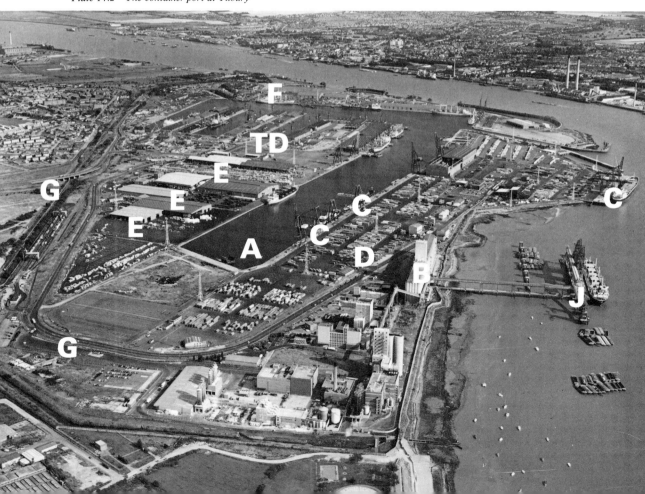

Tilbury Docks

The Port of London Authority has its main container terminal at Tilbury, shown on Plate 14.2. The new extension dock (letter A) and the grain terminal (B) can be seen in the centre and foreground of the picture. On the near side of the dock are two gantry cranes (C), which can transfer a container from the quayside to a ship in about two and a half minutes. The container park (D) lies behind the cranes. The quayside has six new container berths, each capable of taking a large purpose-built ocean-going ship, and of handling ten times the amount of cargo of a conventional berth. The turn-round time for a container ship is about one and a half days, as against eleven to fourteen days by older methods.

The jetty (J) serving the grain terminal can take bulk carrier ships of up to 80 000 tonnes. The grain is discharged from the holds by bucket elevators and pneumatic suction pipes and then taken by conveyor belt to the huge silo (B), capable of holding over 100 000 tonnes of grain. Other modern developments at Tilbury Docks are the transit sheds (E) and the roll-on/roll-off berth, located on Figure 14.1. Figure 14.1 also shows the position of the packaged timber berth. Packaged timber is timber cut into even lengths, secured by strong steel bands, making it much easier to handle than loose timber of varying sizes. Extended facilities for container traffic have been provided in the area near 3 on Figure 14.3.

The original Tilbury Docks (letters TD on Plate 14.2) were opened in 1886, over 40 kilometres from the City of London, and much nearer open sea than the older docks of the port. As a result, Tilbury Docks can handle larger ships than the docks upriver. In this century Tilbury became the main passenger port on the Thames, though this function has declined recently. The passenger terminal (F) lies in the background of Plate 14.2 and is directly connected with Fenchurch Street Station in London. Tilbury Docks suffer less road congestion than the other docks of the Port of London. Plate 14.1 shows new approach roads (G) which speed up the flow of traffic to the new extension dock.

Exercises

1. Lay a sheet of tracing paper over Plate 14.2 and draw and label on the tracing the outline and main features of the Tilbury dock system, the road and railway serving the dock, the town of Tilbury, and an area of flat, open farmland. Refer also to Figure 14.1. In which direction was the camera pointing when the photograph was taken?
2. Explain why Tilbury Docks are the most recently developed part of the Port of London, stating the advantages they have over other parts of the dock system. Why is distance from London no longer a handicap?
3. Imagine that you are in charge of the export division of a large firm in west London, manufacturing a variety of light engineering products, of different sizes and shapes, for sale overseas. Work out some of the preparations you would have to make to arrange for the export of a batch of these products via Tilbury, (i) using conventional methods, (ii) by means of containers. State the advantages of the newer system. Can you think of any possible disadvantages?

The Eastward Shift of the Port of London

Over the years, the River Thames has had to accommodate an increasing number and size of vessels. As a result, the port has had to be extended downriver, from the old Pool of London to Tilbury and beyond.

The City and the Pool of London

Figure 14.2 is a map of the original site of London: a pair of low hills, less than 16 metres in height, which provided firm ground above the marshy banks of the Thames. The two hills were separated by a small tributary of the Thames, the Walbrook. In Roman times there was a fording point on the Thames just below its junction with the Walbrook. Here the lowest bridging point developed: the first place inland at which the River Thames could be crossed by land traffic. On either side of the old London Bridge lay the Pool, which formed London's harbour until the eighteenth century. As the banks of the river were shallow and muddy, ships unloaded in the Pool, and the cargo was taken ashore in

Figure 14.1 Tilbury

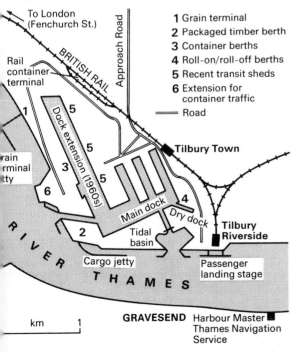

1 Grain terminal
2 Packaged timber berth
3 Container berths
4 Roll-on/roll-off berths
5 Recent transit sheds
6 Extension for container traffic
—— Road

171

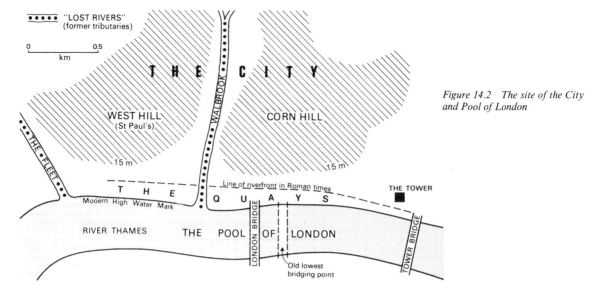

Figure 14.2 The site of the City and Pool of London

flat-bottomed 'wherries'. The bridge, the city and the harbour were defended by the Tower of London (Figure 14.2 and Plate 14.3).

By the eighteenth century the Pool of London had become severely congested. The upper pool was being used by three times the number of ships it was capable of handling efficiently. A great deal of time was wasted, and goods were left standing for long periods, a situation which resulted in much pilfering. The danger of collision in the overcrowded pool was also great. Such problems made clear the need for extending the port.

The Growth of the Dock System

Figure 14.3 gives by dates an indication of the eastward shift of the dock system. Table 14.1 gives the dates of opening (and closing) of the various docks, the main cargoes which each handles (or handled) and the countries traded with.

The Port of London Authority

During the nineteenth-century period of dock growth, the various dock companies were separate bodies and competed with each other for trade. There was no possibility of joint action to keep the river properly dredged, or to deal with problems such as congestion. By an Act of Parliament in 1909, the Port of London Authority was formed, to be responsible for a whole series of improvements. One was to keep the river surveyed and dredged and to remove obstructions. Another was the registration of craft in the port. Many defects had to be made good in port accommodation and equipment. Another service which the PLA came to provide was a port navigation system, based on Gravesend (Figure 14.4).

The most vital function of all is to bring ships safely upriver. Sea pilots join incoming ships at either Harwich or Dungeness, and river pilots take over at Gravesend.

Figure 14.3 The growth of London Docks

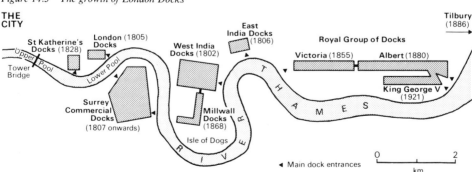

172

Table 14.1 The decline and fall of the older docks

Docks	Opened	Closed	Cargoes and other details	Main trading areas
London and St Katharine's (Plate 14.3)	1805 1828	1968 1968	Only used, in later stages, by barges and coasters. Goods usually transhipped downriver. Main cargoes were *wool* and *wine*. Special warehousing facilities.	Australia, New Zealand and South America (wool), France and other parts of Europe (wine)
Surrey Commercial (11 Docks)	Original dock enlarged 1807. Other docks built during the nineteenth century.	1970	*Softwood timber* by far the most important. Many timber yards and open storage. Much timber was transhipped to barges for movement upriver to timber merchants. A little general cargo.	Canada, Scandinavia, Soviet Union, Baltic states
West India. Today referred to as the 'India and Millwall Docks'	1802	1980	Built originally to handle Caribbean trade. Main cargoes were *sugar*, *fruit* (fresh and dried), *bulk wine*, and some *hardwood timber*. Also grain, fruit and vegetables. Now closed except for bulk wine and timber.	Latin America, West Indies, Mediterranean, Far East, Europe
Millwall	1868 (Connected with West India)			North America, Canary Islands and Mediterranean
East India	1806	1967	Handled mostly coastal and near continental trade.	Other British and West European ports
Royal Group (a) Victoria (b) Royal Albert (c) King George V	1855 1880 1921	1981 1981 1981	Main trade was in *tobacco* (RA and KGV), *chilled beef* (V and RA), *grain* (V), etc. Now closed except for some container trade at Victoria Dock.	South America, Middle and Far East, South and East Africa, Australasia, West Indies, etc.

Tugs lead vessels upriver to the dock entrances or riverside wharves. In times of fog, the PLA radar at Gravesend is an essential aid.

Exercises

4. (a) Compare the riverside scenes shown on Plates 14.2 and 14.3.
(b) Explain why the former is now London's most important port area, and why the latter area was the most important at the beginning of the nineteenth century.
(c) The right foreground of Plate 14.3 shows the new hotel development at St Katharine's Dock, also used as a marina. Outline the advantages and disadvantages of this area for such leisure development. What other tourist facilities can be seen on the photograph?
5. Refer to Table 14.2 which shows London's imports in millions of tonnes in 1980.
(a) Draw a bar graph to illustrate the relative importance of the different imports of the Port of London.
(b) Outline the most significant features of the figures.

Table 14.2 London's imports, 1980 (million tonnes)

1. Crude petroleum and petroleum products	20.22
2. Coal	3.62
3. Cereals, dairy and meat products	2.93
4. Paper	1.53
5. Oilseeds/nuts/vegetable oils	1.36
6. Cement	1.24
7. Iron and steel	1.18
8. Heavy chemicals	1.08
9. Timber	0.87
10. Sugar	0.86
11. Ores and scrap	0.64
12. Pulp and waste paper	0.62
13. Machinery	0.43
14. Non-ferrous metals	0.41
15. Other	2.41
All goods traffic	39.40

Plate 14.3   The Pool of London

The Decline and Fall of the Older Docks

As Table 14.1 indicated, the period between 1967 and 1981 saw the closure of the traditional dock system, with some minor exceptions, such as the bulk wine and timber traffic of the West India and Millwall Docks. Plate 14.3 shows how the land round the old St Katharine's Dock has been converted to leisure purposes. Ambitious schemes are planned for the re-use of derelict dock areas, including new housing, office and industrial development, and even a new airport at the Royal Group of docks which could be used for small-scale aircraft, to take business executives to European centres from a location near the City of London.

The following newspaper extract and Table 14.3 indicate the drastic decline in the number of dockers

174

1,000 jobs go as Royal London's Docks are axed

By JOHN PETTY Shipping Correspondent

A FURTHER 1,000 redundancies and closure within six weeks of the Royal Docks, the last of the East End enclosed docks that once made London the world's biggest port, were agreed yesterday as the price of more Government aid for the Port of London Authority....

Now, trade has slumped so badly that they have ceased to be a vital part of the economy of East London....

What remains of general cargo shipping business at the Royals will mainly switch to Tilbury.

16,000 dockers

Twenty years ago London's East End docks handled 16,500,000 tons of conventional cargo a year, but it has fallen to little more than 250,000 tons.

Dock systems that have already gone include St Katherine's, London, Surrey Commercial and the Millwall and West India. From the end of this month, no bookings will be made into the Royals for ships.

About 900 workers have accepted redundancy in the port this year on top of 2,000 last year....

The request now is for another 600 dockers to go and a further 400 other workers....

The port has debts of more than £100 million and has been kept going for the last three years only through Government aid. It lost £19,300,000 last year.

(*Daily Telegraph*, 18 September 1981)

employed in the Port of London Authority, from 130 000 before the war, to 3500 today. This has created major social and economic problems for the dockland communities of the East End of London.

Table 14.3

Year	1938	1955	1967	1971	1977	1982
Dockers employed	130 000	80 000	24 000	18 000	9000	3500

Note Numerous clerical workers are also employed.

The dockers who remain are better off than those of previous generations. Although there is still much hard and unpleasant work, such as that involved in unloading dirty cargo, there is more assistance from handling machinery. The dockers now work regular hours and get regular pay. At one time, they reported at the dock gates every day, and if there was no work available, they were sent away.

Riverside Industry along the Thames

The riverside zone of industry in the Isle of Dogs is part of a much larger belt stretching over considerable areas of Thames-side (Figure 14.4). The marshlands of the Thames estuary, although expensive to reclaim, are a vital source of level land. The main group of industries uses bulky imported raw materials, such as timber, chemical raw materials, ores and fuels. Coal-fired power stations were built to use coal brought by coasters from other British ports, located near the coalfields (see Chapter 6). Table 14.4 shows the high level of coal shipments in earlier days.

Table 14.4 Amount of coal shipped to London, 1955

Areas of supply	
North-east England	12 million tonnes
Humber ports	1.5 million tonnes
South Wales	0.75 million tonnes
East Scotland	0.5 million tonnes

In addition, about 5.5 million tonnes were brought in from abroad, making about 20 million tonnes in all. In 1980, however, only about 3.5 million tonnes of coal came in. This decline is a result of the increasing use of natural gas at riverside gas works, of oil as an industrial fuel, and the fact that London now gets more of its electricity supply from the National Grid, and relies less on local power stations. Apart from power stations and gas works, other major riverside industries include the manufacture of cement, paper and cars (Figure 14.4).

Cement manufacturing in the Dartford area uses chalk from the North Downs and alluvium from the Thames estuary as a source of clay.

The Ford Motor Company plan at Dagenham has its own private wharves, which import the coke and iron ore used in its blast furnaces, and export cars. The most extensive industries downriver are the oil refineries of Thames Haven, Coryton and Kent, processing imported crude oil. For all these industries, the Greater London area provides a huge market.

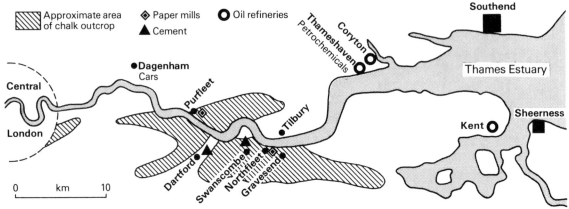

Figure 14.4   The lower Thames: riverside industry

The Advantages of London as a Port

The most obvious advantage is of course the presence of the *River Thames*, which is tidal for over 150 kilometres from its seaward limit. Notice from Figure 14.4 how the estuary narrows inland. This 'funnels in' the tide, helps ships to move upriver on the incoming tide, and provides a natural 'scour' of the channel, reducing the problem of silting. Nevertheless, the channel has still to be dredged artificially.

The *low-lying marshy ground* which once formed the banks of the Thames was easy to excavate for docks. In addition, there was a firmer gravel layer below the alluvium, providing a good foundation for the dock floors.

The *meanders* of the Thames have also been made use of in dock construction. This is made clear in Figure 14.3. Notice how the docks were placed to make it possible for vessels to move into the dock system at one side of a meander, and leave at the other.

The Port of London *faces the world's busiest sea areas*. It is also opposite: the world's largest port, Rotterdam; the most important inland waterway in Europe, the Rhine; and the two most densely populated countries of Europe, the Netherlands and Belgium. London is well placed for trade with most of the countries of Europe, with whom it has enjoyed trading relations for centuries, and this trade has become even more important since Britain joined the European Community.

Apart from its overseas links, London is extremely well situated for dealing with much of Britain's trade. Its immediate *hinterland* (that is, the area which provides the port with its exports and takes imports from the port) is the Greater London conurbation and the whole of south-east England. This region contains over one-quarter of the total population of Britain, and is one of the most important industrial areas.

In addition, London is *at the hub of Britain's communications system*, which radiates out from the capital like the spokes of a wheel (see Chapter 7). The road, rail and air routes which focus on London bring goods for export from all over the country.

For centuries, the trade of the port has been controlled from the City of London, near to which the original wharves were sited (Plate 14.3). The City contains the main commodity markets of the capital. It is also the centre of insurance and banking for Britain. These activities are of international reputation. Lloyd's of London, for example, insure much of the world's shipping.

Conserving the River Thames

In 1964, the River Thames was described as 'dirty, poisoned and fishless'. Later in the 1960s, the following portrayal appeared in a novel, in which the heroine gazes out over part of the river:

The tide was out. Gulls squawked in their sea voices over the low marsh of water between smelling mud banks in search, not of fish in these polluted waters, but of refuse. White preened wings balanced over diluted chemical, between grey cement walls that held such a weight of building. And it was so ugly, so ugly: what race was this that filled the river with garbage and excrement and let it run smelling so evilly between the buildings that crystallized their pride, their history.
(From Doris Lessing, *The Four-gated City*, Curtis Brown Ltd)

Another writer has observed:

Year by year London has made greater demands on the Thames. Besides providing a site for Britain's greatest port and an approach for the port's shipping, the Thames supplies two-thirds of the water for London's domestic and industrial use, disposes of the city's waste, and is a ribbon of open air, offering vistas, sometimes beautiful, always interesting, for the recreation and instruction of Londoners.
(From J. Bird, *The Major Seaports of the United Kingdom*, Hutchinson)

In fact major efforts have been made in recent years to lessen the effects of pollution. The Thames is a long way from being Britain's worst affected river today, and fish can again be found in its waters. This improvement has resulted from the greater control the Port of London Authority and other bodies can now exercise over the activities of organisations polluting the river.

The main problems resulted from: (*a*) *disposal of sewage*, there being eighteen sewage works along the tidal part of the Thames, although the sewage is supposed to be treated before it enters the river; (*b*) *chemical effluent* from scores of industrial concerns along the river and its tributaries, which have been forced by law to treat their effluent so that it is less polluting; (*c*) *the presence of driftwood and other floating debris* thrown into the river, for which the PLA employ two special ships to collect the 7000 tonnes of material affecting the river each year; (*d*) ships illegally *dumping oil* into the estuary, an activity which sometimes threatens beaches of the estuary, such as those of Southend (Figure 14.4). In 1969 there were eleven convictions for dumping oil. There is also the terrifying prospect of a major collision in the estuary involving a supertanker.

Exercises

6. Find out more about **one** of the following Thames-side industries: oil refining; car manufacturing; cement manufacturing; paper manufacturing. For the industry you choose, state the types and sources of raw materials used, and the advantages of its riverside location. Refer to Figure 14.4 and Table 14.2.

7. Refer to the descriptive passage from the novel. State in your own words what you think the writer is 'getting at'. Is it fair to refer to Londoners as part of a race filling rivers with 'diluted chemical' and 'garbage'? The problem could be debated in class, one side taking the point of view of the Port of London Authority, and the other that of a riverside industrialist. You should find out the facts, however, before you debate the matter.

8. Why does one of the writers refer to the river scene as 'ugly', and the other as 'sometimes beautiful, always interesting'? Examine these descriptions with special reference to Plate 14.3.

THE PORTS OF BRITAIN

Leaving aside crude petroleum imports, London is by far Britain's most important port, handling over twice as much tonnage as its nearest competitors. Together with Liverpool, it handles over half Britain's trade in value.

Table 14.5 gives details of the leading ports of Britain in terms of changes in tonnages handled in 1970, 1975 and 1980. A marked feature of recent years has been the *vast growth in imports of crude petroleum*, which make up almost the whole of the trade of some estuaries. Another striking feature has been the *container revolution* which we examined in the case of Tilbury Docks. This most important growth area tends to be concentrated on particular ports, as shown in Table 14.6. (See also pages 96–7.)

Table 14.5

Port	1970		1975		1980	
	Total tonnage (mill. tonnes)	Petroleum	Total tonnage (mill. tonnes)	Petroleum	Total tonnage (mill. tonnes)	Petroleum
Milford Haven	30.0	30.0	45.0	45.0	39.0	38.5
London	56.0	37.0	41.5	22.5	39.5	20.0
Southampton (including Fawley)	27.0	25.0	24.5	21.5	22.0	17.5
Liverpool	29.0	14.0	23.5	13.0	13.0	4.5
Medway (including Isle of Grain)	26.0	24.0	21.5	18.5	17.0	12.0
Immingham/Grimsby	22.0	14.0	20.5	12.0	21.0	11.5
Tees (Middlesbrough and Hartlepool)	22.0	13.0	20.0	11.0	37.5	28.5
Manchester	15.0	9.5	14.0	9.5	11.0	6.0
Clyde (Glasgow, Greenock)	14.5	8.5	12.0	7.0	7.0	2.5
Forth (Leith)	8.0	4.0	8.5	4.5	28.5	25.0
Swansea	7.5	6.5	6.0	4.0	5.0	3.5
Tyne (Newcastle)	7.0	1.5	4.5	1.5	4.0	1.0
Hull	7.0	2.5	4.5	0.75	4.0	0.5
Bristol (Avonmouth)	6.5	3.0	4.5	1.5	4.0	1.0
Dover	1.3	0.3	3.5	0.2	6.5	0.2
Felixstowe	2.2	0.3	4.0	0.3	5.5	0.5
Sullom Voe					29.0	28.5
Flotta					17.5	17.0

Table 14.6 Thousands of containers, 1980

Dover	538
Felixstowe	439
Tilbury	401
Southampton	343
Liverpool	209
Hull	148
Tees/Hartlepool	64
Manchester	61

Since 1975, two main trends have been evident in trading patterns. The first is the gain of east-coast ports such as Dover and Felixstowe. These have the advantages of coming new to the field, with major container and roll-on/roll-off facilities developed at a time of expanding trade with the EEC. Another major feature has been the growth of North Sea oil exploitation, which has led to an enormous growth of traffic along the Forth and the Tees, and the development of new oil ports off the north of Scotland, at Flotta and Sullom Voe (Chapter 6).

By contrast, other ports have declined. Thus despite its new container berth at Seaforth, Liverpool's traffic has declined from 29 million tonnes in 1970 to 13 million in 1980. A number of factors explain this trend. One is the fact that Liverpool is on the west side of the country, facing away from the important growth trade with the EEC. Another is the opening of a deep-water oil terminal on Anglesey, connected by pipeline to Stanlow refinery, resulting in a decline in crude oil imports via the Mersey. Another is the closure of the Shotton steel works on Deeside, for which iron ore was imported via Birkenhead Docks.

SOUTHAMPTON AND FAWLEY

Port and Industrial Development

As Table 14.5 shows, Southampton is one of Britain's major commercial ports. By the 1860s, a dock had been built near the mouth of the River Itchen. Today, the whole of the peninsula between the Rivers Itchen and Test is occupied by port and industrial development (Plate 14.4), as is the eastern bank of the River Test. Southampton's growth into one of Britain's major ports has resulted from the advantages of its site and general position and, above all, the approaches to the port.

Southampton Water is unusual in having *two tides* per day, giving about nine hours of high water level, making it easier for large ships to approach the port. At the same time, the *tidal range* (that is, the difference in height between high and low tide) is not great enough to require the building of expensive lock gates to the docks (Plate 14.4). Many of the ships moor at wharves. The drowned inlet of Southampton Water contains a *deep channel* leading right up to the docks. With dredging, it can take the largest liners and some of the largest supertankers afloat. A supertanker can be seen approaching the jetties at Fawley on Plate 14.5.

Southampton Water *faces south-east* and the land to its west protects it from the prevailing south-westerly winds, as a result of which the waters are relatively calm (Figure 15.2, page 195). The *marshy land* along the shores of Southampton Water, some of which can be seen behind the jetties on Plate 14.5, facilitated the excavation of docks at Southampton and provided a cheap flat area on which the extensive oil refinery at

Plate 14.4 Southampton Docks

Plate 14.5   Fawley, Southampton Water

Fawley could be built (Plate 14.5). Fawley is now part of a major industrial zone which includes a chemical works and two large oil-fired power stations, at Fawley and Marchwood. The *peninsula site* (Plate 14.4) between the Itchen and the Test has allowed the compact grouping of docks and port buildings, not far from the town centre of Southampton (in the right foreground of the picture).

Southampton's *general situation* also provides advantages:

(*a*) it is conveniently placed to serve the London, Birmingham, and Bristol areas, although it would gain considerably from having better motorway links;

(*b*) it is also well placed for the coasts of France, Spain, Portugal, the Mediterranean and Africa, both for trade and for tourist traffic (including ocean cruises). Southampton is by far the most important passenger port in Britain.

The success of Southampton as a port and Fawley as an oil refinery has worsened the pressure on the land surrounding Southampton Water, and is threatening the New Forest (Figure 15.2).

Exercises

9. (*a*)   On an outline map of Britain, mark and name the ports shown on Table 14.5. For the figures for 1980 for the ports on Table 14.5 draw a horizontal bar graph (2 cm for each 5 million tonnes) in proportion to the amount of trade handled, shading in a different colour

the part of the graph which represents petroleum imports.

(*b*)   Which are the main petroleum-importing ports? Find out reasons for the particular location of the four largest of these (see also Chapter 6).

10. (*a*)   Outline the main trends in port trafffic between 1970 and 1980.

(*b*)   Name the ports which go against the main trend.

(*c*)   Try to explain the changes indicated.

11. Draw a large sketch map of southern England and south-western Europe, to show the Straits of Dover, the English Channel, and the Bay of Biscay, and stretching as far south as the Straits of Gibraltar. On it mark the main countries and sea routes, Southampton, Portsmouth and London. In what ways does the map suggest that the strategic positon of Southampton and Portsmouth has contributed to their importance?

12. With the help of an atlas and other maps, explain why Southampton has a less advantageous hinterland than London.

13. Refer to Plate 14.4.

(*a*)   Describe the layout of docks and other land use on the photograph.

(*b*)   With the help of information in the text, describe the site and explain the growth of Southampton as a major commercial port.

(*c*)   Why has Southampton declined as a trans-Atlantic passenger port?

(*d*)   Why is it less important than Dover and Felixstowe as a container port?

14. Which is the nearest major port to your school? For this port (or one well known to you if you live in London or Southampton), draw labelled sketch maps to show its site and hinterland. Compare its site, hinterland, trade and problems with those of London and Southampton.

FISHING PORTS

Methods of Catching Fish

There are three basic techniques of sea fishing: *trawling*, *seining and drifting*.

(1) *Trawling* involves towing a net through a shoal of fish, so capturing the fish in the path of the net. There are two varieties:

(a) *Sea-bottom trawling*, which can be by means of an *otter trawl* (Figure 14.5a), is used for *demersal* fish such as cod, haddock and plaice; and

(b) *Mid-water trawling*, usually used to catch *pelagic* fish such as mackerel and herring.

(2) *Seining* is the technique of encircling a shoal of fish by means of a net and warps, so capturing the fish within the sweep. The most effective way of doing this is by *purse seining* (Figure 14.5b), using huge nets 550 metres long and 165 metres deep. One end of the net is attached to a buoy, then the ship sails round in a circle. On return to the buoy the net is closed. In the case of purse seining this is done like a purse, by zipping up from the foot of the net.

(3) *Drifting* (Figure 14.5c) is a form of passive trapping, involving the attachment of nets to *long lines*, so that fish swimming towards the 'wall' of net become enmeshed in it. This form is little used today. In addition, baited hooks can be attached to lengths of line. This is still used in areas with a rocky sea floor, especially to catch larger fish such as halibut.

Fishing Grounds

The main fishing grounds comprise the waters of the *continental shelf* (Figure 14.6), relatively shallow and rich in *plankton*, microscopic organisms which are the basic food source of fish.

Traditionally, British fishing vessels have used grounds in three areas (Figure 14.6).

(1) The *near-water fishing grounds* include the English Channel, the North Sea, the Irish Sea, and waters off the west coasts of Scotland and Ireland. These were mostly fished by small trawlers, staying away from port for up to ten days.

(2) The *middle-water fishing grounds* include those off the Faroes and Rockall, used by larger trawlers, on voyages lasting about two weeks or more.

(3) The *distant-water fishing grounds* used to be the most important of all. To fish these grounds, voyages of three weeks or more are needed.

Of the distant-water ships, some are 'freezer trawlers' in which the fish are frozen on board. In 1975, Hull had 35 of these, Grimsby eight and Fleetwood one. Even larger and more expensive are 'factory trawlers', in

Figure 14.5   Methods of catching fish

(a) Bottom trawling: otter trawl

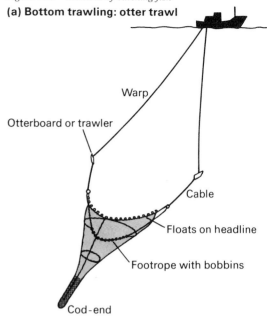

(b) Purse seining

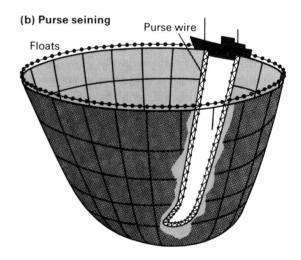

(c) Drifting

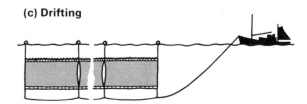

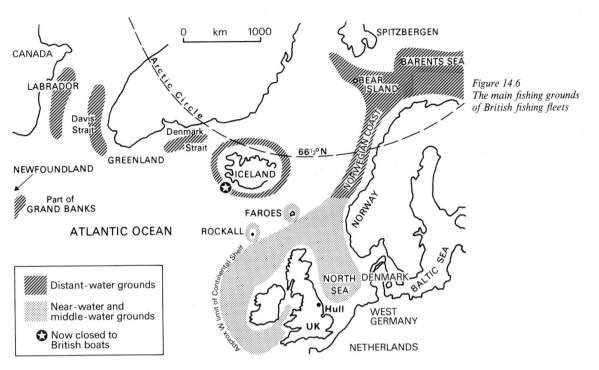

Figure 14.6
The main fishing grounds
of British fishing fleets

Map labels:
CANADA
LABRADOR
Davis Strait
NEWFOUNDLAND
Part of GRAND BANKS
GREENLAND
Denmark Strait
ATLANTIC OCEAN
0 km 1000
Arctic Circle
SPITZBERGEN
BARENTS SEA
BEAR ISLAND
66½° N
ICELAND
NORWEGIAN COAST
FAROES
ROCKALL
NORWAY
Approx W limit of Continental Shelf
NORTH SEA
DENMARK
BALTIC SEA
Hull
UK
WEST GERMANY
NETHERLANDS

Legend:
Distant-water grounds
Near-water and middle-water grounds
Now closed to British boats

which fish can be filleted as well as frozen, and fish meal can be manufactured. *Coriolanus* (Plate 14.6) was the factory ship of the Hull fleet.

The numbers of distant-water trawlers have, however, declined catastrophically since the mid-1970s, from 454 in 1974 to only 20 in 1981. Landings from distant-water grounds by the British fishing fleet in 1981 constituted only 2.1% of the total catch. This has been the result of the Icelandic fishing dispute which closed Icelandic waters to British vessels, and subsequently of the lack of an EEC fisheries policy. Restrictions have been extended to other waters, and even grounds still fished by British vessels (Figure 14.6) are limited in use.

Table 14.7 illustrates the drastic effect of the decline on British fishing ports. The hardest hit has been Hull, Britain's premier distant-water fishing port. Since 1980 there has been a further decline. By 1982, Hull had only eighteen vessels, of which only half were operational. Its fish landings declined from 201 000 tonnes in 1970 to 29 000 in 1980. It is now struggling to remain a fishing port at all.

The near-water and to a less extent the middle-water fishing grounds (although the Faroes catch has been restricted) have now become the main fish source for this country. As Figure 14.7 suggests, this has resulted in major changes in fish catches. The main distant-water fish catch, cod, has dramatically declined, while a near-water fish, mackerel, has equally dramatically increased. There has been a slight increase in whiting,

caught in near-water and middle-water grounds. As we shall see, there has also been a major slump in the catch of another near-water fish, herring, to conserve stocks (page 186).

Plate 14.6   The *Coriolanus*, *a factory trawler*

181

Table 14.7 British white fishing fleet

| | Near-water | | Middle-water | | Distant-water | | | |
| | | | | | Fresher trawlers | | Freezer trawlers | |
	1978	1980	1978	1980	1978	1980	1978	1980
Grimsby	5	3	31	21	21	9	–	–
Hull	–	4	–	2	16	5	34	30
Lowestoft	26	19	34	25	2	2	–	–
Fleetwood	5	3	9	6	4	3	–	–
Milford Haven	6	6	–	–	–	–	–	–
North Shields	1	4	3	2	–	–	–	–
Aberdeen	25	16	30	9	1	–	–	–
Peterhead	9	13	1	3	–	–	–	–
Total British	111	110	112	85	44	34	34	30

The problem of the near-water grounds is that they all come within the 200-mile limit, formally extended by Britain at the beginning of 1977. This was done to exclude fishing vessels from non-EEC countries, such as those of Eastern Europe. But the coastal states of the EEC have also extended their limits to 200 miles, and these overlap with the British. The EEC 'Common Fisheries Policy' is planned to give access to Britain's traditional inshore grounds, even within the former 12-mile limit. This has greatly alarmed the British fishing industry.

The EEC countries are, however, agreed on the need to conserve fishing stocks to prevent over-rapid exploitation of the near-water resources. This is why Iceland has limited catches of cod in its waters. The loss of access to Britain's most important distant-water ground, however, plus increasing costs of fuel, have led to enormous increases in the price of fish in recent years.

Figure 14.7   The landings of fish by British ports, 1980

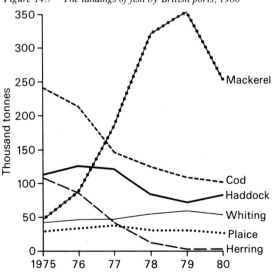

Exercises

15. Refer to Table 14.7 and Figure 14.7, and the text.
(a) Identify the British ports traditionally most concerned with each of near-water, middle-water and distant-water fishing.
(b) Outline the trends which have taken place in fishing since the mid-1970s and the impact on particular fishing ports.
16. Keep a scrapbook of the impact of EEC policy on the British fishing industry.

The Humber Estuary

Hull is not only a fishing port, but also a commercial and, in recent years, a passenger port. The docks of the port of Hull stretch along the north side of the Humber Estuary (Plate 14.7). This estuary contains four major ports: Hull, Immingham, Grimsby and Goole (Figure 14.8). Immingham handles massive imports of petroleum and iron ore, while it and Goole are important coal exporting ports, with access by road, rail and canal (in the case of Goole) to the Yorkshire coalfield. This diversification of port functions has been important in enabling Hull to survive the crisis in the fishing industry.

The main cargo-handling docks of the port of Hull can be seen in the right background of Plate 14.7. The port is particularly well placed for trade with Europe, though it imports goods from all over the world. The Humber Estuary is difficult to navigate but contains a deep-water channel swinging from Grimsby and Immingham on the south side to Hull on the north. Hull has the advantage of being sheltered from easterly gales by Spurn Head and the Holderness peninsula (Figure 14.8).

The Growth of the Fishing Industry in Hull

At the western end of the Hull dock system is St Andrew's Dock (Figure 14.8 and Plate 14.8). The dock was opened in 1883, and extended in 1897. In the early nineteenth century the Thames was the leading centre of the fishing industry of Britain. At this time it was difficult to transport fish to inland markets, and the Thames estuary had the advantage of the large London market on its doorstep. As a fishing port, Hull was then involved only with the whaling industry.

From the middle of the nineteenth century, however, Hull, Grimsby and other coastal towns grew as fishing ports. One reason for Hull's development was the discovery of the rich Silver Pit fishing ground of the North Sea, not far from the Humber estuary (Figure 14.8). Another was the growth of the railway system, which allowed the rapid transport of fish to inland markets such as the West Riding and the Midlands (Figure 14.8). Cheap labour to work on the fishing vessels was brought from the workhouses of large cities such as Leeds.

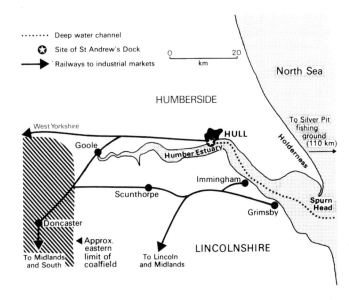

Plate 14.7   Aerial view of Hull docks

By 1863 Hull had 270 fishing smacks (sailing vessels). After 1883, ice was used to conserve fish at sea, allowing boats to travel further and stay out longer from the home port. By 1900, most of Hull's 410 trawlers were steam driven, coal being easily obtained from the Yorkshire coalfield. From the 1920s Hull came to concentrate on distant-water cod fishing, serving the rapidly-growing fish and chip industry.

St Andrew's Dock

Plate 14.8 is a fairly old photograph of the entrance to St Andrew's Dock, showing the dock entrance, the River Humber in the foreground, the river wall backed by warehouses and fishing offices, and some of the smaller trawlers in the dock itself. Behind the dock are railway sidings, and the terraced housing and fish-processing factories (some of which are indicated by the strangely shaped chimneys) of the Hessle Road district of Hull.

The fishing industry was very important to the city of Hull. In 1970 it employed directly about 9000 people. Of these 3000 were fishermen going to sea, over 3200 were engaged in processing fish (either in freezing or 'smoking' fish, or in the preparation of fish meal and cod liver oil), about 650 were occupied in landing the fish, while nearly 2000 were engaged in the maintenance of the ships or in administration. When all those who were indirectly concerned with the fishing industry are added in, probably over 25 000 people in the Hull area were involved. At the beginning of 1977, the number of workers on trawlers had been reduced to 1400. Today the number is negligible. Hull is not far from ceasing to exist as a fishing port.

Like other large ports, with their traditional fish docks, fish markets and fish auctions, Hull has suffered from changes in marketing methods, so far as distant-water trawlers are concerned, since they are able to freeze and process fish catches on the ship. The frozen and processed fish products can then be transported directly over the country by container lorry.

Britain no longer catches enough fish to supply itself, and large quantities are imported, particularly from Iceland, Denmark, Norway and the Netherlands. Although foreign vessels occasionally land fish at major ports such as Hull, there is now no need to do so, as they can be landed at any port, direct into refrigerated transport, and sent to cold stores. In the case of near-water fish, they are often transferred direct to refrigerated cargo vessels for export. Hull and Grimsby (see page 61) remain centres of the frozen food industry, processing fish as well as vegetables. But in a time of easy transport by refrigerated lorry, there is no vital need that the fish be landed at these ports.

Plate 14.8   The entrance to St Andrew's Dock, Hull

Exercises

17. Draw a simple labelled sketch map to illustrate Hull's location in relation to Western Europe. Look up information about the car ferries that connect Hull with the continent for passenger traffic. State briefly how Britain's entry into the European Community has affected (*a*) the traffic of the port of Hull, (*b*) its fishing industry.
18. Lay a sheet of tracing paper over Plate 14.7 and on the tracing outline name: the coast of the Humber Estuary; the dock system as a whole; St Andrew's Dock; railway lines and sidings; areas of industry; an area of mainly terraced housing; and an area of redevelopment. Draw an arrow pointing towards Spurn Head and label the compass direction in which it is pointing.
19. Examine the accompanying newspaper extract about Fleetwood. Indicate how it relates to the trends outlined in this chapter.

Century of tradition ends for fishing port

By Michael Morris

A CENTURY OF tradition ended yesterday when the last deep-sea trawler tied up at Fleetwood. But there was cautious hope among crews on the dockside for a rebirth of the Lancashire port as a haven for inshore fishermen.

The 150ft Jacinta, one of the biggest stern trawlers fishing out of a British port, came in quietly to a dock that has been gradually deprived of the big boats over several years.

But berths in the large Jubilee dock are being gradually filled by vessels of up to 80ft, manned mostly by crews of only two or three. There are about 80 of these now. Fifteen years ago there were only 20.

(*The Guardian*, 30 July 1982)

The Fishing Ports of Britain

Table 14.8 shows the weight of landings of fish at the twelve leading fishing ports of Britain in 1970, 1975 and 1980.

Table 14.8 Landings of fish
(*to the nearest 1000 tonnes*)

Port	Total weight		
	1970	1975	1979/1980
Hull	198	137	29
Grimsby	189	150	45
Aberdeen	122	74	57
Ullapool	45	37	93
Fleetwood	41	34	11
North Shields	39	45	13
Lowestoft	28	20	19
Fraserburgh	20	33	17
Oban	27	13	5
Leith	19	12	7
Lossiemouth	10	10	4
Newlyn	3	9	11

Note The figures for the Scottish ports refer to 'districts' and not just to the port itself.

There are of course many smaller fishing ports in Britain, such as those round the coasts of Devon and Cornwall (for example, Brixham) and South Wales (Milford Haven). Hull concentrates very largely on cod fishing, but the other ports tend to handle a large variety of fish, as their vessels do not concentrate solely on the distant-water fishing grounds. Some of them specialise in particular types of fish; for example, Lowestoft specialises in high-value plaice. Fleetwood and Milford Haven have traditionally supplied hake to much of Britain, but over-fishing has seriously depleted hake supplies in recent years. The small but numerous ports of south-west England are well known for their pilchard and mackerel catches.

Although the major ports distribute fish over large parts of Britain, they were traditionally located to supply a particular area or areas. Grimsby and Hull serve the markets of West Yorkshire, the Midlands and London; Aberdeen and Leith send much of their fish to the towns of central Scotland; Fleetwood to north-west England; North Shields to north-east England; and Milford Haven to South Wales. These close links are now much less significant as a result of refrigerated transport, as we have seen in the case of Hull.

Herring and Mackerel Fishing

Some of the ports marked on Table 14.8, especially those of north Scotland, became in the 1970s more important for herring fishery than for other types of fishing. Unlike the white fish industry, herring fishing in a particular sea area is very seasonal, as Figure 14.9 shows. The herring boats must travel in search of the herring shoals, which are found in different areas off the shores of Britain at different times of the year. Over the years, the herring shoals have been unreliable in their behaviour. In recent years they have been difficult to find over much of the North Sea, as shown by the rapid decline of the herring industry of Great Yarmouth and Lowestoft, once the most important herring ports in England. During the early 1970s, there were abundant herring shoals off the coasts of north-west Scotland, particularly the North and South Minch (Figure 14.9). By the late 1970s, however, the over-fishing of herring in these waters led to the need for conservation measures. Herring fishing was banned off north-west Scotland, and small catches only were allowed from the Clyde area and off the Isle of Man.

The decline in herring catches (Figure 14.7), was matched, however, by an increase in mackerel, although by 1980 there were signs that this was being over-fished also. Figure 14.9 shows how the herring shoals migrate. This is also true of mackerel. There is a minor mackerel fishery in the North Sea in the February–August period; but the main seasons are August to late October off north-west Scotland; and November to March off south-west England. Scottish purse seiners move south at this time, and compete with the hand-liners of the local Cornish vessels.

The main ports for both herring and mackerel are Ullapool, Mallaig (Plate 14.9) and Stornoway, all much smaller than the major white fish ports.

Another interesting feature of the fish trade has happened both with herring and then mackerel catches. This is the resumption of trade to the continent from Scottish west coast ports such as Mallaig and Ullapool, in the form of *klondyking*, whereby foreign vessels, from East European countries in particular, come into local waters to buy freshly caught mackerel (formerly herring), and then transfer them to their own cold stores, before sailing back to their own countries.

Conservation

The decline of the herring fisheries round Britain is just one example of the disastrous consequences of over-fishing. There are many others, ranging from the decline of salmon stocks in British rivers to the extinction of the whaling industry in Arctic waters, and its decline in Antarctic waters. The catching of too many young fish, by using nets with too fine a mesh, means that there is

Figure 153
Seasonal movements of her shoals in British waters

Figure 14.9   Seasonal movements of herring shoals in British waters

Plate 14.9   Mallaig harbour, Scotland

not enough stock left to breed. This leads to a decline in numbers. The consequences are that it becomes un-economic to continue to fish, and eventually a species may die out altogether.

The conservation issue lies at the heart of the disputes over fishing limits. The falling catches from the traditional fishing grounds may lead to the freezer and factory trawlers going further afield, even into the South Atlantic.

Experiments are now taking place to increase fish supplies by fish farming. Many of the rainbow trout we buy in the shops come from fish farms. The technique is only economic with high-value fish, but it is hoped that sole, plaice and others can be raised in this way. Under artificial conditions, the fish can reach a marketable size in two years, instead of four years under natural conditions. Similar experiments are going on all over the world, and may make a useful contribution to the massive problem of feeding the world's growing population.

Exercises

20. Refer to Table 14.8.

(a) On an outline map of the British Isles, and with the help of an atlas, locate and name the ports mentioned. Draw a bar graph by each port to show the weight of fish caught in 1980. Simplify the figures.

(b) Mark on the map the main industrialised areas of Britain, and indicate the main links between these and the fishing ports.

21. (a) With the help of Plates 14.7 and 14.8 for Hull, and Plate 14.9 for Mallaig, compare the two ports in respect of their harbours and the boats using them.

(b) With the help of an atlas, draw a labelled sketch map to show the land transport links of Mallaig. Why is klondyking particularly useful to its mackerel trade?

22. Compare and contrast the changes which have taken place since the mid-1970s in demersal and pelagic fishing.

PASSENGER PORTS

The age of air transport has seen a drastic decline in long-distance passenger traffic. Great ships which used to ply the Atlantic and other sea routes are now used largely for pleasure cruises. The only remaining long-distance passenger port of any importance in Britain is Southampton, although there is still a little from Tilbury. There has, however, been a great increase in short-distance traffic in recent years, especially across the North Sea and the English Channel to Europe, with the coming of car ferries and hovercraft services. Figure 14.10 shows the enormous number of routes which now connect Britain and Europe.

One of the ports engaged in this traffic is Hull. In the background of Plate 14.7 where the river bank bends round, is King George Dock, at which North Sea

Figure 14.10   Passenger ports

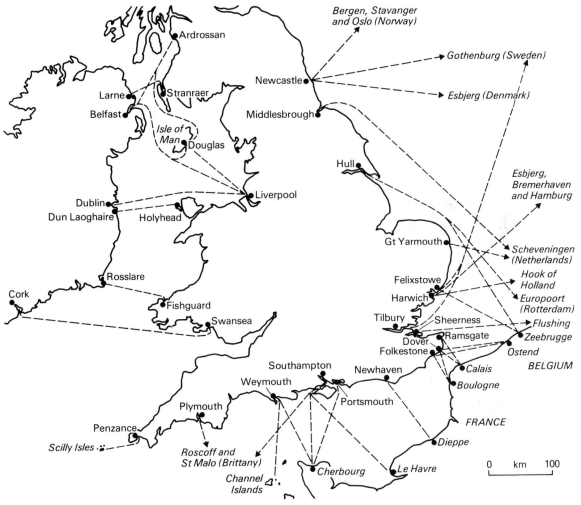

Plate 14.10   The docks at Dover

Ferries have a terminal, from which ships run to Europoort in the Netherlands and Zeebrugge in Belgium. Hull is one of the many new ferry ports which have sprung up in recent years, to take advantage of increasing contacts with Europe.

As Table 14.9 indicates, however, Hull is a relatively minor ferry port compared with those of south-eastern England. One of its main disadvantages is its relatively long sea crossing to the other side of the North Sea. As a result, it runs its services overnight. Hull has, however, the advantages of an existing sheltered harbour (Figure 14.8), and motorway links (M62) to the densely populated industrial areas of West Yorkshire and north-west England. A lot of lorry traffic uses this route. For industrialists in northern England, it is a much longer drive to get to the ports of the south-east than to Hull.

An important feature of a port is its passenger handling facilities. Dover, by far Britain's most important passenger port (Table 14.9), has facilities for handling cross-channel rail services (Plate 14.10) and also car ferries, both by boat and hovercraft. A new road now avoids the town centre, running directly to the terminal for the car ferries (Plate 14.11).

The passenger figures on Table 14.9 include both arrivals and departures. Of the 15.4 million passengers in 1975, almost exactly half were arrivals and half departures. Note that the 1980 figures are given in more generalised form, with one or two exceptions.

Table 14.9 Passenger traffic (millions of passengers)

1975		1980	
Dover	6.80	Dover	11.0
Folkestone	1.60	Newhaven	
Harwich	1.50	Southampton	
Southampton	1.15*	Weymouth	3.3
Ramsgate	0.95	Plymouth	
Holyhead	0.80	Folkestone	
Newhaven	0.60	Ramsgate	2.9
Liverpool	0.40	Sheerness	
Felixstowe	0.30	Fishguard	
Hull	0.29	Holyhead	
Fishguard	0.28	Liverpool	2.5
Swansea	0.18	Stranraer	
Plymouth	0.16	Harwich	1.7
Weymouth	0.15	Hull	
Newcastle	0.13	Newcastle	1.1
Immingham	0.10	Middlesbrough	
		Immingham	
		Great Yarmouth	1.0
		Felixstowe	

* Southampton's figure includes about 0.10 longer-distance passengers.

Exercises

23. Imagine you live in (a) London, (b) Birmingham, (c) Liverpool. Write an explanatory account of the factors you would take into consideration in each case in planning to cross by sea to (i) Sweden, (ii) the Netherlands, (iii) Dublin. In addition to the information in the text and on Figure 14.10 look up maps of motorways and rail services.

24. Refer to Plate 14.10, showing the rail terminal and the older part of the port and the town of Dover; and Plate 14.11 showing more recent development for car traffic. (This area lies to the right of the area in the background of Plate 14.10.)

(a) Outline the problems of physical access to the rail and car terminals and indicate how they have been overcome.

(b) Why do you think the developments on Plate 14.11 were needed?

(c) With the help of an atlas, Figure 14.10 and Plates 14.10 and 14.11, and other information you can find, draw a labelled sketch map to illustrate Dover's importance as a passenger port, and container port (page 178).

Plate 14.11 Dover: the car-ferry terminus

15 TOURISM

SEASIDE RESORTS

Southport

Plate 15.1 is a photograph of the resort and dormitory town of Southport which, until about 1900, was the largest seaside resort in north-west England. At about this time it was overtaken in importance by Blackpool which, with the attractions of the newly built Tower, its lively 'Golden Mile' of Promenade, and its huge pleasure beach, proved a much more effective magnet for holidaymakers from the Lancashire textile belt and places further afield. The line of buildings on Southport's more genteel Promenade is marked on Plate 15.1. Until the late nineteenth century, this marked the sea front. Since then, the former gently shelving sandy beach has been reclaimed for recreational purposes, as shown both on the photograph and on Figure 15.1. Like other resorts, Southport has an urban land-use zone devoted to leisure activities, in this case lying between the town centre, with its shops and offices, and the beach.

Plate 15.1   Southport, Lancashire

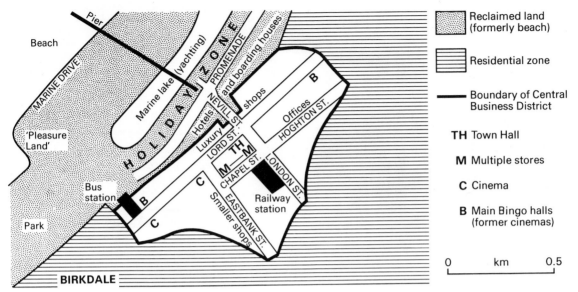

Figure 15.1 Southport: land-use zones

Reasons for the Growth of Southport as a Resort

Slow Early Growth to about 1850

At the beginning of the nineteenth century the coast of south-west Lancashire was somewhat bleak and inhospitable. At first sight it seems surprising that a seaside resort should have developed in this area. In fact the growth of resorts was an important part of urban growth in nineteenth-century Britian, and the story of Southport can be used to illustrate some of the reasons why such places developed.

In the first place, the extensive areas of beach and dunes at the coast were useful natural assets for the growth of a resort. Unlike other British resorts, however, Southport did not have the benefits of attractive cliff scenery or mountains immediately behind.

From the late eighteenth century onwards, doctors in the large towns began to recommend visits to the seaside as a means of improving the health of their patients. This happened in Liverpool, where various medical experts advised their patients to come to Southport for cures. In addition to hotels and boarding houses, convalescent homes, baths and sanatoria were established.

It also became fashionable for well-to-do people to take holidays by the sea. Some south-coast resorts, particularly Brighton, were frequented by royalty. While this did not happen to Southport, it benefited from the general trend towards seaside holidays, especially when the fashion spread to other sections of the population. In Lancashire there was a vast increase in population in the industrial towns in this period, with expanding textile, coalmining, and other industries. The grimy and insanitary conditions in the industrial towns made a trip to the coast, with its clear air and clean sea water, a pleasant prospect for their inhabitants. Southport was the nearest of the coastal resorts to many of the Lancashire towns.

The weather conditions at the coast were a further attraction. It was quite normal to leave the east Lancashire industrial towns under a pall of cloud and smoke, and find bright sunny weather at the coast. There are on average about 1500 hours of sunshine each year at the coast, as against 1000 in the polluted industrial towns (Figure 5.14).

Despite these advantages, the population of Southport only increased from 2500 in 1801 to 9000 in 1851. This slow early growth was also characteristic of many other British holiday resorts.

Rapid Growth from 1850 to 1900

Between 1850 and 1900 there was a much more rapid rate of population growth. By 1901, Southport's population, including its neighbour Birkdale, had reached 63 000.

The Coming of the Railways

Before 1850, rapid growth of the resort was hindered by poor communications. There were no good roads from Southport to the industrial towns.

Some visitors came by canal, for the Leeds and Liverpool canal ran within 10 kilometres of Southport. Southport therefore had a relatively inaccessible location at this time.

191

Plate 15.2   Chapel Street Station before the First World War

The position was improved with the coming of the railways, one of the most important technological developments of the nineteenth century. Plate 15.2 shows Southport's main railway terminus in Chapel Street in the early years of this century. Note the list of places to which it was connected. There was also a line to Preston. Like other resorts, Southport was greatly stimulated by this new and rapid means of travel. Previously Manchester had been over eight hours' journey away. Now it could be reached in one hour. Southport was still just as far away in straight-line distance, but accessibility in terms of *time* was much improved.

Exercises

1. Identify the resort facilities shown on Plate 15.1 and Figure 15.1.
2. Refer to Plate 15.2. State at least five features which indicate that this is not a present-day scene.
3. With the help of an atlas, draw a map of Lancashire, marking and naming the main coastal resorts, the main industrial towns to which Southport was connected, together with the railway links. Compare Southport's links with those of Blackpool and Morecambe.

Twentieth-Century Southport

The Decline of the Resort Function
Fewer people now come to stay for holidays in Southport than in the past, though the town is still crowded with day-trippers on sunny summer weekends. The number of hotels and boarding houses in the town declined from 900 in 1930 to less than 200 in 1971. Between 1931 and 1971 the population remained almost stagnant, growing very slowly from 78 000 to 84 000, and then grew more rapidly to over 89 000 in 1981.

In recent years British resorts as a whole have suffered from the competition of package tours to Spain and other European holiday areas, but Southport's decline as a resort began long before this. From the late nineteenth century Blackpool Local Authority took the initiative in providing a very wide range of holiday facilities to attract the masses from the industrial towns of the north-west, and its population grew from 40 000 in 1900 to over 150 000 in 1971, falling slightly to 148 000 in 1981. Southport, on the other hand, preferred to concentrate on its dormitory function (providing suburbs for city workers). This again shows how human decisions may be more important than geographical factors, because geographically Southport would seem to have an advantage over Blackpool since its location is nearer to most of the Lancashire industrial towns.

The Growth of the Residential Function
(a) *A place of retirement* Part of Southport's residential function is associated with the presence of a suitable environment and provision of accommodation for old people. Many of the town's advantages as a resort are equally helpful to the retirement function, including the flat relief, the mild and sunny climate, and the attractive tree-lined streets and parks laid out in Victorian times as a planned garden suburb (Plate 15.3).

192

Southport's location near industrial Lancashire makes it fairly easy for its people to retain links with relatives and friends in the towns from which many of them have originated. In addition, many old folk's homes have been established, often in large Victorian detached villas. In other cases these have been divided up into flats or adapted as nursing homes, providing further accommodation for the retired.

As medical knowledge improves, people are on average living longer, and an increasing proportion of the population is made up of the over-60s. The 'retirement industry' will continue to grow in the future. Plate 15.3 shows the spacious pattern of Victorian villas and gardens being broken for the erection of apartments or flats (marked F), which are sought by old people coming to retire in the town.

(b) *A dormitory settlement* About 9000 of Southport's working population of about 34 000 people *commute* to work, about half of these to the Merseyside area.

The links established with Merseyside in the nineteenth century have been maintained. The greatest proportion of the commuters are office workers, employed in the central areas of Liverpool and, to a much lesser extent, Manchester. The decline in the rail service to Manchester, and improvements in the 'Merseyrail' service to Liverpool, with an underground section under the city's CBD, have emphasised Southport's relationship with Merseyside. It is now part of the Merseyside Metropolitan District of Sefton, together with Bootle, Crosby, and Formby, all linked with Liverpool along the same electrified line of railway.

Bournemouth: Holiday Resort and Residential Development

Plate 15.4 is an aerial view of Bournemouth, one of the largest holiday resorts in Britain. In the foreground are large villas set in their own grounds, and luxury hotels and flats, carefully laid out on top of the cliffs which overlook a narrow beach. There are many more trees than is usual in a town. The spacious layout does, however, increase the amount of land used up by the built-up area, the extent of which is shown on Figure 15.2. Bournemouth, unlike Southport, has maintained its importance as a resort but, not lying near to a major conurbation, it is less significant as a dormitory centre.

The main reason for Bournemouth's rapid growth in the nineteenth century, as at Southport, was the coming of the railways. Two branch lines had reached the vicinity of Bournemouth by the 1870s. By the end of the century, direct rail services linked Bournemouth with London, the Midlands and the north. Express trains made it possible for people to travel much more widely for their holidays, and the sunny south coast became very popular. Facilities such as piers, promenades, theatres and concert halls, and cliff-top walks, some of which are shown on Plate 15.4, were provided for the stream of visitors.

In 1971 there were over 1000 hotels and boarding houses in Bournemouth. Many of the others were in the resorts of the Isle of Wight (Figure 15.2) including Shanklin, Sandown and Ventnor, which also have attractive coastal scenery and are the sunniest places in Britain, with over 1800 hours of sunshine on average each year.

Plate 15.3   Birkdale, Southport: Victorian villas and modern flats

Plate 15.4   Aerial view of Bournemouth

Apart from the hotels and boarding houses, accommodation is provided by caravans, chalets and camp sites. There were nearly 8000 caravan and chalet sites in Hampshire by the late 1960s. Pressure on land is being made worse by the increasing number of people wishing to retire to these pleasant coastal areas. Bournemouth's population includes well over 40 000 retired people. The stretch of coast from Bournemouth eastwards is being devoted more and more to building bungalows for the retired and, as Figure 15.2 shows, there are now hardly any gaps in the built-up area between Bournemouth and Lymington.

Exercises

4. Refer to Plates 15.1, 15.3 and 15.4 and Figure 15.1 and contrast the sites and layouts of Southport and Bournemouth.
5. Compare the Lancashire and Hampshire coasts as resort areas, in terms of scenery, weather, facilities, and access.

The Seaside Resorts of Britain

Most British resorts grew for reasons similar to Southport, though the period of most rapid growth might be different. Blackpool, as we have seen, has grown more rapidly in the first half of this century than in the latter half of the nineteenth. In addition, different groups of resorts clearly serve different urbanised inland areas, particularly for day-trippers. Unlike Southport, many resorts have the advantages of imposing coastal and inland scenery, as in the case of the North Wales resorts. In general, the south coast resorts have a sunnier climate than those of the north, averaging in some cases over 1800 hours of sunshine per annum, as against 1500 hours at Southport. Some areas, particularly Devon and Cornwall, were less well placed through much of the nineteenth century to serve rapidly growing industrial areas. Their turn has come in the twentieth

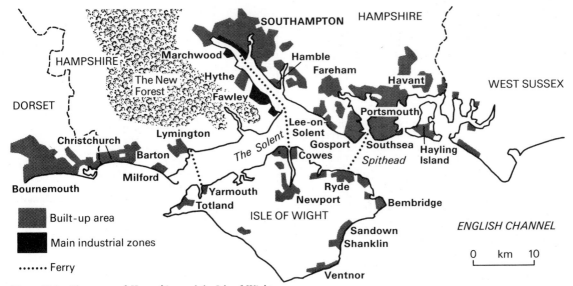

Figure 15.2   The coasts of Hampshire and the Isle of Wight

century, helped by the increased use of the motor car.

It is interesting to check which particular resorts illustrate the following *stages of growth* which we have noted at Southport:

(1)   a *pre-resort* period before 1800;

(2)   a *pioneering stage*, with slow early growth, in the first half of the nineteenth century;

(3)   a *stage of rapid growth* with the coming of the railways in the second half of the nineteenth century;

(4)   an increasing *emphasis on the residential function, and decline of the resort function* in the twentieth century.

To summarise for Britain as a whole, it may be said that people travel for holidays (*a*) from inland areas to the coast (and to a lesser extent from lowland areas to the hills); (*b*) from northern to southern parts of Britain seeking warmer, sunnier places than their home area.

But patterns of holidaymaking have changed considerably over the last twenty-five years or so.

(*a*) Fewer people now take the traditional week or a fortnight's holiday in one place, such as Blackpool or Bournemouth, though many still like to do this.

(*b*) Many tourists now prefer to move about, taking advantage of the flexibility of having a car and perhaps also a caravan. They move from caravan site to caravan site, or from hotel to hotel, often in scenically attractive areas such as the Lake District, the Cairngorms or the New Forest (see below).

(*c*) The coming of 'package tours' by air, rail or road has made it easy and relatively cheap to take holidays in Europe and even more distant parts of the world, seeking sunnier environments than Britain can usually provide. On the other hand, there is also a 'counter-current' of foreign tourists, who can obtain package tours to this country. These tourists tend to be attracted not only by our varied scenery (See Figure 1.1), but also by the historical heritage of old cities such as London, York and Edinburgh.

Figure 15.3   Holidays in Britain: a sample from a school in Ormskirk

(d) The access provided by motorway connections, as well as rail transport, has increased the number of day-trippers to resorts such as Southport and Southend. The M6, for example, makes it possible to travel to the Lake District from the Midlands and return the same day.

Exercises

6. (a) Refer to Figure 15.3, and, with the help of an atlas, draw your own map and name the main resorts, marked by dots, of England and Wales. You can add any others with which you are familiar, even if they are not marked on the map, so long as you locate them accurately.

(b) Compare Figure 15.3 with Figure 6.7 (page 79) which shows the main coalfield areas of Britain. Name the main resorts nearest to (i) the Yorkshire coalfield; (ii) the East Midlands coalfield; (iii) the South Wales coalfield; (iv) the London area.

7. Table 15.1 shows the number of hotels and boarding houses in the major resorts and coastal areas of England and Wales in 1971:

(a) On an outline map of England and Wales, use different symbols (see Figure 15.3) to indicate the relative importance of the different resorts and coastal areas, naming each.

(b) Discuss the distribution shown, in the light of your answer to exercise 6.

(c) Southend is well known as an important resort, yet comes low down in the list of hotels and boarding houses. Can you explain this? Is the number of hotels and boarding houses a good index of importance?

(d) Is Southend more similar to Southport or Bournemouth? Give reasons for your answer.

(e) How does the importance of the areas on your map compare with Figure 15.3, which shows the preferred holiday areas of a sample of children from Ormskirk in Lancashire? Try to explain the differences.

Table 15.1

Number of hotels or boarding houses	Resort
Over 2000	Blackpool
1000–2000	Bournemouth
	Torbay
	Cornish coast (as a whole)
250–1000	Scarborough
	Isle of Wight (south coast)
	Thanet coast (Kent)
	Brighton and Hove
	Eastbourne
	East Devon coast (excluding Torbay)
	North Devon coast
	Dorset coast
	North Wales coast
	Morecambe area
150–250	Great Yarmouth
	Weston-super-Mare
	Southport
	South Devon coast
	South Kent coast (excluding Dover)
100–150	Hastings
	South Pembrokeshire coast
	West Wales
	Southend
	Essex coast (excluding Southend)
	Suffolk coast
	Norfolk coast (excluding Great Yarmouth)
	Dover
	Worthing
	Skegness–Mablethorpe

(Source: 1971 Census, County Tables)

TOURISM AND CONSERVATION

The expansion of townscape leads to a reduction of farmscape and wildscape. A large proportion of Britain is already consumed by urban development, and the increasing time allowed for the leisure of town dwellers has posed threats to two types of area in particular: the coast and the mountains. People are no longer content to be taken by rail to resorts such as Blackpool and Bournemouth. Their cars and caravans are taking them into the heart of the wildscape.

The Attack on the Coast: Hampshire

Figure 15.2 showed how much the coastal area of Hampshire has been built up. In Hampshire there are three small but growing conurbations based on Bournemouth, Southampton and Portsmouth. The built-up areas of Southampton and Portsmouth have almost joined up. In addition, there is a scatter of smaller towns round the coast of the Isle of Wight. The rapid growth of population in the three main urban areas is shown below.

Table 15.2 Growth of population

Year	Portsmouth	Southampton	Bournemouth
1801	33 000	8 000	—
1851	53 000	35 000	700
1901	188 000	77 000	69 000
1951	233 000	178 000	145 000
1971	196 000	215 000	153 000
1981	179 000	204 000	145 000

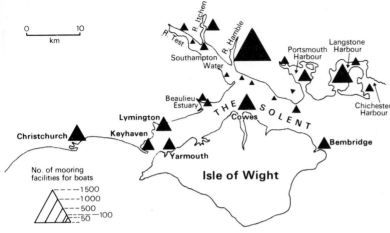

Figure 15.4   The coasts of Hampshire and the Isle of Wight: yachting facilities

There is no slackening off in the population growth. Although the number of people in Portsmouth itself has fallen considerably in the last twenty years this is because people are moving out of the town into adjacent areas. Hence nearby Fareham's population grew from 58 000 to 88 000 between 1961 and 1981, while over the same period Havant and Waterloo (Figure 15.2) increased from 75 000 to 117 000.

Hampshire as a whole has seen a population increase from nearly 1.2 million people in 1951 to nearly 1.5 million in 1981. Of this total, about 1.2 million are living at or near the coast. It is anticipated that there will be 2 million or more people wishing to live on this coastal stretch by the end of this century.

Congestion in Coastal Waters

The sheltered coastal waters of this area make it perhaps the most important in Britain for yachting and other kinds of pleasure boating. Cowes is the most famous centre, while the Hamble estuary (Figure 15.4) is the most congested. Every inlet is an important yachting centre. The building of marinas, or 'boat parks', is becoming popular, and is necessary to provide for the 7000 sailing boats using the coastal waters at the beginning of the 1970s. It is thought that there might be 20 000 by the end of the century.

Pleasure craft are of course the smallest of the boats using Southampton Water, the Solent and Spithead. At the other extreme in size come the huge liners and supertankers. In addition there are large cargo ships and naval vessels, while numerous ferry boats (Portsmouth–Ryde; Southampton–Cowes; and Lymington–Yarmouth (Figure 15.2)) link the mainland with the Isle of Wight. Adding to the congestion are hovercraft and hydrofoil vessels, speeding up the connection between Southampton and Cowes. Cowes is a major centre for the construction of hovercraft.

This congestion creates serious collision hazards. It is fortunate that these coastal waters are relatively free from fog and gales. There are other dangers created by the over-use of Southampton Water and the Solent, of which oil pollution is one of the most worrying. In addition, the increasing use of sheltered inlets for boating is affecting the wild life, as in the case of Langstone Harbour (Figure 15.4), famous for its marine birds.

The Attack on the Mountains: The Cairngorms

Recreation in the Cairngorms

Tourists are also attracted to the mountains, of which the Cairngorms are almost unique in the British Isles in having become in recent years an important winter sports area. Plate 15.5 shows the chairlift which carries skiers up the steep slopes of Cairn Gorm, down which runs one of the main ski slopes.

The scenery is equally attractive for summer holiday-makers. For example, there is the beautiful Loch Morlich, part of which can be seen on Plate 15.6. The loch is much visited by tourists, especially in the summer, when it is used for boating and fishing. Beyond the loch is the extensive forested area of Glen More Forest Park (Figure 15.5). Above the forest the steep rocky slopes of the Cairngorms are visible in the background of the photograph. These north-west facing slopes are broken by large, armchair-shaped hollows known as corries, which were eroded out by glaciers during the Ice Age. The steep backwalls (or headwalls) of these corries, seen in the background of Plate 15.6, attract rock climbers (Figure 15.5).

The low-lying area in the north-west corner of Figure 15.5 is part of the Spey valley. The river itself runs past

197

Plate 15.5   Cairngorm chairlift

Plate 15.6   Loch Morlich

the small town of Aviemore. Aviemore is the largest of the winter tourist centres of Scotland, the others being Glencoe, Glenshee and Lecht. The Spey valley also attracts holidaymakers for fishing, canoeing, rambling and pony-trekking.

The Aviemore Centre

The tourist trade in the area has expanded rapidly since the opening of the Aviemore Centre in 1966. The facilities include an indoor swimming pool and restaurant, luxury hotels, chalet accommodation, shops, a theatre, a discotheque, a dance hall, an indoor skating rink and a skittle alley. In the first eighteen months after its opening, about 2 million people visited the Centre. The impact in recent years of tourism in general, and the Aviemore Centre in particular, on this part of the Spey valley may be judged by comparing Plate 15.7, a photograph of Aviemore taken before the Second World War, and Plate 15.8, a more recent picture, taken soon after the beginning of Aviemore's 'boom' period.

Exercises

8. (*a*)   Refer to Plates 15.4 and 15.8. Outline the major differences between the built-up areas.
(*b*)   Why is Bournemouth so much bigger than Aviemore?
9. With the help of Figure 15.5, draw a labelled 'field sketch' of Plate 15.6, naming the Cairngorms, Loch Morlich, rock climbing slopes, and parts of Glen More Forest Park.

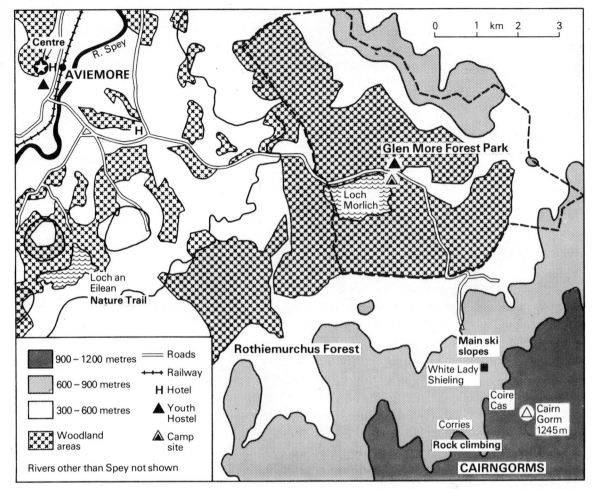

Figure 15.5   Aviemore and the Cairngorms

10. (*a*)   Lay a sheet of tracing paper over Plate 15.8 and on it outline the edge of the Spey valley floor and the surrounding hills. Also mark in the railway line and the main road; buildings present before the war (Plate 15.7) and those built since. Label the Aviemore Centre. Mark by labelled arrows in opposite directions the places the railway is leading to (see Figure 15.6).
(*b*)   What are the main changes which have taken place in recent years, as shown by the two photographs?
11. Write a brief account of the advantages Aviemore has for tourism, using information given in the text and illustrations, and worked out by you in answers to other questions.

Weather Conditions

In the last twenty years, there has been a rapid increase in the demand for winter sports facilities which, as we have seen, have been provided in the Aviemore area. This provision has been made possible because of certain characteristics of local weather conditions. The Cairngorms have on average the highest snowfalls of any part of Britain. The snow lies from December to April, and sometimes in November and May as well. It stays for a particularly long time in the corries, such as Coire Cas (Figure 15.5) where deep drifts of snow accumulate in the hollows, and form ski slopes. Many of the corries face the north-west and are shaded from the sun for long periods. Plate 15.5 shows a deep snow bed in the Coire Cas.

The heavy snowfalls of the Cairngorms occur for a number of reasons. (*a*) They often receive cold winds in winter. Figure 2.6 (page 33) indicates that the mountains are open at this season to cold winds from the north, north-east and east, that is from the Arctic Ocean, Scandinavia and the USSR respectively. (*b*) In each case, these cold winds have to pass over long stretches of sea to reach north-east Scotland, including the Norwegian Sea, the Baltic Sea and the North Sea, and thus pick up moisture. (*c*) When they reach Scotland, therefore, they are cold and moist, and are

199

Plate 15.7   Aviemore before the Second World War

Plate 15.8   Aviemore in the 1970s

then forced to rise by the Cairngorm mountains, giving precipitation in the form of snow in winter. This is partly because the winds were cold and moist to start with and partly because of the low temperatures which exist on high ground.

These are the monthly average temperature figures (°C) for 1964 at Coire Cas (750 metres):

Jan.	Feb.	Mar.	Apr.	May	June
2.3	0.2	−0.4	3.5	7.7	8.0

July	Aug.	Sept.	Oct.	Nov.	Dec.
9.7	9.2	8.7	5.2	3.1	−0.7

Normally temperature figures are averaged out over a long period of time, but records have only fairly recently been kept at Coire Cas. Generally, January and February, rather than March, are the coldest months, and many winters have colder conditions than prevailed in 1964. Temperatures are higher in the valley of the Spey. Here the snow lies for a much shorter period, which means that road access to the Cairngorms can usually be kept open.

Weather Problems

The Cairngorms sometimes experience long *mild spells* during the winter, usually when the winds are blowing from a westerly direction rather than from the east or north (see Figure 2.6, page 33). This is a particular problem on the lower ski slopes. Melting occurs and the snow beds become slushy, a serious drawback for skiers.

The Cairngorms are also prone to gale-force winds, which cause *blizzards*, snow drifting and even avalanches. When the winds are too strong, the chairlifts cannot operate. On the exposed plateau summits, conditions become truly Arctic. In November 1971, six teenage pupils from an Edinburgh school died from exposure in a blizzard in an area just off the south-east corner of Figure 15.5.

Despite the chances of bleak, wintry conditions, no other part of Britain provides such good winter sports facilities as the Cairngorms. Over the Easter period, when snow is still lying, weather conditions often become very pleasant. In addition, the facilities of the Aviemore Centre ensure that there are plenty of activities available for visitors, even in periods of severe weather.

Routes to Aviemore

Figure 15.6 shows the main routes which lead to Aviemore, including a number of main roads and the main-line railway between Perth (connecting with Glasgow, Edinburgh and London) and Inverness. Most

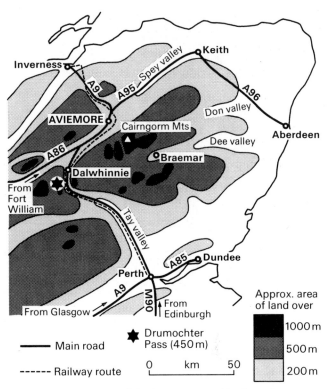

Figure 15.6   Aviemore and the Cairngorms: position in north-east Scotland

visitors travel to Aviemore by car or train. During the summer season, about twelve trains a day each way stop at Aviemore. There are also motorail services from London, Crewe and Birmingham, to Perth and Inverness.

The Effects of the Tourist Industry on the Cairngorms Area

Advantages

In the past, most hotels in the Aviemore area had to shut down for four or five months in winter, because of the lack of visitors. Local people who worked in the tourist industry were often unemployed at that season. Today, the hotels are open all year to cater both for summer visitors and for winter sports enthusiasts. Instead of there being winter unemployment, people have had to be brought in from outside the area to work in the hotels and the restaurants. Continental ski instructors are hired. On an Easter weekend, there may be 20 000 tourists on the Cairngorm slopes. Over 40 000 people come to the area in the course of a year to stay for a full week's holiday or more.

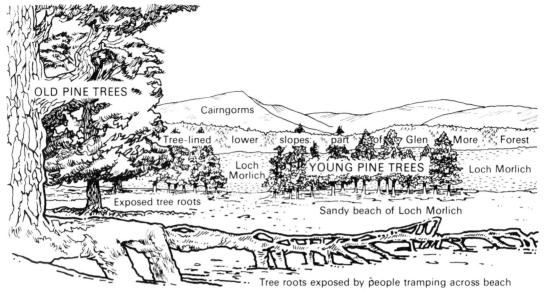

Figure 15.7   Field sketch of Loch Morlich

Disadvantages

There is no doubt that the rapid expansion of the tourist industry, and especially of winter sports activities, has disturbed the natural peace and seriously affected the landscape of the Cairngorm mountains. The same problem is present in areas such as the Lake District and Snowdonia. During the tourist season, thousands of visitors encroach on the countryside, congesting the roads, crowding the car parks, and too often leaving a trail of litter.

The Aviemore area is notable for the fine specimens of old Scots pine trees which have remained, though they have been cleared in the past from most other areas of the Scottish Highlands. Some of the best of the trees are found in the Rothiemurchus and Glen More forests, shown on Figure 15.5. One of these pines can be seen on the extreme left of Plate 15.6. A fine natural plantation of birches survives behind the Aviemore Centre (on the right of Plates 15.7 and 15.8).

These trees, as well as the more recent conifers planted by the Forestry Commission, are endangered by the presence of tourists. One hazard is forest fires. Another occurs round the shores of Loch Morlich, where the tramping of people across the beach has exposed the roots of the old trees (Figure 15.7). This process will, if unchecked, cause the death of the trees. Higher up, on the bare slopes of the Cairn Gorm, the construction of the chairlifts and ski-runs has caused soil erosion. Fortunately, conservation is being practised by the tourist organisations and by the Forestry Commission, and great efforts are being made to

educate the public to preserve the countryside. It is a difficult job to balance the benefits of the tourist industry against its possible serious consequences for the countryside.

Exercises

12. (*a*) Explain briefly what is meant by accessibility. How accessible is Aviemore from your home?
(*b*) Plan a journey from your home to Aviemore. Work out carefully the route you would follow, state the means of transport you would use, calculate the time the journey would take, and try to find out how much it would cost.
13. Write a short account of the effects of the tourist industry on the Cairngorms in the form of a dialogue (a discussion between two people), representing opposing points of view: (*a*) an Aviemore hotel keeper; (*b*) a conservationist (someone who wishes to conserve the beauty of the countryside). Alternatively, you could debate this subject in class, making use of the knowledge you have gained from the text.
14. Write a short account of the advantages and disadvantages of the Cairngorms area for the tourist industry, under the headings:(*a*) scenery; (*b*) weather conditions; (*c*) facilities; (*d*) accessibility, to form a summary of the points you have noted earlier.
15. *Finding the Nature Trail*
Refer to Figure 15.5. The Aviemore area is a magnificent one for studying plant and animal life. Apart from the old Scots pine trees and the newer coniferous plantations, many of the younger forests of pine and birch are carpeted with heather, which also covers the lower slopes of the hills, giving them an attractive purple colour in autumn. In the forests, wild deer can be found

in winter. The forests also shelter wild cats, foxes and red squirrels which are, however, rarely seen. In addition, there is a variety of bird life and to the north of the area shown on the map is one of the few nesting places in Britain of the osprey. Birds such as the osprey, eagle and others need protection if they are not to become extinct.

(*a*) Trace Figure 15.5 into your exercise books, marking lakes and streams in blue, roads in red, woodland in green, and land over 450 metres in brown.

(*b*) You are required to find another nature trail in the area, because the one shown is being over-used. Your nature trail must be (i) in an area of woodland; (ii) within approximately 2 kilometres of a lake; (iii) not more than 3 kilometres from a hotel, youth hostel or camping site; (iv) below 450 metres. (Note that you will need a pair of compasses to do (iii); (ii) need only be approximate.)

(A) Shade in an area, fulfilling all the above conditions, in which your nature trail could be placed.

(B) Shade in a different way areas of woodland which fulfil none of the other conditions.

(C) Make a list of notices you would put up on your nature trail to remind visitors how they should and should not use the trail.

(D) Find out whether there is a nature trail in the area of your school. One of the staff at your school may be able to inform you and show you how to use the trail, if there is one.

Figure 15.8 is a map showing the distribution of areas which in different ways are subject to conservation laws, designated as 'protected areas'. These include National Parks, Forest Parks, Areas of Outstanding Natural Beauty, and Country Parks.

Figure 15.8   Great Britain: conserving the countryside

National Parks

National Parks were established by Act of Parliament in 1949, the provisions becoming law in 1950. The purposes of National Parks were seen as:

(*a*) the preservation of the natural beauties of the landscape of these areas;

(*b*) the provision of access and facilities for the enjoyment of the general public;

(*c*) the protection of wild life and places of architectural and historical interest within these areas;

(*d*) the maintenance of established farming use.

As Figure 15.8 shows, the National Parks are to be found in the hills and mountains of 'Highland Britain' (Figure 1.1, page 4). One of the largest is the Snowdonia National Park (Plate 1.16).

When an area becomes a National Park, people continue to live and work in it, and to own land and property. But the National Park Authorities are able to preserve the natural beauty by strict planning controls, limiting new building, setting high standards of design, and dictating the choice of materials for new buildings.

While areas are allotted for parking, picnicking, camping and caravanning (fulfilling the second purpose of the National Parks), these are generally very carefully sited, and screened to prevent them spoiling the natural view. They are concentrated at certain points, often on the edges of the National Park, or near the roads, to leave the rest of the area unspoilt. Footpaths and nature trails are laid out with grants from the government. Wardens and information services are also provided.

The Lake District

As we have seen (Chapter 5), the Lake District is an area of outstanding natural attraction. It was 'discovered' by tourists in part as a result of the poetry of Wordsworth, and people flocked in after the coming of the railways in the nineteenth century. Resorts such as Keswick, Windermere and Ambleside sprang up to cater for the visitors.

Plate 15.9   Holiday crowds in the New Forest

Since the Second World War, the area has come under much greater pressure, particularly since the M6 has brought the area within day-tripping distance of places as far away as the Midlands. Peaks such as Helvellyn have become heavily 'over-populated' in the holiday season.

Conflicts of interest have inevitably arisen, in this and similar areas:

(*a*)   between the hill sheep farmers and the tourists, who leave gates open, let dogs off the leash, which worry the sheep, and so on;

(*b*)   between the indigenous inhabitants and well-to-do people from the industrial towns, who in recent years have been buying second homes in the Lake District, paying prices local people cannot afford;

(*c*)   congestion on the roads, especially on the overloaded trunk road, the A 591, running from Kendal through Windermere and Ambleside to Keswick. Attempts to build a by-pass at Ambleside, however, have been resisted by conservationists, who claim it would ruin a beautiful piece of countryside on the edge of the town;

(*d*)   Quarrying is a less serious problem in the Lake District than in other National Parks, as there is not much slate quarrying left and, in any case, from a distance, slate quarries blend in better with the natural landscape than, say, the limestone quarries of the Peak District and the kaolin quarries and tips of Dartmoor.

Forest Parks

One of the duties of the Forestry Commission is to open up its forests, mostly of coniferous trees, to the public, by supplying sites for camping and caravanning, laying down nature trails, and providing information services.

The New Forest

We have already referred to the Glen More Forest Park in the Cairngorms (pages 197–202). One of the finest forests in England is the New Forest in Hampshire, containing trees hundreds of years old, planted by the kings of previous eras, and jealously preserved for hunting purposes.

Although the New Forest has been a settled area, with competing land uses, for centuries, it is only in this century that it has come under serious attack from outside. The main-line railways, built after 1850, and the main roads, covered with tarmac early in this century, now cross the forest and have made it increasingly accessible to visitors. Today there is a serious conflict between those who are interested in conserving the natural landscape of the New Forest, and those who wish to exploit it for recreational purposes. Apart from the holidaymakers, there is pressure for increased residential development. Farms are being sold for building land, to provide homes for retired people and commuters.

Conserving the New Forest

The pressure of so many visitors on the New Forest has serious effects on the landscape and wild life. Plate 15.9 shows a typical scene on a summer's day near an easily accessible crossroads in the forest. Here the open grassland becomes very congested with cars, deckchairs, sunbathers and, in this case, children paddling. The aftermath of a busy weekend can be seen in Plate 15.10, with unsightly litter blown against the bracken.

Problems

Litter is just one of the many problems created by tourists in the New Forest. While it is ugly and offensive, it is not the most damaging of the effects of visitors on the area, though it can create a health risk to animals. The litter problem is of course far more widespread than in the New Forest alone.

The natural *appearance* of the New Forest is not improved by congestion of cars and people, as Plates 15.9 and 15.10 indicate. Views of attractive glades and open woodland are obscured by congregations of cars, caravans and tents. The enjoyment of the countryside is also disturbed by noise.

The *effects on wildlife* are becoming increasingly serious. Already large numbers of birds, small animals, and deer have been disturbed in their natural habitat, and have either disappeared from the forest or can only be found in the remotest parts, away from the roads.

The *effects on vegetation* are even more obvious. Driving cars off the road on to grassland damages or even destroys the turf, leaving large bare patches of earth and mud embedded with tyre marks. In the forest glades, compacted earth round the trees exposes the roots (see also page 202) and leads to the destruction of trees. In dry weather, there is a fire hazard to the forest from the dropping of lighted matches, cigarette ends, and the leaving of camp fires.

The increase in the number of cars has made worse the *danger* to the forest ponies and other animals, and also to pedestrians, on the many narrow forest roads. There are approximately 160 kilometres of public highway in the New Forest, and 1200 access points for cars. In 1971, 121 ponies, 40 cattle, and 52 deer were killed on its roads.

Remedies

The New Forest Study Working Group indicated that the most important remedy was to confine cars to certain routes in the forest, with the dispersal of car parking sites over the area. This channelling of cars along particular highways would leave large *car-free zones* in the New Forest.

Associated with this idea was the provision of an increased number of *caravan and camp sites*. One of these, at Holmsley in the south-western part of the forest, is shown on Plate 15.11. This is one of the 'equipped' sites with full toilet and other facilities. There are also a number of 'informal' sites for campers, which have litter bins, chemical toilets and in some cases water standpipes.

To encourage a deeper interest in and appreciation of the New Forest, *nature trails* and *scenic drives* have been established. Apart from going on the drives themselves, people can park off the road and take a forest walk, helped by detailed information given on leaflets provided by the Forestry Commission. Some of the finest coniferous woodlands in Britain are found in this area, and include massive pine trees planted over one hundred years ago. The placing of bins at parking sites has helped to improved the litter problem.

In these and other ways the Forestry Commission has helped to check the serious 'human erosion' which continues, however, as a threat to the animals, the vegetation and the general attractions of the New Forest. In the New Forest at present, the chief 'conflict' is between the Forestry Commission and the 'commoners', people with grazing rights in the forest, who wish to increase forage production for the intensive grazing of their animals.

Plate 15.10   *Picnic litter in the New Forest*

Exercises

16. Take one of the National Parks shown on Figure 15.8.
(*a*)   Draw maps or diagrams to illustrate its main features.
(*b*)   Show how it is related to heavily populated areas.
(*c*)   Identify the main conflicts of interest which have arisen.
17. (*a*)   Describe the different 'uses' made by tourists of the New Forest, as shown on Plates 15.9 and 15.10.
(*b*)   Do you see the provisions on Plate 15.11 as adequate protection of the natural landscape?

Areas of Outstanding Natural Beauty

These are more widespread than the National Parks. They are of equal scenic attraction, but less fully part of the 'wildscape' than the National Parks. They are more likely to be in easily accessible areas and contain a large proportion of farmland. These areas are protected from indiscriminate building of houses, roads, etc. in the same way as the National Parks.

Country Parks

Another major Act of Parliament, designed to open up the countryside, was passed in 1968. This was the *Countryside Act*, which established the *Countryside Commission*. The emphasis was changed from protection and conservation of the countryside, though the countryside was still to be protected and conserved, to

205

Plate 15.11   Holmsley camp site, the New Forest

an encouragement of enjoyment of the countryside for open air recreation, but in a responsible way.

The work of the Countryside Commission has been to concentrate car access on to car parks, camping and picnicking sites. Special attention has been paid to making use of lakes, reservoirs, and flooded gravel pits, as well as canals and coastal areas, for increasingly popular water sports. Another outcome has been the establishment of *Country Parks*, which are much smaller than National Parks, and established by Local Authorities with the help of government grants. Thus in the Merseyside area a 'Wirral Way Footpath' has been established on the densely populated Wirral Peninsula, near built-up areas, and making use of a disused railway track. In addition, long-distance footpaths such as the Pennine Way, the Cleveland Way and the Pembroke-shire coastal path have been established.

Conclusion

One of the success stories of the post-war period has been the reduction in pollution of the air and rivers. Although urban air remains polluted, there is much less smog (and more sunshine) in London and the industrial towns of the Midlands and North than there was at one time. Although many rivers are still polluted, fish can again be found in the lower Thames.

Attention is increasingly being focused on new dangers, such as the threats of nuclear waste and poisonous materials such as blue asbestos. Ignorance of the harmful effects of such substances has lost many lives in the past.

The purpose of legislation for the countryside since the war has been to maintain a balance between *conserving* it and opening it up as an *amenity*. The promotion of principles of conservation has become a well-established advertising campaign. But many people seem to respond more readily to advertisements

to buy cars and chocolates than to appeals to treat the countryside well, as Plate 15.10 indicates only too clearly. Townscapes are equally badly treated.

Bodies such as the National Parks Authority, the Forestry Commission, the Countryside Commission, and the National Trust, are faced with built-in conflicts between different interests. Reconciliation of such interests is often difficult and sometimes impossible. Do you have a view, for example, on the siting of a new nuclear power station at Torness, about 45 kilometres from Edinburgh, in Lothian in south-east Scotland? As Plate 15.12 indicates, the power station is to be built on what was a relatively unspoilt stretch of rocky coast. Does this disturb you on environmental and social grounds? Or do you feel that the economic advantages outweigh any disadvantages?

One of the purposes of 'environmental education' is to try to help the younger generation to grow up better informed than their elders about the issues involved; better able to balance the advantages of one course of action against the disadvantages of another; more determined to take a stand when vital principles are at stake; but realistic enough to accept that most conservation and anti-pollution measures are expensive and have to be paid for. It is hoped that this study of Britain's changing geography has alerted you to some of the problems of living on a densely crowded island, but one which has the exceptional advantage of an attractive and varied natural and cultural heritage, both in the countryside and in the towns and cities.

Plate 15.12   The site at Torness at which a nuclear power station is planned

INDEX

air masses 31, 34
airports 100–4; location 102–3
alluvia 14, 41; farming 42
anticyclones 35
aquifers 10, 47
arêtes 17, 18

bars, bay head 24
basalt scenery 6
beaches, raised 26
Beaufort wind scale 28
beef production 54, 55, 62, 66
bergschrund crevasses 17
Birmingham: central 150–1, 153; growth 152; housing 155–8; immigrant population 129–30; traffic problems 153; water supply 44–5
blow-holes 21
bluffs, river 14
boulder clay 41; deposition 19; farming 66
Bournemouth 193–4
bus services 138

Cairngorms: tourism 197–203; weather 31, 199–201
canals 77, 107, 191
car ferries 187–8
car industry 121–4, 152, 175; government policy 125; manufacturing process 121–2; siting 121
carboniferous limestone: economic contribution 11; scenery 6–8
castle locations 140–2
Castleford 70–2
cattle: beef 54, 55, 62, 66; dairy 54, 66
caves: limestone 7; sea 21
cement industry 11, 175
cereal crops 59, 60, 66
chalk: economic contribution 11; scenery 9–11
chemical industry 11, 87, 117–18; siting 117
china clay 11
cities: growth 126, 142–9, 152; inner, decline of 127, 129; new *see* towns, new
clay: boulder 19, 41, 66; china 11
clay vales 11
clays 41; and farming 42; texture 39
cliffs, formation 22
climate, British 29–30; factors affecting 30–7; *see also* weather

clints 6
coal: Industrial Revolution 79, 105, 107, 110, 119; mining 70, 74–9; towns 70–3; transport 77; uses 77
coal measures 75, 109, 110
coalfields: of Britain 79; North Yorkshire 75–6, 77; Selby 70–3
Common Agricultural Policy 50, 68
commuters 154, 162, 193
conservation: conflict of interests 44, 67–8, 196, 204; fishing 185, 186; promotion 206; Thames 177; tourism 196–206; water supplies 48, 68; *see also* environment
container transport 96, 170, 177, 184
conurbations 126, 127, 129; south coast 196; West Midlands 150, 158–6
convection 37
Corby 114–5
corries (cirques, cwms) 17, 18
cottage industries 119
Country Parks 205–6
Countryside Commission 205–6
crag and tail structures 21, 139
crevasses, bergschrund 17
Crewe 97–9
crofting 64
crop rotation 42, 59, 63
cuestas 9

deltas: glacial 18; river 14
deposition: glacial 18, 19; marine 23; river 14
depressions 33, 34
desalination 48
Development Areas 114, 124, 125
dip slopes 9
dockers 175
docks 171, 172, 174, 184
downlands 10
drumlins 19
dry point sites 11, 52, 132

Edinburgh 139–48
electricity 88–91
energy resources 70–91
Enterprise Zones 114, 124
entertainment 136
environment: airports 102, 103; education about 206; housing spread 127; manufacturing industry 108, 118; North Sea oil 85; tourism 196–7, 202: water supplies 48, 68; *see also* conservation

erosion: glacial 16–18, 21; lateral 14; marine 21–3; river 12, 14; soil 40, 41; vertical 12; wind 41, 42
escarpments 9
eskers 21
European Community (EEC): aid to industrial areas 124, 125; effects on farming 50, 68; fisheries policy 181, 182

farming: drainage 59, 66; EEC 50, 68; economic factors 54–5, 59–60, 66, 68; factory 67; fertilisation 42, 59, 67; fish 186; government aid 55, 60, 66, 68; irrigation 42, 47, 67; Lake District 50–5; Lincolnshire 56–62; marketing 60, 65, 66, 67; mechanisation 59, 67, 68; physical factors 49, 50, 52–4, 55, 56–8, 66; post-war developments 67–8; second sources of income 55, 119; soils 42, 53, 57, 66; types 49; weather 53, 57, 66; *see also* *specific types*
farmscape 49
Fawley 178–9
Featherstone 73
ferries, car 187–8
fish: conservation 185, 186; farming 186; marketing 184
fishing: grounds 180–2; herring/mackerel 180, 185–6; industry 182; methods 180; ports 181, 182–5
fjords 18, 26
flood plains 13, 14, 25
fog 36
Forest Parks 197, 204
Forestry Commission 68, 202, 204, 205
freightliners 96
frozen foods industry 61, 184
fruit growing 65

gas, natural 80–2
geology: economic 11; scenery 4–11
Giant's Causeway 6
glaciation: effect on soil 41; lowland 19–21; mountain 16–18
glaciers 16; corrie 17; valley 17
glass manufacture 105–8
gorges: limestone 8; slot 12
government involvement: farming 55, 60, 66, 68; manufacturing industry 114, 117, 120, 125
granite: economic contribution 11; scenery 5

grasslands 59
gravels 41; deposition 19
green belts 161
grikes 6
growth areas 124
groynes 23
gullying 40, 42

hierarchies *see* settlement, hierarchies
holiday resorts 190–5
hops 64–5
horn peaks 17, 18
housing: estates 124, 127, 147; high
rise 158; industrial 105, 109, 111,
120, 146, 156; miners' 73; New Towns
165; overspill 159; Redevelopment
Areas 155–8; slum 109, 146, 155, 158,
162
Hull 182–4
hummocks 9

ice and landscape 15–21
igneous scenery 5
immigration 120, 128, 152
industrial inertia 111
industry: capital-intensive 88; labour-
intensive 88; nationalised 79; *see
also* manufacturing industry *and
specific industries*
iron industry 110–13
iron ore 109, 110, 111
isobars 29

Jurassic limestone: economic
contribution 11; scenery 9–11

Kaolin 11

Lake District: conflict of interests
203–4; farming 50–5; scenery 17, 18
lakes: corrie 17, 18; ox-bow 15;
ribbon 18
land: competition for 67; use 49, 60
landscape: geology 4–11; ice
15–21; rivers 11–15; sea 21–7
landslides 9; river valleys 12
levées 14; artificial 15
light industries 114, 121, 124
limestone: carboniferous 6–8, 11;
Jurassic 9–11
loams 39; farming 42
Lincolnshire: farming 56–62;
settlements 132–5
local government: reorganisation
160; West Midlands 159
loess 19
London, Port of 171–7
longshore drift 23
Louth 133–5
Luton 123–4

manufacturing industry 105–30,
152; adaptibility 111, 120;
development 106–8; 'footloose' 121;
government policy 125; mass

production 121–2; New Towns 165;
pollution 108; transport 107, 119,
120, 124
marginal fringe 49
market gardening 66–7
marketing: farm produce 60, 65, 66,
67, 133; fish 184; manufacturing
industry 118, 119, 121
meanders 14, 15; incised 25, 141
millstone grit: economic contribution
11; scenery 8–9
mining: safety 75; settlements 73;
see also coal *and* iron ore
monoculture 59
moraines 18, 19
motorways 92–4, 154; goods transport
107, 120, 124; holiday resorts 196

National Parks 203–4
natural gas 80–2
New Forest 179, 204–5
North Atlantic Drift 29
North Sea oil: effects of 82;
discovery 80; environment 85;
exploitation problems 84; ports 177,
178; refining 86–8; resources 82
nunataks 16, 18

oil: North Sea *see* North Sea oil;
onshore 82; refining 86–8, 175, 178
overspill 127, 159, 163, 169
ox-bow lakes 15

peas 60
peat 39, 41; and farming 42
petrochemicals 84, 117–8
podsols 41
pollution: coastal 197; industrial 108,
118, 177; reduction 206; of Thames
176–7
population: distribution 127, 159;
growth patterns 126–7,
159; immigrant 120, 128, 152; *see
also* towns, growth of
port(s): of Britain 177–8; cargo
170–9, 182; fishing 180–7; industry
175, 178; of London 170–6;
passenger 179, 182, 187–9
poultry rearing 66, 67
power stations: coal-fired 77–8, 89,
175; hydro-electric 91; location
89–91; nuclear 89, 206; oil-fired 89,
179; pumped storage 91
pressure, atmospheric: 29, 31–4, 35–6

quarrying 11, 204

railways 95–9; commuter 154, 162,
193; development 97–9;
modernisation 95–6; tourism 191–2,
193
rain shadow 35
rainfall: in Britain 29, 34;
convectional 37; and farming 53, 57,
66

recession, economic 124, 152; *see also*
unemployment
refineries, oil 86–8, 175, 178
relief and weather 34–5
reservoirs 44, 45, 48
resorts, seaside 190–5
retirement areas 127, 192–3, 194
rias 26
rivers: industrial sites on 86, 119,
175; landscape 7, 11–15; pollution
109; terraces 25
roads 92–4; urban 153–4, 158, 166,
168, 171; *see also* motorways
roches moutonnées 17
rurban fringe 49, 126, 161

St Helens 105–9
salt marsh 24
sands 41; deposition 19; Shirdley Hill
42, 66
scarpland scenery 9
scars: landslip 9; limestone 7
scenery *see* landscape
scree 16
Scunthorpe 111–3
sea: changes in level 25; landscape
21–7
settlements: hierarchies 132, 150–67;
mining 73; sites 11, 25, 26, 47, 52, 58,
132; *see also specific types*
sheep farming 46, 54, 55, 68
Sheffield 110–1
shipbuilding industry 116–17
Shirdley Hill Sand 42, 66
silt 39
site location: airports 102–3; car
industry 121; chemical industry
117; defensive 139, 140–1,
171; frozen food industry 61,
184; glass industry 107; light
industries 121; manufacturing
industries 105; market towns
133; new towns 163; petrochemical
industry 84, 118; power stations
89–91; refineries 86, 87; settlements
11, 25, 26, 47, 52, 58, 132; steel
industry 110–13; sugar beet factory
60; textile industry 118, 119, 120
skerry guard 18
slip-off slopes 14
smog 36, 108
soil profiles 40
soils 39–42; factors affecting
40–2; farming 42, 53, 57; fertility 40,
41, 42; properties 39–40; *see also
individual types*
Southampton 178–9
Southport 190–3
spheres of influence 136–8
spits 24
spring lines 10, 47, 58, 132
springs 10
spurs: interlocking 12; truncated 17,
18
stacks 23